THE VARIATION OF
ANIMALS IN NATURE

MIMICRY OF BEES BY FLIES IN BRAZIL

1. Centris atriventris (Bee) mimicked by Mallophora   3. Euglossa dimidiata (Bee) mimicked by M. fasciipennis, 4.
xylocopioides (Asilid fly), 2.

After STUDY Zool. Jahrb. Syst, 42. 1926 by permission.

THE
VARIATION OF ANIMALS
IN NATURE

BY

G. C. ROBSON, M.A.

Deputy Keeper of Zoology, British Museum (Natural History)

AND

O. W. RICHARDS, M.A., D.Sc.

Lecturer in Entomology,
Imperial College of Science and Technology

WITH 2 COLOURED PLATES AND 30 ILLUSTRATIONS IN THE TEXT

LONGMANS, GREEN AND CO.
LONDON • NEW YORK • TORONTO

LONGMANS, GREEN AND CO. LTD.
39 PATERNOSTER ROW, LONDON, E.C.4
6 OLD COURT HOUSE STREET, CALCUTTA
53 NICOL ROAD, BOMBAY
36A MOUNT ROAD, MADRAS

LONGMANS, GREEN AND CO.
114 FIFTH AVENUE, NEW YORK
221 EAST 20TH STREET, CHICAGO
88 TREMONT STREET, BOSTON

LONGMANS, GREEN AND CO.
480 UNIVERSITY AVENUE, TORONTO

First published February 1936

Printed in Great Britain

PREFACE

In 1928 the authors of this work commenced to collect and arrange data on the variation of animals in Nature. Any naturalist, particularly the systematist and the student of geographical distribution, will realise that there are many methods and subjects of inquiry which might be usefully adopted in analysing the vast amount of detail which has accumulated on this subject. We felt, however, after some time that we could make our analysis most useful if we tried to show the relation between natural variation and the main problem of the causes of evolution. We came to the conclusion that, in spite of the many valuable contributions to this subject, a review which was both synthetic and critical was still necessary. The subject has become so complex of recent years, so many special lines of research have been opened up and the accumulated literature relevant to the subject has become so intractable, that a synthesis of the sort we have attempted is an urgent necessity. To exemplify the need for such a synthesis we would point out that of the observations, experiments and theories made by workers a generation or more ago some have become the matter of text-books and current biological teaching, some have been neglected and forgotten, and others again are still the subject of ill-informed controversy. There is a great need for an overhaul of our heritage of research and observation and for an exact valuation of much that is either summarily neglected or accepted without question or scrutiny of the original publications.

We do not claim that in this work we have produced either an exhaustive survey or a novel viewpoint which might illuminate an old and contentious problem. The method we have adopted differs very little from that elaborated by Darwin, though we have tried to formulate the problem in accordance with the many generally accepted changes which have taken place in biological thought and procedure since his time. We do not suggest that the attempts at a synthetic treatment that have been made in recent years are to be lightly disregarded. To some of these, indeed, we are deeply indebted. We feel, however, that many new and fundamental questions are left still unrelated one with another. Moreover, no adequate attempt has been made to see how far the data of variation in structure and behaviour confirm particular theories of evolution.[1]

We are under obligation to numerous fellow workers who have given time and trouble in assisting us, and tender our thanks for their generous help and the trouble they have taken on our behalf.

G. C. R.   O. W. R.

[1] Owing to the illness of one of the authors the publication of this book was delayed, and no references to literature later than 1933 are included.

CONTENTS

PRÉCIS OF CONTENTS

CHAPTER I

INTRODUCTION

CHAPTER II

THE ORIGIN OF VARIATION

The establishment of permanent isolation. Analysis of the various methods of establishment. Discussion of (*a*) Seasonal occurrence ; (*b*) Time of breeding ; (*c*) Loss of means of dispersal, etc. (indirect methods) ; and (*d*) various bars to intercourse, and (*e*) various sources of sterility (direct methods). Conclusions : Importance of biological races.

CHAPTER VI

CORRELATION

Use of the term ' correlation ' ; Dürken's analysis. ' Physiological ' and ' gametic ' correlation (Graham Kerr). The correlation of specific characters very variable in degree, probably on the average rather low. The two fundamental types of correlation (' causal ' and ' coincidental '), their causes and importance. Methods of deciding the basis of the correlation of specific characters. Segregation and specific characters in relation to correlation and variation. Highly correlated characters are probably those for which large populations are homozygous. ' Lineages ' and the correlation of specific characters. Independence of characters as revealed by the study of ' lineages.' Difficulty of reconciling the apparent independence of characters in phylogeny with our conception of development and organisation. Specific characters as mosaics of fortuitously associated units. Their incorporation in the general unity of the organism and transformation of their basis from a fortuitous to a permanent one.

CHAPTER VII

NATURAL SELECTION

Introduction. Darwin's presentation of the evidence. Subsequent modification and development of the theory. Conditions of proof required and procedure to be adopted in this work. The origin of domesticated races and its relevance to the problem of Evolution. Selection experiments with pure bred stock. Pearl's requirements of proof that selection has altered the character of a race.

Direct evidence for the selective incidence of death-rates in nature. Twenty cases of direct observation on the selective incidence of death-rates examined. Summary of the examination (p. 212). Direct observation on the alteration of natural populations. Summary (p. 215).

The nature of variation considered in relation to natural selection. The mutation-rate and survival-value of mutations. Mathematical treatment of the subject. The problem of random mating. Summary (p. 229).

Indirect evidence for and against the efficacy of selection.

I. Standard cases. Protective coloration. Mimicry.
II. Less intensively studied cases. The adaptations of torrent-living animals. The colour and pattern of Cuckoo's eggs. The adaptations of (*a*) abyssal animals and (*b*) cave-dwelling animals.

CHAPTER X

SUMMARY AND CONCLUSIONS

The fundamental divergences in evolutionary theory—the organism as the product of variation guided by environmental change and as endowed with an internal momentum. Limitations of our knowledge. The origin of groups and the production of adaptation are the outstanding features of evolution. The apparent unitary nature of the evolutionary process ; are group-formation and adaptation produced by the same process ? The evolutionary relationship between specialisation and organisation. Natural selection and the unitary concept of evolution. Discussion of the evidence for the efficiency of natural selection. The rôle of Lamarckism and ' induced ' mutations. The importance of certain ' orthogenetic ' phenomena. Summary of the main theories of evolution. The ' spread ' of variants an acid test of evolutionary theories. Difficulty of regarding organisation as a product of natural selection.

ACKNOWLEDGMENTS

For kind permission to make use of illustrations from already published works the authors are indebted to :—

The Director of the Carlsberg Laboratory, Copenhagen, for Figure 1 from Schmidt, J., in C.R. Trav. Lab. Carlsberg, **18,** 1930 ;

Firma Julius Springer, Berlin, for Figure 2 from Zimmermann in Zeitschrift für Morphologie und Oekol. Tiere ;

The American Museum of Natural History for Figures 3, 10, 11, 12 ;

Firma Johann Ambrosius Barth, Leipzig, for Figure 4 from a paper by Sikora, H., in Arch. für Schiffs-und Tropenhygiene ;

The United States Government Printing Office for Figure 5 from Mickel, C. E., in Entomological News, **35,** and for Figure 22 from Journal of Mammalogy, **7** ;

The United States Department of Agriculture, Bureau of Biological Survey for Figures 6A, B and C from Howell, A. H., in Bulletin, **37** ;

The Carnegie Institute, Washington, for Figures 7, 8, 18 from Crampton, H. E., Studies on the genus *Partula* in publications **228** and **410,** and for Figure 25 from Lutz, F. E., in publication **101** ;

Brighton and Hove Natural History and Philosophical Society for Figure 9 from an article by H. Toms in Report, 1920 ;

The Wistar Institute of Anatomy and Biology, Philadelphia, for Figures 19, 19A and 21 from the Journal of Experimental Zoology ;

The Royal Entomological Society of London for Figure 13, a plate from the Presidential Address, Proceedings, **5,** 1931 ;

The Zoological Society of London for Figure 14 from Ingoldby, C. H., in Proceedings, **1927** ;

The British Museum (Natural History) for Figure 15 from the ' Handbook of British Mosquitoes ' ;

Messrs. Ernest Benn, Ltd., for Figure 16 from J. R. Norman's ' A History of Fishes ' ;

Professor Nuttall and University Press, Cambridge, for Figure 26 from Parasitology, **4,** 1911 ; and

University Press, Cambridge, for Figure 30 from Himmer in ' Biological Reviews,' **7,** 1932.

Beneath each illustration is the reference to a source which is set out in full in the Bibliography at the end of the volume. The Table on page 97 is translated from Rensch, R. B., in Arch. Naturges. **1,** by permission.

LIST OF ILLUSTRATIONS

THE VARIATION OF ANIMALS IN NATURE

CHAPTER I

INTRODUCTION

THE term *variation* is generally used in biology to connote the differences between the offspring of a single mating or between the individuals or groups of individuals placed in a single species, subspecies, or race. It is sometimes used in a more general way to connote, *e.g.*, the differences between genera and other groups above the rank of species (*cf.* Pelseneer, 1920 ; Gardner, 1925). The former usage, which is more common and is regularly used in evolutionary, genetical and taxonomic studies, is the one employed in this work.

A division of the study of variation in animals according to whether they are living under natural conditions or in domestication is arbitrary from one point of view. We have no reason to believe that either the origin of variation or its mechanism of hereditary distribution is different in any essential as between wild and domesticated animals. Nevertheless the various procedures employed in the mating of domesticated animals have, in the mixing or isolation of hereditary strains, such different effects from the matings of animals in nature that the distribution and evolutionary fate of variant characters in domesticated and wild forms can rarely be comparable. Whether the study of variation under domestication has the importance in evolutionary studies that Darwin originally assumed is very doubtful : but if the study of variation is to yield any results of value in assessing the causes of evolution, it should primarily be conducted in natural populations.

B

The facts of variation impressed themselves on the early systematists and the collection and utilisation of such data are a part of systematic zoology. The analysis of the vast body of facts thus accumulated and the extraction of general principles from them were, of course, stimulated by the work of Darwin and Wallace and became important items in the technique of evolutionary studies. Various aspects of the problem have been dealt with in a number of synthetic works: Bateson (1894), Woltereck (1919), Philiptschenko (1927), Rensch (1929). The origin of variation and its hereditary distribution has become one of the commonplace matters of biological literature. The majority of the synthetic works are concerned with the special problems presented by what is after all a very extensive subject. The object of this work is, like that of the majority of its predecessors, a special one. It does not set out to review the problem of variation in all its aspects, but to gather together all the leading facts and principles that emerge from a study of variation and have any bearing on the causes of evolution.

On account of the vast numbers of books and papers that have been produced on evolution, some word of excuse is perhaps needful in adding to the number. In spite of all that has been written on this subject and the fresh prestige which, after a period of intense criticism, the doctrine of Natural Selection has acquired from mathematical and genetical studies, we believe that the causes of evolution are still obscure and the relative importance of the presumed causative agencies is still to be assessed. We further believe that many principles and much recorded data still need to be worked into the general scheme of inquiry and that in a number of directions much more research is still necessary. Even such a subject as geographical distribution and variation, which might be thought to be worn threadbare, is still in need of systematic study.

As we are mainly concerned in this work with the causes of evolution it may well be asked whether a survey of this subject based only on zoological data can be of much assistance. We think that a comprehensive work including both botanical and zoological data and principles of the kind brought together here is eminently desirable. At the same time we do not feel that such conclusions as we have formulated

are in any way invalidated because they are based on zoological data alone. We are concerned with the evolution of
animals and are content to let our conclusions speak for themselves. It is very probable that there are certain evolutionary
principles and phenomena that are peculiar either to animals
or to plants. Polyploidy and certain other chromosomal
phenomena seem at present to be almost restricted to the
latter. We do not, however, believe that the truth or falsity
of any theory of evolution is likely to be decided by an
acid test provided by exclusively botanical or zoological
data.

The importance of variation in the study of evolution is
too well known to require much explanation. Whatever we
may hold to be the cause or causes of the evolutionary process,
it is almost invariably recognised that it has proceeded by the
progressive accumulation of changes of the same dimensions
as are found in the variation within a species. In spite of the
considerable changes that have taken place in evolutionary
inquiry, the fundamental idea enunciated by Darwin and
Wallace that evolutionary divergence is the summation of a
series of changes having the status of individual differences
is still almost universally accepted. Students of evolution are
still concerned with the questions—how do such variations
arise and by what means are they amplified so as to give
progressive change in given directions ?

Some measure of variation is of universal occurrence among
all living organisms, and the capacity to display this phenomenon might be given as one of the attributes of living matter.
It is doubtful indeed whether it is an exclusive property of living
organisms or even of organic compounds (Reichert, 1919) ;
but it is far more marked in them than in inorganic bodies.

The origin of variation is fully discussed in Chapter II.
The most generally accepted view, of course, is that, while
the somatic tissues are readily modified by environmental
factors, *heritable* variation is due to spontaneous changes at
single loci in the chromosomes (gene- or point-mutations),
to various kinds of chromosomal abnormalities, or to the
combination of maternal and paternal genes. In certain
conditions, however, it seems that mutations may be induced
by environmental factors. Whether this is a correct view and
whether all heritable variation may not in the last resort be

due to modification by the environment will be discussed in Chapter II. The term *mutation* is used in the narrow sense of a change at a single locus (*e.g. cf.* Hämmerling, 1929, p. 1) or in a less restricted sense for both gene-mutations and the results of chromosomal abnormality (Morgan, Bridges and Sturtevant, 1925).

Though it is quite certain that part of the variation induced by the action of the environment is not heritable (somatic variation, ' modification,' ' fluctuation '), such variation is not to be distinguished by inspection of its visible effects from heritable variation and it is quite common to find that a given variation (*e.g.* in size) is heritable in some cases and non-heritable in others. The heritability or non-heritability of a character can be determined only by experiment, and even the argument as to the status of a given character based on analogy with other cases in which heritability has been experimentally proved, is insecure.

Somatic variation is a very widely occurring phenomenon and is due to a great diversity of environmental factors. It ranges from minute changes in size, shape and colour to excessive and ' monstrous ' changes. The causes may be operative over large areas and whole populations may be affected by them, or they may be local and operative only in exceptional circumstances. There is an unfortunate tendency to use the term ' purely phenotypic ' for such variation, but ' phenotypic ' has a precise and totally different meaning, so that this usage is undesirable. The term ' Dauermodifikation ' (for which no English equivalent is in common use) has been given by Jollos and others to temporary and reversible alterations of the hereditary constitution.

In distinguishing between hereditary and non-hereditary kinds of variation we touch on what is the most important distinction from the evolutionary point of view. We ought, however, to remember that hereditary variation may be either due to the combination and recombination of pre-existing factorial material or to the introduction of new hereditary material. Moreover, as is well known to systematists, variation may be due to the divers combinations into which the characters of the zygote enter. Thus series of species are known which represent the permutation and combination of a common stock of characters, *e.g.* :

Species *a* may have the constitution ABCDEF
    ,,   *b*   ,,   ,,   ,,   ,,   BCEFGH
    ,,   *c*   ,,   ,,   ,,   ,,   ABDEGH

The nature of variation may be further studied according to whether we are considering (*a*) the part of the organism affected, (*b*) the extent of the deviation from the norm, or (*c*) the mode of its occurrence having regard to (i) its spatial distribution, (ii) its frequency of occurrence, and (iii) its limitations.

(*a*) By far the greatest part of our knowledge of variation relates to the structural characters of animals. Herein it appears to be practically universal and it affects the size, form and arrangement of parts and also appears in the form of meristic as opposed to substantive variation (Bateson) as well as in the phenomena of homeosis (replacement of one part by another). It is much open to discussion whether certain parts or areas of the animal body are more subject than others to variation. For example, Pelseneer (1920, p. 409) holds that ectodermal derivatives are more subject to variation than those derived from the other germ-layers. This opinion has been combated by Robson (1928, p. 48).

Variation is also seen in the various functions and activities of animals. Our knowledge here is more scanty and in need of systematisation : but there is ample evidence, *e.g.* from the data in ' Tabulae Biologicae ' and such a work as Winterstein's ' Vergleichende Physiologie,' that variation occurs in the majority of the vital activities and their products. It is hardly necessary to state that variation in ' performance ' is a familiar phenomenon in applied genetics. Finally, there is evidence of very considerable variation in habits, food- and habitat-preferences and similar activities.

(*b*) It was originally customary to draw a distinction between *continuous* and *discontinuous* variation. The former were held to consist of the slight differences found between individuals, even when they are of identical genotypic constitution. The latter were the clearly marked and uncommon variations sometimes alluded to as ' sports.' Genetical study has tended to minimise the importance of this distinction. Originally held to be distinct in kind the first were thought to be non-heritable, the latter to be heritable (' mutations ' of de Vries). It is now realised (*cf.* Chapter IV) that there is no essential difference between the two; both marked and slight variations are known to be heritable.

(c) (i) Variant individuals are not distributed in space at random and in a chaotic fashion. In the first place there is a very marked correlation (more marked in some groups of animals than in others) between the ecological background and the type of variation, which is one of the most obvious effects of the susceptibility of the living organism to its environment. There is also a tendency for variant individuals which demonstrably do not owe their peculiarities to their environment to be distributed in certain specific ways. The most familiar example of such distribution is the geographical race.

(ii) The frequency of heritable variation is one of the most important topics of modern evolutionary study. It is now generally agreed that gene-mutations are of the greatest importance, as they are regarded as the only source of new evolutionary material. It is usually stated that they occur very infrequently, and this conception is of prime importance in the modern statement of the theory of Natural Selection (Fisher, 1930; Haldane, 1932). How true this conception is it is impossible to say, as the subject has only been intensively studied in two species kept in artificial conditions. However, it is desirable to keep in mind the probability that the very great profusion of variation among animals in nature is due mainly to somatic differences and factorial recombinations.

This conception has introduced a rather different outlook on the rôle of Natural Selection. Darwin in no place in ' The Origin ' or any other of his works, as far as we know, committed himself to any pronouncement as to the frequency of heritable variation. He repeatedly insisted indeed on the slowness of the selective process. This we imagine was due to his belief in ' blended inheritance ' and his realisation of the smallness of the individual steps and the comparative infrequency of serviceable ones, rather than to any idea of the infrequency of any heritable variation. Nevertheless he conveys the distinct impression that he thought that the stock of heritable variation was plentiful. We are now confronted with the suggestion that *any kind of mutation* is very rare, so that the additional qualification that it must also be serviceable renders it highly necessary that Selection must act with great efficiency ; it also introduces the question—how frequently will such rare mutations coincide with the selective circumstances that confer on them an advantage? This matter will be discussed at greater length at a later stage in this work.

(iii) On surveying the general field of variation in all its aspects the first impression one gains is of the very great plasticity of animals. This is, it is true, more clearly seen in some groups than in others, but marked variability is very general. Nevertheless variation is subject to strict limitations. The living organism is not capable of variation in all degrees and directions. Pantin (1932, p. 710), in an interesting essay, refers the limitations of variation to the fact that protoplasmic materials comprise a limited number of standard parts of limited properties. In spite of the seemingly infinite plasticity of morphological parts the variation of the living substance is limited by the character of its molecular structure. Thus Pantin (*l.c.* p. 709) cites the fact that only four respiratory pigments have been evolved capable of combining reversibly with oxygen. He suggests that the same limitation affects the capacity for morphological variation. We might explain on these lines the very notable occurrence of parallel evolution and the development of similar variation in allied species.

The limitations of variability in a particular group of animals (*Dinoflagellata*) has led Kofoid (1906, pp. 251–2) to stress the analogy between the variation of a group of 'elementary species' and a group of related organic compounds. 'The seeming reversion in these mutants (?) of *Ceratium* to old and fundamental subgeneric types, the occasional reversibility of mutations elsewhere and the limitations in the range and number of mutant types appearing in nature and under culture suggest that the chemical nature of living substances . . . place certain rather definite restrictions upon the number and amplitude of the departures which mutants make from their sources . . . the relation which exists among the members of a group of elementary species . . . presents a striking analogy to that which is found to exist among the various radio-active substances or members of a chemical series of related organic substances.'

In the preceding paragraphs we have considered the origin and nature of variation, and for the purpose of defining our particular problems it is now desirable to discuss a little more fully the way in which variants occur in nature.

At the offset the exact study of natural variation is rendered obscure by the relatively slight amount of precise knowledge as to which variants are heritable and which are mere fluctuations. Every population will contain a certain element of individual forms having the latter status and sometimes (possibly quite often) large sections of a population will be of this nature ; this is particularly true of plastic organisms, such as corals and hydroids, in which 'ecological types,' the products of the peculiar environmental conditions found in various habitats, have been often reported.

When fluctuations have been allowed for, as far as possible, we are left with the important heritable elements. Of these we may distinguish three kinds—(1) individual variants ; (2) groups ; and (3) special categories of various types.

(1) **Individual Variants.**—Individual variants occur in nature with very different frequencies and there is every gradation between the variant which occurs sporadically throughout a population and groups of appreciable size. In some classes and orders sporadic individual variation is common; in others, group-formation is more characteristic. The divergence of such individual variants may be in one or several characters.

(2) **Groups.**—Although no two individuals are ever exactly alike in all their characters, it is a commonplace that individuals can be classed together in assemblages or groups of various kinds. For the study of the origin of variation the constitution and status of such groups are irrelevant, but, inasmuch as we find that variant individuals tend to form groups characterised by the possession of a set of common and peculiar characters and that such group-formation seems to be the initial stage of evolutionary divergence, it is clearly part of our business to inquire into the process by which recognisable groups are formed.

These groups differ among themselves not only in their degree of distinctness, but also in the nature of the distinction. Thus a clone is a different kind of assemblage from a physiological race. The various kinds of groups recognised are discussed in Chapter III. For the moment we are concerned only with a single general question, viz. the relation between taxonomic units and the concept of the natural 'population.'

The facts of variation, and indeed all the phenomena with which the biologist deals, are most often given in association with a specific name. The very idea of variation assumes deviation from a norm which is invariably the character of a group defined (whether as species, subspecies, or race) by taxonomic procedure. To anticipate the discussion on the species (Chapter III) we must point out that the latter is not a group with standardised properties by which it can be invariably recognised as such. It is an abstraction from a number of individuals varying in such a way that any group or groups defined must do some violence to the natural divergences that certainly have always occurred in time and very frequently occur in place. There are further difficulties to note which arise from the actual imperfections of taxonomy. The vast literature of taxonomy and the categorical nature of its definitions obscure the incompleteness of our knowledge in this branch of zoology. In certain limited groups in which abundant series have been collected and studied critically the status of the species at least rests on a solid foundation. In many groups, however, particular species are known only from a few individuals, sometimes of one sex only. Sometimes our knowledge of the range of variation of a species depends on whether two forms found in different areas are really identical and no adequate comparison of them has ever been made. Often purely nomenclatorial difficulties intervene, *e.g.* where one species is known under more than one name in different countries. All these difficulties are intensified when we are dealing with the finer taxonomic units, such as very closely allied species or geographical races. Many generalisations about the variation of particular species are still rendered dubious in this way, probably many more than is usually supposed. The imperfections of taxonomy in this respect are doubtless temporary, but they are at the present time a great practical difficulty in the investigation of variation in nature and not uncommonly they produce an element of doubt in generalisations as to distribution and similar matters.

A species, like a molecule, is a statistical summary, and a comparison of its properties with those of related forms can most efficiently be made with the aid of statistical methods involving tests of significance. When simple measurements, such as those of size, are being made or when the material studied consists of numerically small samples, these tests are often indispensable, but in a broad survey like the present

one we are limited in two ways.   First, we are bound to give
some weight to statements not verified by these methods, when
the author alone has had, and perhaps can have, access to
the material.   Secondly, many problems in the study of
variation appear at present to be outside the field of statistics,
because it is not yet possible to obtain sufficiently accurate
measurements for statistical tests to be applied, *e.g.* to differences in habit or to some of the finer structures.   Often those
characters which are most easy to measure have no biological
significance, while those for which measurement is most needed
are least susceptible to it.   Finally, all taxonomists are familiar
with differences between races and species which depend on
a general ' facies ' ;   the individual characters which go to
make up this facies can be measured singly and the correlation
between any pair of them determined, but no single formula
can express the whole.

We have laboured this point in order that at the offset it
may be amply clear that the study of variation within groups
is bound up with systematic procedure and is liable to errors
arising out of the inevitable defects of the latter.   We do not
wish to minimise the risks to which theories of evolution are
liable through defective systematics.   But although species and
other systematic categories are important reference points and
significant episodes in the course of evolution, with modern
intensive collecting-methods and the intensive study of large
numbers of individuals, the centre of interest is passing from
the systematist's species to the ' natural population ' from
which the species is abstracted.

The term *natural population* (*cf.* Chapter III) is given to
any assemblage of individuals of a species living in nature irre-
spective of its systematic relationships, *i.e.* whether it is homogeneous or whether it contains diverse genotypic elements.
A ' population ' consists of a number of more or less genotypically similar individuals which are better able and have
more opportunity to interbreed with one another than with
the individuals of other populations.   Such populations
considered taxonomically may be only a group of individuals
isolated topographically (*e.g.* on an island) from other structurally identical individuals, or they may form a definite
variety, geographical race or species.   The taxonomic name
given to the population depends on a variety of circumstances,

but we are concerned with the character of the population rather than with the name given to it. In the study of such populations we can use for convenience any name that may have been given by a taxonomist, even though groups put into the same taxonomic category are not necessarily equivalent in degree of isolation or divergence. Nevertheless the distribution of variants in nature does not, in general, appear to be at random ; they are arranged so that different types of populations can be recognised. Populations may be distinguished by a varying number of physiological and structural characters which may be correlated in different degrees with one another. Further, the size of the area inhabited and the nature of the factors limiting the area may differ.

Topographical groups.—By far the most striking manifestation of natural variation is the occurrence within a population of larger or smaller groups of some measure of homogeneity. Usually these are defined by at least partial isolation and they range in size from a small patch of individuals (colony), peculiarly characteristic of small sedentary animals like land snails, to a group occupying an extensive area (geographical race). Such groups may be rigorously isolated from neighbouring races, or they may overlap. In the growth of these assemblages we may note as in (1) that the divergence of one or more characters may be involved.

(3) **Special Categories.**—The terms *polymorphism* and *dimorphism* are sometimes used without any general agreement as to their meaning and it is necessary to clear up this ambiguity. In its clearest and most usually employed sense dimorphism is applied to the occurrence within a species of two strongly marked and discontinuous phases, such as we see in the difference between the colour, etc., of males and females, between seasonal forms, or between mimetic forms (*e.g.* the East and West African female of *Acraea alciope* (Lepidoptera), Eltringham, 1910, pp. 44–45). The term has also been given to other contrasted types within a species, whose occurrence is not apparently related to bionomic needs, *e.g.* by Bouvier (1904 : dimorphism of the Atyidae).

Polymorphism has been used either in a general way to denote that a population is very variable (*cf.* Coutagne, 1895) or with a special significance to denote the occurrence of several well-marked phases which inhabit the same area.

The latter meaning is the one used in this work. The phenomena to which it is applied are best exemplified by the mimetic
phases of certain Lepidoptera. Rarely, seasonal variation
may also be found to produce a polymorphic series, *e.g.* in
Daphnia acutirostris Woltereck (1928) found an unusual cycle
consisting of spring, summer and winter forms.

Over and above the variation just described a population
may contain other special elements such as castes (*e.g.* in
Hymenoptera), ' high ' and ' low ' males (Scarabaeidae) and
developmental phases.

General theories of evolution have usually concerned
themselves with questions as to the origin and importance of
new characters and the processes by which the continuous
transformation of such characters is brought about. The
reference to group-formation in the previous paragraphs
stresses an aspect and a result of the evolutionary process
which, though they are universally recognised, are perhaps too
little regarded. Darwin has been taxed for naming his most
important work ' The Origin of Species.' We may admit that
he thus gave undue prominence to the species as opposed to
other systematic categories ; but the implication that the
problem of evolution is closely bound up with that of the origin
of groups shows that he realised what to our minds constitutes
one of the essential problems of evolution. The formation
of groups having some degree of distinctness seems to be a
universal property of living organisms, and the whole scheme
of animate nature reveals itself as a hierarchy of groups beginning with simple aggregates of the status of the pure line, the
clone and the colony and developing in distinctness and individuality through the local race to the species and higher
categories.

The main qualitative changes in evolution no doubt begin
with changes in single characters, and for the essential features
of the process, the linear changes in the history of organs and
of one individual type into another, the occurrence of groups
is perhaps at first sight irrelevant. As long as the necessary
changes occur, the question as to whether they occur in one
or 1,000 individuals might seem unimportant. But evolution
does not proceed by the transformation of single organisms,
but by the mass changes of populations. The outstanding
feature of the process as it is seen in palæontological and

systematic data is the continued break-up of populations, the divergence of the groups thus formed along different paths, and the replacement of groups having one kind of constitution by other groups having a different constitution. What we have to account for is not only the changes in single characters or groups of characters in single individuals, but also the means by which they become characteristic of populations. We stress this obvious and generally accepted truth, because in the generalisations based on experiments and observations in the laboratory, or in the genetical and mathematical treatment of the subject, emphasis is usually laid on the origin of new characters and their chances of survival and the fact of group formation are neglected. Moreover, various authors (*e.g.* Kinsey, 1930, pp. 34–35 ; Hogben, 1931 ; Guyénot, 1930, p. 211 *et seq.*) have suggested that any mutant might spread, if it was not actually harmful to its bearer. Darwin also was evidently of the same opinion and seemed to think that ' neutral ' characters might survive. Haldane and Fisher, however, have clearly shown that the mere fact of re-emergence from a cross does not confer on mutations the power to spread through a population. The spread of variants is, indeed, one of the most crucial problems in the study of evolution.

We will now proceed to formulate what we believe to be the chief problems which a study of natural variation raises.

(i) A population inhabiting a definite area may gradually change in the course of time, or two populations, originally similar and practically homogeneous, but inhabiting different areas, may diverge so as to become two distinct groups. The two processes are probably much the same, though in the latter case it may be possible to point out definite differences in the environment of the two areas to which the divergence might be due. In either case we have to explain the origin of the new characters by which the diverging groups differ from those they used to resemble, *i.e.* we have to consider the *causes* of *variation*.

(ii) As indicated on pp. 8–11, variants are not found distributed chaotically but in groups of various kinds. It is necessary to define *what these groups are* and *how they occur in nature*.

(iii) It is evident that our definition of the term ' population ' depends not only on a morphological criterion but also on differences in ability to interbreed, populations being more or less isolated from one another. We may distinguish between populations separated by temporary topographical barriers, populations which, if the barriers were removed, would interbreed freely and soon become homogeneous, and those separated by permanent reproductive barriers either of instinct or due to sterility. In the latter case the populations remain distinct even when inhabiting the same area. The study of variation, therefore, is much concerned with the *origin* and *causes* of *isolation*.

(iv) In different individuals of a population are many more or less peculiar characters, but only those will be called specific which are found in association in the bulk of the members. Thus the specific characters are more or less correlated with one another and we have to investigate the *origin* and *causes* of this *correlation*.

(v) The divergence of populations depends not only on the occurrence of new variations but on their accumulation to give rise to those groups of characters by which species are recognised. Any new character to become specific, if it does not first appear in a number of individuals simultaneously, must arise in one or a few individuals and then spread through the species. We must further consider, then, the *spread of new characters* within the population.

(vi) We have finally to consider what is the relationship between the establishment of groups and the main tendencies of evolution. It is almost universally held that the main adaptive divergences which constitute the most striking feature of evolution are merely group-divergences progressively raised to a higher power by the continued operation of the same processes that produced group-formation. We consider that this is a questionable doctrine. Chapters IX and X are devoted to a consideration of the relation between variation and organisation.

The problems enumerated above will be treated in the following order. In Chapter II we consider the origin of variation. In Chapter III we enumerate the types of groups recognised as the result of various methods of study (systematic, genetical, etc.), and in Chapter IV we detail how variants and groups of variants are actually found in nature.

The action of isolation in producing discontinuity is dealt with in Chapter V and that of correlation in Chapter VI. The efficacy of Natural Selection as the most generally accepted theory of the spread of new characters is examined in Chapter VII. It is shown that the scope of this process is questionable. In Chapter VIII we examine the other theories of evolution, and in Chapter IX the nature of adaptation and the special difficulties of explaining its origin are detailed. In a general summary (Chapter X) we attempt to define the relationship between adaptation, variation and group-formation and to distinguish between their presumed causes.

We may conclude this chapter with some remarks on procedure in evolutionary inquiry in so far as our methods are involved.

Many of the subjects mentioned above can be investigated experimentally. The origin and mode of inheritance of variation are almost exclusively to be treated in this way. The validity of the selection hypothesis, as an explanation of the spread of variants, has been likewise tested by experiments in the field and in the laboratory, and the formation of new habits, food preferences, reactions to the environment, etc., have been similarly investigated. The behaviour of animals, their interrelationships, seasonal occurrence and the incidence of actual environmental pressure on animal populations are most profitably studied by direct observations in the field. For the study of the distribution of variants in nature, the formation of groups and the incidence of correlation we fall back on the methods of taxonomy and statistical analysis, though the findings of genetics are of service here : of supreme importance is the method of population-analysis, which is a combination of statistics, field observation and taxonomy. This has been much in vogue during the past thirty years. It dates further back indeed, viz. to the pioneer work of Coutagne, Gulick, Duncker and Heincke, and to other studies, particularly of economically important animals (fishes). More intensive and critical work supported by modern genetical and statistical methods has been conducted by such workers as Crampton, Schmidt, and Sumner.

In this work we are approaching the subject of evolution primarily as taxonomists. We believe that all theories of evolution should be tested by the results of taxonomy (dealing with both living and fossil forms) and population-analysis. These two studies, more than any others, bring the theories of evolution into contact with the gross facts of nature. We realise their specific limitations and in particular the need to supplement them by observations on habits and behaviour, but we feel that they constitute an acid test of evolutionary theories based on other studies. This test has been insufficiently applied in the past. It is well worth while to try to describe the facts of nature as they actually are and to see what are the *simplest* deductions suggested. There has been a tendency to ignore or distort certain observations because they fail to fit in with the theories, *e.g.* some of them seem to suggest a neo-Lamarckian explanation of evolution, but this idea has been nearly always ruled out on *a priori* grounds. The occurrence of non-adaptive specific characters, and certain palæontological and other evidence suggest that variants can spread without any adaptive qualifications. But recently mathematical theories have been invoked to prove that this is impossible. We believe it is advisable to make new contacts between theories so obviously developed by deductive methods and the large body of recorded observations from which they have been so long divorced.

It appears that on the whole modern writers on evolution fall into three classes. The first are impressed by the obvious facts of adaptation. They take variations for granted and tend to describe the assumed effects of selection. The second argue from a relatively few animals which have been studied under laboratory conditions. They tend to assume that, when once a mutation has occurred, it can look after itself and that, as long as it is not harmful, it can spread through a population. The third class, recognising that the spread of variants needs explanation, have given exact mathematical expressions for the efficiency in this respect of Natural Selection without, however, first showing that that process is actually operative in nature.

In our attempt to evaluate the evidence put forward on behalf of the various theories of evolution we discuss the logical conditions for an exact proof of certain theories and in particular (p. 186) Woodger's account of the stages by which a theory attains the status of an accepted truth. It is unfortunate that along with the development of theories as to the causes of evolution no serious methodology has been developed and very little attention has been paid to the logical requirements of such inquiry. The ground is partly covered by Woodger's admirable 'Biological Principles' (1929) ; but there is still need for an inquiry into the methods of evolutionary research and the logical procedure by which the main and subsidiary theories may be tested.

CHAPTER II

THE ORIGIN OF VARIATION

IT is generally held at the present time that there are three main types of variation differing in their mode of origin, viz. : (1) *fluctuations* or non-heritable somatic variations, (2) the effects of *recombination of existing genes*, and (3) *mutations* in the wider sense (Chapter I, p. 4). Most biologists believe that there is a real distinction between *spontaneous* germinal change, which is heritable, and non-heritable fluctuations, and they experience great difficulty in accepting any evidence that changes wrought either on the body cells or on the germ cells by external agencies, by use or by changed habits, are inherited. It is our object in this chapter to examine the evolutionary importance of the different modes of origin of variation. After estimating the importance of those processes we consider whether fluctuations can ever become hereditarily fixed. We deal with these questions in the following order :

1. Fluctuations.
2. The basis of heritable variation.
3. Recombination.
4. Mutation in the restricted sense—Gene-mutations.
5. The inheritance of induced modifications :
   - (a) General considerations.
   - (b) Experiments.
   - (c) Circumstantial evidence.
   - (d) Habit-formation.
   - (e) Summary.

Finally, we attempt to summarise the data and to evaluate their importance in the study of evolution.

Before proceeding with this programme we may consider what importance the origin of variation has in the study of evolution. An intelligent layman once observed to one of us : 'Why do you worry how variations arise : surely it is their fate that matters?' Up to a point this is a valid criticism. But, if we anticipate what is discussed in later chapters, it is of considerable importance to decide whether new variants arise only in a few scattered individuals or whether in some cases whole populations are changed simultaneously. In the former case we have to explain how the rare variants spread. Again, any factor seriously affecting the rate of mutation might have some influence on the chance of establishment of mutants, especially in a rare species. In fact, apart from its logical value in completing the theory of evolution, some knowledge as to the origin of variations is necessary to form any theory at all.

1. FLUCTUATIONS

That animals are more or less 'plastic' or modifiable by the environment in their structure, reactions and physiological properties and activities is a fact of general knowledge.[1] We do not propose to describe the many and varied effects which external factors produce. They have been sufficiently detailed in a number of works, and the varying action of temperature, salinity and other chemical factors, humidity, etc., is familiar to most biologists. Surveys of the subject have been made by Hesse (1924), Cuénot (1925), and others, and studies of the effects of all known environmental factors on a single group of animals have been made for the Mollusca by Pelseneer (1920) and less fully for the Insecta by Uvarov (1931) and Chapman (1931).

In actual practice the proof of the non-hereditary nature of a variation is relatively infrequent and the great bulk of 'fluctuations' is diagnosed as such on *a priori* grounds. Yet no variation, as far as we know, declares its origin by its mere 'appearance' (p. 78). Whether it is a fluctuation or of fixed heredity can be determined with certainty only by experiment. Nevertheless many systematists and other writers proceed as if it were possible to determine the nature of a variant by mere

---

[1] The ease with which some animals are experimentally or otherwise modified by their environment should not lead us to ignore the marked constancy with which others retain their specific characters. Nabours (1929, p. 55) lists a long series of environmental factors which have no effect on the colour-patterns of the grouse-locusts (Tettigidae).

inspection and write-off many forms as ' mere fluctuations ' or ' due to the environment.' It may be claimed that this procedure is justified by analogy with effects known to be produced by experiment. But actually a number of experiments has been claimed to show that certain effects are due to the environment, though no examination was made of the behaviour of the affected characters in heredity. Further, the amount of variation that is treated as non-heritable is far in excess of the number of cases that have been experimentally verified.

It is not easy in fact to obtain more than relatively few instances of characters which have been shown experimentally to be non-heritable. Among the Mollusca, the form *albolateralis* of *Arion empiricorum (ater)* (Collinge, 1909), the carinate and ecarinate forms of *Paludestrina jenkinsi* (Robson, 1929), and various forms of *Limnea peregra* (Boycott, Oldham and Waterston, 1932) seem to be definitely fluctuations. Pelseneer (1920, p. 641) catalogues a list of ' variations non héréditaires ' in the Mollusca ; but in all his cases, except that of *Arion ater*, there is no evidence that the character in question was not acting as a simple recessive, since the breeding test was not extended to more than one generation. In the insects, which have been so much used for genetical research, rather more cases are available. Some of the naturally occurring colour-variations of the bug *Perillus bioculatus* (Knight, 1924) and of the parasitic wasp *Microbracon brevicornis* (Génieys, 1922) are certainly not inherited. As for variations known only under artificial conditions, we may mention a white variant of the moth *Ephestia kühniella* (Kühn and Henke, 1929) and a number of variants in *Drosophila*, especially reduplications of various organs (Morgan, Bridges and Sturtevant, 1925, p. 71 *et seq.*). Amongst birds, Beebe's (1907) experiments on the effect of a humid atmosphere on doves of the genus *Scardafella* are well known. In the rotifers, Kikuchi (1931) shows that in *Brachionus pala* lateral spines are developed when the animal is fed on the alga *Scenedesmus* ; the spines are lost when it is fed on *Polytoma*, and the action is completely reversible.

A point worth remembering in discussing this question is that a given character may be heritable in one form and not in another. This is especially evident in the matter of the total size of an organism which is determined not only by the available food and the temperature at which development occurs, but also by numerous genetic factors. It seems also to be the case in some of the naturally occurring strains of *Daphnia* studied by Woltereck (1908) ; *e.g.* the low-helmed form from the Lund See could be easily transformed into a high-helmed form, but the apparently similar variant (mutant E) of the Frederiksburg See could not be modified by the same conditions.

These facts are of some importance. In the minds of most workers there is a general idea that animals live in a variety of places and are exposed to a diversity of environmental factors that produce a great amount of merely somatic modifications —that all animals are in varying degrees plastic and receive a more or less marked amount of modification from the food they eat, the soil on which they live, and so on, and that much variation is without moment in evolution, because it is not heritable. The assumption that animals are plastic is no doubt a sound one ; but each case ought to be considered on its own merits and tested by experiment.

In practice what is done, in taxonomy at least, is to proceed by no particular principle except some such idea as that, if a short form of a marine Gastropod (*e.g.*) is found in brackish water, it is a ' stunted ' (somatic) form. The result is that species and their variation are described according to the systematist's very varying knowledge of experimental work. This is, of course, a matter of systematic procedure ; but it is important, as to a certain extent the work of the systematist is taken as evidence of the plasticity of animals. As we suggest later (p. 55) we do not know if this plasticity is actually without evolutionary significance. Moreover, most workers would probably agree that more of the alleged fluctuations are hereditary than was at one time supposed.

The rôle of intrinsic and extrinsic factors in the production of fluctuations deserves considerably more attention than it has yet received. Investigations are often carried out under insufficiently standardised conditions and there is a consequent tendency to attribute variation to unknown differences in the environment. Again, there is usually a considerable probability that the species studied are genetically very diverse. The two loopholes so provided are quite sufficient to prohibit much generalisation. It would, however, be a matter of some interest to discover how far variation can be eliminated by rearing stringently selected strains under thoroughly controlled conditions. It appears by no means impossible that a certain, not altogether negligible, range of variation might remain under the most severe precautions. The complex organisation of the higher animals would appear to be inherently unstable and liable to irreversible changes. The data with regard to conditioned reflexes suggest that this may be the case in the nervous system and it is likely that other organ-systems may be liable to similar 'habit-formation.' Under severely controlled conditions it might still be possible for permanent 'deformations' to result from intrinsic causes. There are, of course, good grounds for believing that physiological rhythms may be permanent in at least the lifetime of the individual. Thus Payne (1931) found that in the parasitic wasp *Microbracon hebetor*, adults taken from cultures reared at high temperatures lived a shorter time at all temperatures than those taken from lower temperatures. In the future it may be hoped that the large amount of research now being conducted into the effects of controlled conditions of temperature and humidity on insects will provide significant data.

2. The Basis of Heritable Variation

The nature and distribution in heredity of the visible characters of an organism are to an important extent determined by the way in which they are represented in the chromosomes of the germ cells. Thus some characters are determined by a single gene, others by several genes, and others again by complementary genes. Or again the distribution of certain characters will depend on whether linkage occurs or not. The way in which characters are genetically determined will thus influence their variation.

In discussing the origin of variation we have to distinguish carefully between the origin of new hereditary material and the occurrence of variation due to differences in the way in which characters are genetically represented. The latter includes, for example, the effects of recombinations and complementary genes. We have, therefore, to examine the various ways in which characters are genetically determined in order to distinguish the sources of new evolutionary steps (mutation) from other forms of hereditary variation.

Haldane (1932, p. 37 and foll.) has distinguished six modes of genetic representation which are tabulated below, though it is by no means clear that all are found among animals.

(1) Characters determined by extra nuclear factors (plasmons). Haldane thinks that some of Goldschmidt's results (1923) on sexuality in moths illustrate this (*cf.* also Boycott, Diver and others (1930); Toyama (1912) on heredity of voltinism in silkworms).

(2) Characters determined by a single gene.

(3) ,, ,, ,, several genes.

(4) ,, ,, ,, genes which undergo re-arrangement (but not alteration in number and quality).

(5) ,, ,, ,, genes some (but not all) of which are represented more or less than twice in aberrant types of individual, *e.g.* non-disjunction.

(6) ,, ,, ,, genes the total diploid number of which is increased by one or more whole sets (polyploidy).

Before proceeding to discuss these various modes of genetic representation we ought to remind the reader that the term ' mutation ' is applied either in a narrow sense to changes in a single gene or to the various phenomena of chromosomal abnormality and other variations dependent on variation in the genetic basis of characters. It seems clear that in Haldane's list the differences enumerated under 2, 3 and 4 are chiefly related to differences in the distribution of characters and to recombination. Differences in sex and fertility are also associated with 4 (attachment of X to Y chromosome).

Morphological change seems to be associated with 5 in plants, and Haldane states (*l.c.* p. 52) that the presence of an extra chromosome generally produces a very unhealthy type (*cf.* production of intersexes possessing the second and third chromosomes in triplicate and the X in duplicate in *Drosophila* (Morgan, Bridges and Sturtevant, 1925, p. 156)). It is not clear if any morphological changes are associated with this abnormality. As to 6 the position is uncertain. Polyploidy is not completely absent from animals, but according to Gates (1924, p. 177) there is nothing comparable to the condition found in plants. Varieties *univalens* and *bivalens* with 2X and 4X chromosomes have been recorded in *Ascaris megalocephala*, *Artemia salina*, etc. In three out of the four cases noted by Gates 'no particular significance seems attached to the bivalent or tetraploid conditions' (*l.c.* p. 177). In the Phyllopod *Artemia salina* it appears to be associated with differences in reproduction, a tetraploid form of that species being parthenogenetic. Tetraploids have been found in *Drosophila* (Morgan, Bridges and Sturtevant, *l.c.* p. 21), but 'as yet their chromosomes have not been studied.' As regards the appearance of entirely new characters from any of the various modifications of chromosomes (either those treated here as abnormalities or those figuring in 4 to 6) in Haldane's list, it seems clear that new characters or at least new complexes of characters have arisen, *e.g.* as seen in the appearance of the 'Diminished' mutant due to the loss of a 'fourth chromosome' (Morgan, Bridges and Sturtevant, *l.c.* p. 136). But, owing to low viability (*l.c.* p. 137), it certainly seems that this type and probably other similar ones are of small evolutionary importance.

Up to the present we have had little opportunity outside the study of *Drosophila* to distinguish between the various causes of mutation (in the broad sense, p. 4), so that it is not possible to distinguish between gene-mutation and chromosomal abnormality, etc., from the evolutionary point of view. On the other hand, in the many experiments on induction, etc., that have been carried out, we do not know what kind of mutation is involved. From Mavor's experiments (1922) it seems clear that X-ray treatment causes non-disjunction of the X-chromosome.

3. RECOMBINATION

It is sometimes not realised what an enormous scope for variation lies in the permutation of a relatively small number of gene-differences. Fisher (1930, p. 96) points out that in a species with a hundred segregating factors the number of different true-breeding genotypes would be so large as to require thirty-one figures to express it, or forty-eight if the heterozygotes are included. Thus, even if thousands of millions of individuals are produced in any one generation and no two individuals are genetically alike, only a small fraction of the possible combinations would actually be realised. The possibilities of recombination are much enhanced by the variation in the expression of genes when combined with different gene-complexes.

Outside domesticated forms it is not very easy to find good examples of the effects of recombination. Permutations of specific characters within a genus are, of course, very familiar, but owing to the occurrence of sterility, etc., are rarely capable of genetical investigation. Amongst domestic animals recombination, leading to novel forms, was early recognised in poultry, rabbits and pigeons. In a wild insect we may mention the cases of *Papilio polytes* investigated by Fryer (1913) and of *Aricia medon* studied by Harrison and Carter (1924). In the latter species two forms meet on the Durham coast and a wide range of variants, many not known elsewhere, is produced. More usually the meeting of two geographical forms leads merely to the production of *simple intermediates* (see p. 89). It is probable that recombinations of numerous small gene-differences in wild populations are responsible for a considerable part of the continuous range of variation in size, colour, etc., often alleged to be fluctuational.

It is very difficult to assess the actual evolutionary value of the variation arising in this way. Some authors, such as Lotsy, have supposed recombination, especially after crosses between very different varieties or species, would supply all the variation required for evolution. This theory is more plausible in the case of plants—in which interspecific sterility is not so much developed—than in that of animals. The problem is not one of very easy direct approach, for genetical experiment on a sufficient scale is lacking, but some indirect evidence may be obtained. If the individuals of a species often differed from one another in a large number of genes we should expect that crosses of such individuals would give rise to a wide range of variation, including some forms perhaps quite distinct from either parent. Continued inbreeding of such a stock would give rise to a large number of distinct lines. Apart from domesticated forms, which are in quite a different category (*cf*. p. 188, Chapter VII), it is not easy to find good examples. In some of the most obvious cases, such as polymorphic butterflies or snails, the evidence suggests that the various forms differ in a rather small number of genes and the range of variation on crossing is not very great.   If we except geographical races and poly-morphic species, crosses within the species rarely give rise to a large series of variants.   We are not aware, however, of any serious attempt to discover by prolonged inbreeding how many genes might be present.   Duncan (1915) crossed specimens of *Drosophila* from widely separated localities, but found that no unusual amount of variation resulted.   Unfortunately, the flies of this genus are so largely spread by commerce that they are not suitable material for such an investigation.   Timofeef-Ressovsky (1927) obtained seventy-eight wild females of *Drosophila melanogaster* from a house in Berlin.   It was supposed that each of these had already mated with more than one male. As a result of interbreeding it was deduced that eighteen of the females and thirty-four of the males were heterozygous for at least one mutant.   Ten different genes were identified, some of them already known in cultures.

Geographical races when crossed often give a consider-able range of variation, usually intermediate between the parents.   If the types produced by recombination are few, the chances of a beneficial variant are smaller, while the larger the number of types, the fewer the individuals of each that will appear.   As far as the evidence goes, it would seem that most individuals of a species are homozygous for a large common stock of genes, so that little or no recombination would occur on crossing.   The geneticists' idea of a ' wild type ' is partly based on this assumption.   Of course we cannot say how far this is true of genes producing only very minute external effects, but we must judge by what evidence we have. When forms differ considerably, so that recombination would be expected to produce much variation, sterility in one form or another seems usually to intervene.   It is quite possible that the majority of animal species have *always* been homo-zygous for most of the genes carried at any one time.

No doubt some crossing between species, subspecies, etc., occurs in nature.   How far such unions are fertile is a very debatable point.   When we consider the diversity of means by which isolation is brought about (Chapter V) it does not seem likely that successful crossing is very common or that it occurs between individuals of markedly contrasted genetic constitution. In view of this, Lotsy's speculations as to evolution by crossing appear unlikely to have a wide application in the animal kingdom. There is a further difficulty in the way of Lotsy's theory. If it has been something more than a minor factor, we would have to admit that all the material of variation was in existence in the earliest forms of life, and evolution has consisted in the allocation to the forms which diverged from an ancestral stock of various portions of this fund of material and the recombination of parts of it to form new genetic groupings. That a good deal of factorial recombination (with the appearance of 'novelties' due to this cause) has taken place we do not doubt. But, if recombination is the only or even the main source of variation, we have to imagine evolution as merely the revelation of latent possibilities—a picture very difficult to harmonise with the facts, for, looked at in the broadest way, evolution undoubtedly leaves the impression of the *continuous* emergence of *new* types of organisms. Thus, while recombination has an obvious importance in trying out all the permutations of the material lying to hand, we feel the need of another process which will provide new material.

4. GENE-MUTATIONS

In spite of the vast amount of genetical research carried out during the past thirty years our knowledge of the origin of gene-mutations is still extremely slight. In the first place, if a given variant is a mutation and not merely a recombination, it should appear suddenly in an inbred stock. Thus only in very quick-breeding forms can much information be accumulated.

In the second place a distinction must be made between agencies which actually produce mutations and those which accelerate mutation-rates. We may illustrate this distinction by recalling the effect of temperature on growth in invertebrates. Here, while differentiation, within wide limits, proceeds independently of temperature, the actual rate at which it goes on is directly dependent.

In actual practice there is no known treatment which regularly produces a high proportion of any definite type of mutant. Such agencies as X-rays induce variation in all directions, while other treatments which have been supposed to produce 'one way' mutation have given only a very low percentage of mutants.   It is possible, therefore, that all these agencies merely alter a mutation-rate which, even without special treatment, would slowly lead to the production of mutations which the treatment makes more numerous.

Before considering the experimental evidence for alteration of the mutation-rate, there is one other point that must be considered.   Those who do not believe in the possibility of the inheritance of acquired characters sometimes write as if the experiments carried out in this connection were designed to investigate the factors controlling the mutation-rate.   Thus Sonneborn (1931), commenting on Macdougall's experiments on rats (see p. 40), writes as if Macdougall had produced a series of adaptive mutations (*i.e.* assuming Macdougall's claim to be technically sound).   In our view this is a confusion of the point at issue.   The question is rather whether there is not a special process, in addition to mutation, by which characters *gradually* become inherited under prolonged environmental influences.   We have to distinguish between (*a*) *induced mutations* which are hereditarily stable from the start and do not revert back to type except by a jump as sudden as that by which they arose, and (*b*) *induced modifications* which gradually become more intensified and more stable as the stimulus lasts longer and are often slowly lost when the stimulus is removed.   Variation of this second category is considered in our next section.   At the moment we shall consider only examples of what is clearly induced mutation.

It was long thought that gene-mutations were spontaneous because they are so rare, so erratic in occurrence, and apparently so unrelated to any known factor in the environment. It has been held that mutations observed in animals kept under standard cultural conditions cannot be related to an environmental cause, and the mode of origin of the *Drosophila*- and *Gammarus*-mutations has been regarded as evidence of first-class importance.   It may be noted that a great deal of the evidence relates to mutations in eye-colour and development (20 per cent. in *Drosophila*, 100 per cent. in *Gammarus*) and nearly all the mutants are more or less of the nature of defects.   This cannot but arouse suspicion that some disturbing external agency may be involved.

In so far as the vital activities are physico-chemically determined it is impossible to imagine that mutations can be truly spontaneous. Doubtless all that this term has meant in the writings of those who have thought out its implications, is that the agencies responsible for gene-constancy or gene-mutation are so numerous that it is difficult or impossible to speak of any one as *the* cause. A theoretical discussion has been given by Schmalfuss and Werner (1926) with reference to the hypotheses that the genes are enzymes (Goldschmidt) or autocatalytic substances (Hagedoorn), and the conclusion is favoured by them that mutations are produced by the action of external factors on specific catalysts.

More recently good experimental evidence has been put forward to show that high temperature, β-rays (of X-rays) or γ-rays (of radium) have a marked effect on the mutation-rate. We shall mention these experiments briefly in the order indicated.

A. *Effect of High Temperature.*—Goldschmidt (1929), Jollos (1930) and Rokizky (1930) have shown that the mutation-rate of *Drosophila* is very much raised when the late larvæ are subjected to a temperature so high (35°–37° C.) as to kill most of them. The attempts of other workers (*e.g.* Ferry and others, 1930 ; *cf.* also Muller, 1932) have been partially or completely unsuccessful. Apparently the mutations produced are all types that have already been recognised. Jollos obtained evidence that the mutations were largely in one direction and the effect cumulative. This is very suggestive of the actual causation of mutation, but more evidence is required on this point. The results should be compared with the Dauer-modifikation-experiments (p. 35).

B. *Effect of X-Rays.*—Muller (1928) showed that the mutation-rate of *Drosophila* was raised about 150 times by subjection to X-rays. Hanson, Heys and Stanton (1931) have recently shown that the increase in mutation-rate, as measured by the number of sex-linked lethals, is directly proportional to the X-ray dosage. Similar results have been obtained by Little and Bagg (1924) and Dobrovolskaia (1929) with mice. Most of the mutations are not unknown in normal cultures, though some of those in mice are apparently novel. The effect would seem to be one of general disturbance, since Mavor (see Morgan, Bridges and Sturtevant, 1925, p. 116) found that the amount of non-disjunction of the X-chromosome in *Drosophila* was also materially increased. Many papers have been published on this subject during the last few years, but these seem to be the essential facts.

Huxley (1926) and Haldane (in Robson, 1928) at one time suggested that naturally occurring radiations might cause the apparently spontaneous mutations. But Muller and Mott Smith (1930) have shown that this is highly improbable.

C. *Effect of Radium.*—Hanson and Heys (1928) obtained lethal mutations in *Drosophila* by exposing the males to the whole radiation of radium or to the γ-rays only. Similar results have been obtained in plants. On the whole it appears much more difficult to obtain positive results with radium than with X-rays.

D. *Experiments with Salts of Lead and Manganese.*—Harrison and Garrett (1926) and Harrison (1928*a*) claimed to have produced melanic mutations in certain Lepidoptera by feeding the larvæ on food-plants which had absorbed these metallic salts. Plunkett (1927) criticised the 1926 results chiefly on the score of the low number of individuals involved in the experiments. Recently, Hughes (1932) and Thomsen and Lemche (1933) have repeated the experiments on a very large scale without producing any melanics. It appears probable either that melanic mutations occurred as a very rare coincidence in the stock that Harrison was using or, as suggested by Haldane (in Hughes, *l.c.*), that the original parent was heterozygous and the recessive melanic factor is linked with a lethal. (*Cf.* also Harrison, *Proc. Roy. Soc.*, London, 117 B, 1935.)

We see therefore that in a few cases the mutation-rate has been directly affected by external agencies. It must not be forgotten, however, that some of the agencies used (*e.g.* X-rays) are not likely to be influential in nature. In the same way we should disregard the experimental induction of hereditary defect by such toxic agencies as alcohol (Stockard and Papanicolaou, 1916) and lead acetate (Cole and Bachuber, 1914), which really amount to a direct poisoning of the reproductive organs.

5. THE INHERITANCE OF INDUCED MODIFICATIONS

(a) **General Considerations.**—This subject has been discussed almost *ad nauseam* and there are numerous critical summaries. The most judicious and well informed, though by now a little behind the time, is that of Detlefsen (1925), which is admirable in its judgment and analysis. It omits some important experimental work (viz. that of Agar, Sumner and Woltereck) and does not discuss some of the circumstantial evidence (*e.g.* that based on geographical distribution) in detail. The analysis given by Robson (1928), which is largely based on Detlefsen's summary, contains a more detailed reference to these subjects, though the question of 'Dauer-modifikationen' (p. 35) is only lightly touched on, and it does not include mention of Woltereck's work. The following discussion is largely based on the two studies just alluded to, with an extended consideration of certain circumstantial evidence in addition.

There is no need for a long account of the historical controversy as to the origin of variation. It is enough to say that in the period up to and including the first acceptance of the theory of Natural Selection the heritable effects of environmental change or of use-inheritance were freely held, and Darwin himself, as is well known, accepted the idea.

The theoretical delimitation of the germ-cells from somatic tissues and the idea of the organic integrity of the former were due to Weismann, though he made a concession in favour of 'parallel induction' as the result of his acceptance of Fischer's experiments. Thus the matter stayed (with a few exceptions, mostly among the palæontologists) until the past two decades, when the matter has again been called into question by the work of Kammerer, Harrison, Przbram, Woltereck and Rensch, and by the advocacy of MacBride in this country.

Opponents of the theory of the 'inheritance of acquired characters' and even those who were prepared to accept the possibility that induced variation might be heritable have always found a serious objection in the difficulty of explaining how a modification of the parental soma might be transferred to the germ cells. The experiments of Castle and Phillips (1911) on ovarian transplantation in guinea-pigs have been held to show that germ cells having a given hereditary constitution are not modified by being transplanted to a new 'somatic' environment. These conclusions have been criticised by Detlefsen (*l.c.* p. 257). The latter goes on to show that there is much evidence to prove that our present cytological knowledge of the origin of germ cells suggests that they are not, at least in their early stages, likely to be immune from influences affecting the somatic tissues, inasmuch as they are, in many cases, morphologically indistinguishable from the latter (*cf.* also Gatenby, 1916).   However, the fact remains that no mechanism by which a true Lamarckian effect could be brought about has as yet been demonstrated. It is very easy to imagine that a new habit or a far-reaching somatic modification involving both structural and physiological re-organisation and readjustment might have a profound effect on the constitution of an animal. But the proof is still lacking that such readjustment would have a specific effect on the hereditary material of such a kind that the original somatic modification was reproduced.

It is customary to attach very great importance to the experimental evidence on this subject. Now the value to be set on experiment in such a matter is open to some doubt. It has the unfortunate limitation of being incapable of dealing (as Calman (1930) has pointed out) with the historical background of animal morphogenesis. This question becomes crucial when we consider the negative evidence brought forward to disprove the inheritance of induced variation. If such-and-such a stimulus repeated for a few months or a few years on a few generations fails to modify the germ cells, is there any reason for assuming that it will have no effect if the stimulus is applied, as it may well be in nature, for many years and decades and over innumerable generations? We cannot point to any case in which the duration of an induced effect is proportionate to the time-intensity of the stimulus ; but that such a contingency is possible ought not to be ignored and negative results have to be accepted subject to this reservation.

Before considering the experimental evidence we shall briefly set out what appear to be the essential conditions for a really convincing experiment. It is one of the misfortunes of the controversy that so much of the evidence is equivocal. The following are, we believe, the necessary precautions to ensure definite results.

1. *The Use of Inbred Stock.*—In our section on natural variation (Chapter IV) we show how often species consist of a mixture of strains. It is the universal experience of those who breed animals under artificial conditions that inbreeding for

several generations sorts out the strains. These may differ from
one another in all sorts of characters, both morphological and
physiological. If an environmental factor modifies the appearance or physiology of an animal, it is always necessary to make
sure that similar modifications, if not perhaps of the same
degree, do not occur in certain strains in nature.

There are two ways of guarding against this source of error.
The most satisfactory is to use an inbred stock. Ten generations of close inbreeding will probably isolate a reasonably
homogeneous strain. In many cases, however, this procedure would be very lengthy or even impossible. The only
method is to employ adequate controls, which indicate that
the modification does not occur normally in untreated portions
of the same stock. It is impossible to say how many control
animals should be maintained ; in a variable species the
number necessary for stringent experimental procedure might
be so large as to make some preliminary inbreeding almost
essential. Even with large numbers of controls a mutation by
a coincidence may happen to arise in the experimental animals,
but the reduplication of experiments with different stocks
reduces the risk of misinterpretation.

2. *The Elimination of Selection.*—The experimental treatment to which animals are subjected frequently causes considerable mortality. If the survivors show some modification,
it is always possible that the mortality has been selective
and the survivors are that part of the original stock which was
genetically fitted to live in the novel environment. The
'modification' of the survivors may be therefore only the
expression of their particular genetic constitution. Such
forms will be especially liable to lead the investigator to wrong
conclusions, because their characters will of necessity be
inherited.

The safest way of guarding against this error is to bring
to maturity every individual of every family throughout the
course of the experiment. If the experimental treatment
necessarily leads to considerable mortality, it may be almost
impossible to arrive at any convincing result, though the use
of highly inbred stock would be a great safeguard. In certain
cases (many insects) the size of the family is so great that the
stock would rapidly become unmanageably large if every
specimen was allowed to breed. In these circumstances it is

D

necessary to kill off part of each family, but the greatest care must be taken to avoid any selection. With adequate statistical treatment such material may still lead to a definite conclusion.

This difficulty arises in its most acute form when only some of the experimental animals show a modification. It has often been the practice to carry on the stock only from these modified individuals, thus introducing a stringent selection in the direction of the modification. Two suggestions may be made in this connection. First, repeated experiment with different strains may show that the modification always tends to arise in the experimental animals and never in the controls. If the experiment stops when the modified individuals first appear, no selection can have been exercised in that particular direction. If repeatable results of this sort can be obtained, the effect of selection in later experiments is relatively unimportant. Secondly, if the modification is an *induced mutation* and is permanently heritable from the start, selection is evidently only a secondary issue. To prove that there has been an induced mutation is chiefly a matter of reduplicating experiments with different stocks.

3. *Persistence of the Modifications.*—It is necessary to distinguish at the offset between induced mutations and any other sort of induced modification. Induced mutations resulting from subjection to high temperature or to X-rays are now well known in *Drosophila* and in mice. The discovery of other equally effective agencies would be a matter of great interest ; but it is evident that experiments of this sort throw no light on the point at issue here. If one admits that it is unlikely that mutations are really ' spontaneous,' the discovery of agencies which raise the mutation-rate need not excite great surprise, even when the mutations tend to be in a particular direction. The question is whether there is any process by which modifications *gradually* become hereditarily stable. There is a sharp distinction here from mutations which are stable from the start.

To prove that an induced modification gradually acquires stability is certainly a difficult matter and there is a danger that experiment will lead to a vicious circle in interpretation. If the process alluded to can occur, then the modification induced by experimental conditions must be expected to be *lost* when the animals are returned to the control environment. It is very difficult to decide what degree of permanence in the modification must be established to prove the possibility of the process. It is at least necessary that the modification should be partially maintained for at any rate one generation after the return to control conditions. Actually, in quite a number of experiments no return to the control environment was ever attempted.

4. *The Value of Negative Evidence.*—No amount of unsuccessful experiments can prove that modifications do not gradually become hereditarily stable. Under natural conditions it might require many thousands of years for the modification to become permanent.

On the other hand, the experiments should not entail subjecting the animal to conditions very unlikely to be met with in nature. If many thousands of years are required to produce a stable modification, it is probable that only a few simple agencies, such as low or high temperature or changed salinity in the sea, can be effective. Few other environmental factors are likely to operate steadily for long periods.

(b) **Experimental Evidence.** (i) *Experiments on Protozoa.*— This work has been summarised critically by various authors (see references in Robson, 1928, p. 168 ; and Hämmerling, 1929). The bulk of the work (Jennings, Jollos and others) concerns such forms as *Paramoecium* and *Arcella* and consists in their habituation to altered temperature-conditions or to doses of arsenic or calcium salts. Reversible modifications (' Dauermodifikationen ') are frequently found. Some (*e.g.* ' calcium-dauermodifikationen ') are in all probability determined by changes in the cytoplasm and reversion follows on the return to normal asexual reproduction after conjugation (*e.g.* in *Paramoecium*). In Bacteria also the changes are still manifested after transplantation to a new medium.

(ii) *Experiments on Metazoa.*—There is substantial evidence that lesions are not inherited. We need mention only such practices as circumcision, modification of shape of head or feet, docking of tails, etc., which produce no heritable effect after hundreds of generations (*cf.* also Agar, 1931).

There is a large number of experiments which may be set aside or regarded as so questionable as to be practically worthless as evidence. These are dealt with very briefly.

Author	Experiment	Criticism
i. Ferronière (1901)	*Tubifex* ; change of medium	No controls. ? Direct adaptation.
ii. Kellogg and Bell (1904)	*Philosamia* ; reduced diet	? Direct weakening of P and F_1 generations.
iii. Pictet (1910)	*Lymantria*; change of diet	? as ii. Possibly a 'Dauermodifikation.'
iv. Schröder (1903*a*)	*Gracilaria* ; change of habit	Lack of information as to natural variation in habits.
	Phratora ; change of food plant	Low number of cases (*cf.* Detlefsen, p. 262).
v. Fischer(1901, 1907)	*Arctia* ; effect of low temperature	? Genetic purity of stock.
vi. Standfuss (1898)	*Vanessa* ; effect of low temperature	? Genetic purity of stock.
vii. Schröder (1903*a*)	*Abraxas* ; effect of high temperature	? Genetic purity of stock.

v, vi and vii are suggestive of induced mutation, but there were no adequate controls.

viii. Guyer and Smith (literature in Guyer, 1923)	*Cavia* ; modification of lens by sera	Repeated unsuccessfully by Silfrast (1922), Finlay (1924), and Huxley and Carr-Saunders (1924). (Experiments not identical in the first two cases.) Diverse interpretations are possible (see Detlefsen, *l.c.* p. 266).
ix. Kammerer (1919)	*Alytes* ; modification of male thumb	Procedure questioned (*cf.* Noble, 1926).

x. Kammerer (1923)	*Ciona* ; truncation of siphons	Repeated by Fox (1924), who did not obtain the same result.

xi. Tower (1906). Colour changes induced in *Leptinotarsa* by alterations in temperature and humidity.

This very extensive series of experiments brings to light the fact that, if the stimuli were applied to the eggs or larvæ, little or no change was effected. If they were applied to the pupæ, changes were induced which were not inherited. But if the adults were exposed to the stimuli during the period of maturation, the offspring alone were modified and the effects were inherited. Tower's results have been very adversely criticised, unfortunately on the score of the actual accuracy of the results claimed. It is difficult to judge whether the criticisms are finally destructive or inspired by prejudice. The work has not been repeated, so that in all fairness it cannot be used as evidence.

More recent work on the effects induced by temperature and humidity in insects suggests that Tower's results must be at least very exceptional, though sublethal temperatures may induce mutation (p. 29).

xii. Dürken (1923) and Harrison (1928a). Colour changes in *Pieris*-pupæ.

Dürken studied *P. brassicae* ; Harrison, *P. napi*. In the former species under normal conditions about 4 per cent. of the pupæ are green, in the latter about 21 per cent. If the pupæ are exposed only to orange light a much higher percentage becomes green—in *P. brassicae*, 69 per cent. in the first generation, 95 per cent. in the second ; in *P. napi*, 93 per cent. and 95 per cent. respectively. In Dürken's experiment offspring of the first generation reared in normal light gave 41 per cent. green. Harrison's broods of the second generation gave 100 per cent. green in the third generation and 58 per cent. in the fourth. In both experiments the initial stock may have been somewhat mixed and there was considerable mortality, which may have involved some selection. Further, in both experiments only green pupæ were bred from to obtain the pupæ which were returned to normal conditions. In both experiments, and especially in Harrison's, the inherited modification occurred in far more of the offspring than would be expected if the result was entirely due to selection, considering the small amount of elimination involved. Further, in another experiment of Dürken's (see his fig. 8) selection of non-green pupæ did not eliminate the individuals with power to become green, so that there is no reason why reverse selection should have given a pure line of green. We believe a *prima facie* case has been made out for the inheritance of this modification.

xii*a*. Wladimirsky (1928). Colour of pupa of *Plutella maculipennis*.

In this moth the amount of black pigment in the pupa case appears to depend jointly on temperature, light and on hereditary constitution. In view of this complicated relationship it is rather difficult to come to certain conclusions. Wladimirsky's experiments, which were carried on over twelve generations, gave results not unlike those of Dürken and Harrison, though the author himself does not regard them as evidence for the inheritance of induced modifications, selection being at least partly responsible. The question how far selection was exercised in this case is a difficult one to decide, owing to the heterogeneous nature of the material.

xiii. Kammerer (1913). Induced colour-change in *Salamandra*.

These experiments were carried out and the results are presented in such a way as to make it impossible to draw any conclusions as to the inheritance of induced modifications. They were initiated with wild material, which may well have been genotypically diverse. No exact numerical data are given, so that it is impossible to discover whether any form of selection may have been practised. The number of individuals in which the induced changes were supposed to have been inherited is not explicitly stated.

xiv. Metalnikov (1924). Immunity of *Galleria* larvæ to the Cholera *Vibrio*.

The account of these experiments is not sufficiently detailed to enable one to draw any certain conclusions. There is no description of the stock used, no detailed lineages are set out, and the system of mating adopted is not stated. As far as can be gathered, larvæ were immunised against the *Vibrio* and the survivors in each generation were bred from. There was thus a stringent selection in favour of immunity and it is not surprising that the percentage of immunity eventually rose.

xv. Agar (1913). Effect of temperature and medium on *Simocephalus*.

Agar succeeded in inducing heritable changes in the size of *Simocephalus vetulus* (Cladocera) by raising the temperature of his cultures. He also experimentally induced an outward flanging of the edges of the carapace by keeping his cultures in Klebs' solution. These modifications were reproduced in F_1 individuals, the mothers of which had been restored to normal conditions just before the eggs were laid, and persisted for some generations, though they became progressively modified, *i.e.* they behaved as ' Dauermodifikationen.' Agar interprets them as effects of ' parallel ' modification. As reproduction was parthenogenetic, inheritance may have been through the cytoplasm.

xvi. Woltereck (1908, 1911, 1921, 1928). Modification of the ' helm ' in *Daphnia*.

The work of Woltereck on the modification of the ' helm ' of *Daphnia* stands in a rather different category from the work just described. Woltereck claimed to have induced a temporarily heritable change in the form of the ' helm ' by transplantation to a different medium and to have found natural races exhibiting characteristics similar to those which he induced, living in appropriate natural conditions. Woltereck's conclusions have been seriously challenged by Wesenberg-Lund, who supplies a totally different explanation, and the matter must be left very largely in abeyance, with the qualification that as far as Woltereck's experiments are concerned they bear a striking resemblance in the results to those of Agar.

xvii. Sumner (1932, summary). Geographical races of *Peromyscus*.

Sumner conducted for many years an extensive series of observations and experiments on the species and races of *Peromyscus* (deer-mice of N. America). He has summarised the work in a survey which involves the modification of views previously published. As he states (1932, pp. 2–3), he started the investigation ' with a distinct bias in favour of the cumulative effect of climatic influence.' This bias was due to the results of certain experiments on white mice. The animals were subjected to different temperatures and it was found that in 'warm room' temperature there was an increase in tail-, foot- and ear-length. The offspring of these were born and reared in normal temperature and had longer tails, ears, and feet than the progeny of animals kept in 'cold room' temperature. This was found in three out of four lots. In the fourth lot the relations as regards tail and foot were reversed. F_2 animals were not studied. For various reasons the experiments were not very satisfactory (see Robson, 1928, p. 170). It should be pointed out that similar results were obtained by Przibram (1909).

Transplantation experiments were undertaken with *Peromyscus* (1932, p. 27) and it was found that mice transplanted from one environment to another (*e.g.* from the Mohave Desert to La Jolla) showed no change over six to eight years and that there was no convergence in transplants of various races under the influence of a common environment. This fact and others (*e.g.* p. 58, the wide range in an unmodified condition through a diversity of environments of *P. maniculatus gambeli*) induced Sumner to abandon his belief in the effect of climate in producing subspecific characters, at least over a few generations.

xviii. Macdougall (1927, 1930). The inheritance of training in rats.

Macdougall has presented evidence to show that rats trained over twenty-three generations may be definitely modified. The animals had to escape from a tank full of water. They could attempt to escape either at a lighted platform (in which case they received an electric shock) or at an unlighted one (without a shock). There was evidence that the number of mistakes made by the rats before they chose the exit where they did not receive a shock was gradually reduced with each generation. The data are not treated statistically, but seem convincing. They have been criticised by Sonneborn (1931) on various technical grounds, especially that there may have been unconscious selection [1] or that the strength of the shock varied. We believe that Macdougall has made out a good *prima facie* case, but confirmation is required. Somewhat

---

[1] But *cf.* Rhine, J. B., and Macdougall, W., 1933, *Brit. J. Psychol.* (Gen. Section), 24, pp. 213–235. (The authors show that in fourteen generations selected adversely for ability, marked improvement took place.)

similar results claimed to have been established by Pavlov have now been withdrawn by the author (see Macdougall, 1927).

xix. Harrison (1927). Oviposition of the sawfly *Pontania salicis*.

Harrison found that the galls of this sawfly in any limited area tended to occur on only one species of willow, though in the whole range of the sawfly many species of willow were attacked. He therefore took sawfly galls from one willow and exposed them in a locality where only another species was available. In the most convincing experiment, in the first year there were few galls and many of these aborted, but later the sawfly became entirely attached to the new host, and, when tested five years later, the original host was no longer attractive. Harrison regards these experiments as a proof that an induced habit-change is inherited. It is possible to regard them as an evidence for ' larval memory ' (see remarks on biological races, pp. 50–52), the oviposition of the females being influenced by the nature of the site in which their larval life was spent. It has been suggested that crosses between certain moths show that oviposition-response segregates as a typical unit character and that therefore such responses must always be germinally fixed. We do not doubt that in many cases the oviposition-response is germinally fixed and it is possible that the temporary fixture by means of ' larval memory ' is a sort of ' half-way house.' But this is by no means proved, and, indeed, any attempt at direct proof would be likely to meet with invincible technical difficulties.

xx. Tornier and Milewski (literature in MacBride, 1924). Experiments with ' fancy ' types of *Carassius* (Goldfish).

Certain domesticated ' fancy ' breeds of Goldfish have been cultivated for a long time in China and Japan. They are characterised principally by abnormal development of the fins and the snout and head and by certain colour-changes (Ryukin and Ronchu types, *e.g.*). In the course of a long period of culture these aberrant types have been detected, iso-lated and bred from for ' fancy ' purposes. It is said that they breed true, but how far this is a fact is uncertain. In experi-ment (*e.g.* Milewski's) they seem to be relatively unstable. Tornier discovered by experiment, both on *Carassius* and other forms, that the abnormal structural features were due to scarcity of oxygen, and it is a fair inference that the original 'mutants' were produced by the unhygienic conditions of the culture practised in China, in which oxygen-starvation in particular was inevitable. We need not detail the particular action on the growing embryos of the oxygen-starvation, its specific effect on particular structures (to which Tornier devoted some very interesting study), nor Tornier's special theory of 'plasma-weakness,' which he held to be ultimately responsible for the malformations in question. What is not apparent from Tornier's and Milewski's experiments is that specific malformations produced under observation by a verifiable environmental factor are regularly transmitted to the offspring. It seems quite clear from some of Milewski's experiments (MacBride, *l.c.* p. 8) that embryos of one of the 'mutant' types (the Ryukin) born in conditions of oxygen-starvation, but reared in oxygenated water, give a high percentage of 'Ryukin' types (80 per cent.). It is nevertheless by no means apparent how far the experimental animals were genetically pure. If the regular causation of the abnormal condition by specific environmental factors is established, and if the original abnormal breeds were indeed produced by this cause, we might be disposed to admit that the inheritance of the character in control conditions suggests that an induced modification had acquired some degree of stability. But it is very uncertain how far we can eliminate an original selection in the production of the 'fancy' types. The relative instability of these forms under experimental conditions makes it very difficult to judge the value of this work.

We may sum up this survey of the experimental work by concluding that there is a small amount of evidence that induced modifications of certain types may be inherited. We shall defer any further discussion until we have considered the circumstantial evidence.

(c) **Circumstantial Evidence.**—There is a large body of observations and suggestions for consideration under this head. There are two principal groups which are available for examination.

(A) *The effects of use and disuse.*—So much evidence (of a sort) is available from human heredity that the effects of use and disuse are not inherited that it might seem superfluous to discuss this question. Nevertheless the matter cannot be dismissed without some discussion. A single case will make the difficulty clear. Duerden (1920) has shown that the sternal, alar, etc., callosities of the ostrich, which are undoubtedly related to the crouching posture of the bird, appear in the embryo. The case is analogous to the thickening of the soles of the feet of the human embryo attributed by Darwin (1901, p. 49) 'to the inherited effects of pressure.' As Detlefsen (*l.c.* p. 248) points out, this would have to be explained on selectionist grounds by the assumption that it was of advantage to have the callosities, as it were, preformed at the place at which they were required in the adult. But it is a large assumption that variations would arise at these spots and nowhere else.

Detlefsen (*l.c.* p. 248) reasonably asks ' why it is necessary to have these anticipatory hereditary callosities appear in the embryo before there is any demand made upon the organism . . . why do they not recur in each lifetime entirely through individual adaptation, as indeed it appears they can? . . . What advantage . . . would an inherited callosity . . . have over an equally effective ontogenetic one? ' We cannot see what selective advantage is involved in having them formed so early, unless we appeal to some principle of ' developmental convenience.' Moreover, Detlefsen asks (p. 250), ' is it not extremely improbable that chance variations in the germ plasm would arise to determine such callosities at exactly those points and nowhere else? Why not fortuitous variations for callosities elsewhere or almost anywhere on the body—which should persist, for they would have little or no lethal effect in the process of natural selection? '

This is a particularly interesting, but at the same time a very baffling case. On the one hand we have the general lack of evidence to support the ' Lamarckian ' explanation ; on the other the apparent absence of any advantage in having the formation of the callosities pushed back in ontogeny to a stage preceding the period at which they come into use. One might construct a purely hypothetical explanation in terms of ' developmental convenience ' to make a case for selection, but it would have very little weight if it were not supported by an exact and intimate study of this particular ontogeny.

The blindness of cave-animals and deep-sea forms (*cf.* p. 269, Chapter VII), and the atrophy of limbs in aquatic mammals are examples of this kind of difficulty.   In general the principle of physiological economy on which the selective explanation of atrophy from disuse is based, seems to us very unsatisfactory. Where an organ or structure is definitely inconvenient in a new mode of life its disappearance may be expected ; but when it is merely useless it is very difficult to see how slight variations in the direction of reduction could be effectively selected, more especially if they are infrequent.

We do not consider that this line of evidence is particularly helpful, as it seems incapable of exact examination.   Experiment may show us that a given organ does or does not atrophy through disuse and, if it could be experimentally proved that complete atrophy took place in conditions in which selection could be excluded, it would go a long way to proving that the results of disuse are progressively inherited.   Up to date no such experiments are available.   It may be pointed out that Payne (1911) subjected sixty-nine generations of *Drosophila ampelophila* (*melanogaster*) to total darkness without any modification of the eyes or the reaction to light.

(B) *Correlation of environmental differences with structural divergences known or presumed to be hereditary.*—Under this heading we have a very large body of facts summarised in a very able fashion by Rensch (1929).   This author maintains that there is much evidence tending to prove that lines of structural differentiation are very frequently correlated with environmental ' trends,' that there is a ' parallelism ' between ' phenotype ' and genotype of such an order that ' modifications ' can be artificially induced which are the same as, or more or less the same as, characters known to be ' genotypic,' and that there is an inference that such externally induced ' Phänovarietäten ' become genotypically fixed. He admits (p. 161) that the latter stage in the thesis has never been quite unexceptionally proved ; but he holds that this parallelism is of the highest significance.   He gives great weight to the production of identical variants in natural and comparable experimental environments, but actually there are very few instances of such parallelism.   His evidence, indeed, consists only of Sumner's (1915) experiments, already shown (p. 39) to be of dubious value.   He does not, however, refer to the later experimental work of Sumner (*cf.* 1923), in which it was shown that ' environmental ' forms of *Peromyscus*

taken from the desert to a new environment remained unchanged for two to ten generations. Sumner, in fact (1932),
abandons the theory of the direct environmental origin of
' desert ' pigmentation. On the other hand, the proof that
the racial characters are now germinally fixed does not show
that they were always so. Still, for the present at least, the
Peromyscus experiments cannot be held to favour Rensch's
views. We shall mention later other instances of characters
which are racially diagnostic in some species and known to be
due to external causes in others (*cf.* Robson, 1928, p. 166).

The alternative explanation to Rensch's hypothesis would be
that all the races whose differences are correlated with trends
are merely ' somatic ' forms or produced by selection. Rensch's
theory is, we hold, no more than suggestive, and in the light of
Sumner's conclusions as to the intensive study of gradients,
perhaps less impressive than is at first sight apparent. It is,
however, more fully examined later on (p. 46). In the same
category is Ekman's theory (1913) of the origin of the lacustrine
crustacean *Limnocalanus macrurus*, which, it is claimed, has
arisen in many places from the brackish-water *L. grimaldii*
(*cf.* Gurney, 1923) owing to the progressive freshening of the
lakes which it has occupied since the Glacial Period. This is
a case for which we would require experimental evidence,
especially as the various lacustrine forms are not all similar,
though, as Gurney admits in his critical review (*l.c.* p. 428),
the tendency has been in the same direction.

Rensch's data (with some supplementary evidence) may
now be considered in detail. Some of his most important
conclusions in the present connection are summarised in the
following three rules :

(1) *Bergmann's Law.*—In nearly related warm-blooded
animals the larger live in the north, the smaller in the south.
This is also true to some extent of invertebrates, provided they
are compared within their optimum range, outside which
dwarfing may appear.

(2) *Allen's Law.*—The feet, ears, and tails of mammals
tend to be shorter in colder climates, when closely allied forms
are compared.

(3) *Gloger's Law.*—Southern races tend to be black, brown,
grey and especially rust-red ; northern forms are paler and
greyer. Humidity here has an important modifying influence.

The whole weight of Rensch's argument depends, of course, on accumulating a large number of examples which it is not desirable to reproduce in the present chapter.

His first point is the extremely gradual changes shown by geographical races arranged along a climatic trend, *e.g.* in the five races of *Parus atricapillus* between North Siberia and the Rhine district the mean wing-length changes regularly from 66·5 to 60·5 mm. The changes are quite regular and even the two extremes vary enough to overlap. A number of similar examples is quoted. He stresses the fact that geographical variants are normally distinguished by several characters rather than by one major character. Next are set out numerous instances of parallel geographical variation, showing that in any one district related forms tend to be all modified in one direction. Examples in the Vertebrata, Crustacea and Mollusca are given. Allen's Law concerning the relative lengths of projecting parts is illustrated by a number of tables. It is seen to hold for the tail-length in a variety of mammals (chiefly rodents), when Alpine or northern races are compared with the representative race occurring in warmer districts. Interesting tables (pp. 149–151) show the same relation between wing- and body-length in North American Picidae, Bubonidae, etc. In 80 per cent. of the species the wings are longer in the southern races. On p. 152 he turns to Gloger's Law, and in a table on p. 155 he shows its application to twenty-five races of nine species of European tits and tree-creepers. It is naturally more difficult to grade species accurately according to colour.

Rensch has collected together a bigger body of information of this sort than has ever been presented before. For more detailed information his book and bibliography must be consulted.

Certain analogous or additional examples, not mentioned or not fully treated by Rensch, may be added. Alpatov (1925, 1929) has recorded some interesting investigations on the Honey Bee (*Apis mellifera*) in Europe. The data are very extensive and have been subjected to rigorous statistical treatment. He has been able to show that southern forms are smaller on the average and have longer tongues, wider wings, longer legs and small wax glands. The number of hooks on the hind wings is greater and the colour is yellower. The change

from north to south is extraordinarily gradual, and except
when extreme forms are compared, it is only the averages that
differ. The comparisons must be made between individuals
occurring on the same line of longitude, the change occurring
more quickly in the east than in the west, the lines of equal
change probably corresponding with the summer isotherms,
which have a similar slope. Exceptions to this regularity are
found only in the Caucasus, where development of a special
geographical race of the Honey Bee introduces a fresh complication. Experiments on the effects of temperature are as yet
not very extensive, but they, like the seasonal changes observed
in *Apis*, show that cold produces artificially the same effects as
those found in nature. Nevertheless transportation experiments have shown that the various naturally occurring types
are to a large extent hereditary. Alpatov's attempt to explain
his results is so characteristic of the orthodox way of dealing
with such facts, that it is worth setting out at some length.

The possibility of the inheritance of a long-continued
environmental effect is dismissed ' because of the lack of any
credible experimental evidence of the inheritance of acquired
characters.' He goes on to attempt to show that the observed
characteristics of the southern forms may really be adaptive.
Thus ' the longer tongue of southern bees is probably connected with the peculiarities of nectar secretion in the south
as compared with the more northern localities. Michailov
suggested that the longer tongue of southern bees is an adaptation to dry conditions which lead to a lower level of nectar in
the south, and thus compel the bee to have a longer working
organ. We expressed the hypothesis that the southern bees
are obliged to have a longer tongue, not only because of a
lower nectar level, but also because of a probable difference
in the composition of the whole nectar-secreting flora. It
has been reported by many beekeepers that the southern, and
particularly the Caucasian, bees can fly longer distances
gathering nectar, and it is probable that in consequence their
wings are more developed and have a larger number of hooks.
The smaller size of the wax glands is probably connected with
the condition that the bees in the south have perhaps less
need to work upon the reinforcement of their nest. Hence
the difference in the tongues, the wings and the wax glands
(also probably in the first joint of the tarsus of the last pair of

legs) may be considered as adaptations of different biological ends. It is probable that these characters have been developed by means of natural selection. Other characteristics like the general size of the body and coloration cannot at the present moment be even hypothetically evaluated as having any biological importance for the organism.'

Allen's Law is corroborated in the diminished length of the tails of the island races of certain British mice. It is possible, however, that there is a further special effect due to island life. In all the British mice and shrews which have races in the Shetlands, Orkneys and Hebrides, the proportion of the tail-length to that of the head and body is almost invariably less in the island races (figures taken from Barrett-Hamilton and Hinton, 1910–21). Unfortunately, the majority of the insular forms are found in the north, while the measurements of the mainland forms were based on southern specimens, so that it is not possible to separate the effects of latitude from those of insular life.

Le Souef (1930) has published an interesting note on the changes of three species of wallaby and an opossum imported sixty years ago from Australia to New Zealand. All have varied in the same way, the fur being now longer, more silky, and less dense.

Rensch's ornithological examples illustrating Gloger's Law may be supplemented by the data brought forward by Banks (1925). Here a number of subspecies or of specimens from different parts of the range of a species were compared and their colours correlated with the average meteorological conditions obtained during the breeding season. A very general positive correlation was found to exist between temperature and dark colours. The relation between pigmentation and humidity is not nearly so simple, being sometimes inverse, sometimes direct, but it appears in any case that the darkening effect of higher temperature is evident only in the presence of a moderate humidity. In areas which are very dry the colours tend to be pale in spite of a high temperature. This general result agrees with the well-known results which Beebe (1907) found by experiment. Dealing with doves of the genus *Scardafella* he found first that, in nature, there was a regular increase in dark pigment as one passes from Mexico to Brazil, the centre of least pigmentation being the driest area and the pigment

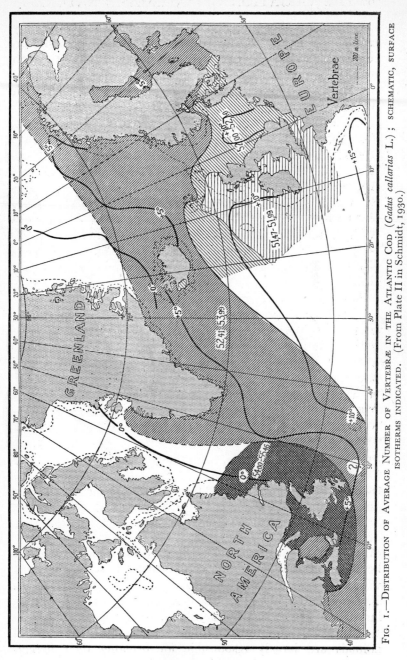

Fig. 1.—Distribution of Average Number of Vertebrae in the Atlantic Cod (*Gadus callarias* L.); schematic, surface isotherms indicated. (From Plate II in Schmidt, 1930.)

E

increasing in either direction as the humidity increased. By exposing the lightly pigmented form to very humid conditions he was able to show that pigment was slowly acquired through a course of moults, till finally a stage was reached darker than any known in nature. Of other examples of the correlation

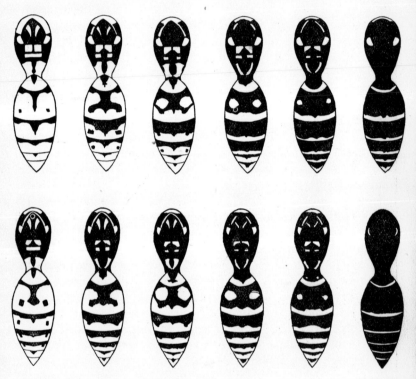

Fig. 2.—Correlation of Yellow Markings with Climatic Conditions in the Wasp *Polistes foederata* (♀ above, ♂ below). The Yellow Markings increase in Warm, Dry Areas.
(From Zimmermann, 1931.)

of structural characters and environmental trends one of the best known is that of the number of vertebræ which is associated with a temperature trend in the Atlantic Cod (Schmidt, 1930). The correlation of colour and temperature is also known in insects, *e.g.* in *Polistes* (Zimmermann, 1930, 1931).

(d) **Habit-formation.**—The habits and instincts of animals are largely responsible for bringing their heredi- tary make-up into play with the environment. No account of the evolution of the more highly organised animals can be complete that does not explain the evolution of instinct as fully as that of structure.   Unfortunately, this is a matter of which we are largely ignorant.   Instincts are less fixed than structures and their heredity and modifications are much more difficult to study accurately.   Undoubtedly in the vertebrates it becomes difficult to distinguish inherited aptitudes from traditions handed directly from one generation to the next. Even in Arthropods there may well be a bigger element of tradition (of rather special sort) than has usually been allowed.

As an introduction to the subject we will consider the predacious habits of the wasps of the family Crabronidae which have been discussed by Hamm and Richards (1926). Most species, in the store of dead or paralysed prey laid up for their offspring, include flies, but particular species capture insects of most of the more important orders.   In a few species members of two or more orders are mixed, while in others there is great specialisation, the prey being sometimes practically restricted to one sex of one genus.   From the present point of view the most interesting species are those which, while tending to specialise on one kind of prey, always capture some or many individuals of a widely different systematic category.   Such a species is *Crabro leucostomus*, which always captures a high proportion of Stratiomyid flies, but includes also Diptera belonging to a large number of other families. This habit is independent of the habitat in which the wasp is nesting.   The behaviour of *C. leucostomus* suggests rather a special form of 'larval memory,' the insect having a tendency to capture the food that it received during its own larval life, as has been suggested by Wheeler (1923, p. 57), who points out that the central nervous system is almost the only larval structure not radically modified at metamorphosis. Such a larval memory would not at first be hereditary in the ordinary sense, but may well have become so in those species which are now strictly specialised.

The general question of biological races in Arthropods is reviewed elsewhere (p. 119) and the facts need only be briefly dealt with here.   The most important conclusions are the following :

(1) There are numerous instances of species which are

divided into one or more strains differing little, if at all, morphologically, but with different habits, *e.g.* different larval food, host of parasite, etc.

(2) Experiment has shown that, if one race is, for instance, forcibly maintained on the food of another, there is at first little oviposition or breeding and a heavy mortality. Often a few individuals manage to perpetuate the race on the new food, to which it eventually becomes adapted. This would suggest at first sight that there has been a selection of a suitable stock, but this interpretation breaks down (*cf.* (3)).

(3) It has been possible in several cases to take a race A, normally feeding on a food *a*, and adapt it to the food *b* of race B. In these circumstances it may be as difficult to make the survivors of A (on *b*) return to *a* as it was to make the original change. This does not fit in with the theory of strain-selection, and Thorpe (1930) definitely postulates a process of more or less permanent habit-modification. It is by no means necessary that this change should at first be incorporated into the normal hereditary mechanism as claimed by Harrison (1927).

(4) There is some evidence that there is a tendency for these biological strains to mate within the race and therefore to stabilise their constitution.

From the evolutionary point of view, instinct is, as we have said, a particularly important subject, but unfortunately we do not know how new instincts arise nor how they are inherited. When an instinct is very firmly established it is naturally handed from parent to offspring like any somatic character, but this is by no means necessarily the case in the early stages of instinct-acquirement. In the songs of birds, for instance, while there is a large hereditary element, there is also much that is local and individual. Yet it is very plausible to suggest that the former element was originally built up from the latter without, in all cases, the actual selection of individuals with a particular song-type.

A further phenomenon which may be considered under the heading of habit-formation is that of voltinism in insects. The subject has recently been discussed in an interesting paper by Dawson (1931), who summarises the main theories and presents some very valuable experimental data (see also Baumberger, 1917). The problem is seen at its clearest in temperate countries in the many insects which have two or more broods a year. In these the pupæ from the early broods produce adults in the same year, whereas the pupæ of the last brood hibernate. It is difficult to imagine how any such system could keep in step with climatic seasonal changes, if it were not ultimately controlled by temperature or some other climatic variable. When, however, the determinative factors are investigated experimentally, a very perplexing state of affairs is laid bare, recalling in detail the complex problem of seasonal variation in colour. There is little doubt that the gradual sinking of the mean temperature in the autumn is the main controlling factor. Pupæ which have been exposed to such a gradual cooling tend to become dormant. But even in one family (of brothers and sisters) the effect is not uniform ; in a number of experiments some individuals become dormant, while others do not. Probably genetic factors partly determine the response to temperature, but Dawson was unable to find any simple scheme of segregation. Previously Toyama (1912), in the Silkworm (*Bombyx mori*), had suggested matroclinous inheritance.

In the Cornborer (*Pyrausta nubilalis*), Babcock (1927) and Babcock and Vance maintain that ' the seasonal rhythm is to a certain extent persistent and is due to the formation of a physiological condition which forces the insect to develop a certain type of seasonal cycle. This physiological condition is formed by continued impress of a particular type of normal environment and persists after the impress of the environment is removed ' (1929, p. 53). The whole question of seasonal rhythms in animals is still in urgent need of experimental investigation.

Since the genesis of instinct is still so obscure there is some value in putting on record a number of instances of aberrations in instinct. Some of these appear to be merely individual, but others have been more widely manifested. In birds and mammals, where social tradition has some weight, even individual aberrations have importance.

Insects.—One of the best known instances of a sudden change in habits is that of an English bug, *Plesiocoris rugicollis*, which, prior to 1918, was known to feed only on willow, but since that date has increasingly turned its attention to apple, so that it is now a serious pest. The flies which ' blow ' sheep in Australia did not become a serious pest till about 1895, apparently owing to a definite change in habits (references in Carpenter, 1928, pp. 111–113). Manhardt (1930) records that a beetle, *Luperus xanthopus*, after stripping all the willows on the banks of the Elbe, made its way inland in large numbers and attacked fruit trees. In some parts very serious losses resulted. In view of what has been recorded as to the formation of biological races, such invasions have some significance. Still more individual aberrations are seen in the genus *Vespa*, where species normally subterranean sometimes nest above ground and *vice versa* (see Stelfox, 1930).

Mollusca.—An octopus (Bristowe, 1931 ; Robson, 1932*a*) was found eating spiders, though the diet is normally restricted to Crustacea.

Limax maximus (Taylor, 1907) is usually found in gardens or near houses, but in Ireland is never found in cultivated ground or gardens.

Reptilia.—*Lacerta muralis* according to Eisentraut (1929) is found on the shore in the Balearic Islands, feeding on Halophytes because the normal supply of insects and snails is reduced.

Birds.—The Black-headed Gull (*Larus ridibundus*) (Lack, 1933) sometimes feeds on land in spite of its adaptations to aquatic feeding. The same species (Gray, 1930, p. 170) has been observed flying in a V-formation like geese. This is very unusual for the species.

The Reed Bunting (*Emberiza schoeniclus*) (Lack, 1933) is typically a marsh form, but is very occasionally found nesting in typical Yellow Bunting habitats.

The Great Tit (*Parus major*) (Darwin, 1884, p. 141) sometimes behaves like a shrike and kills small birds. Darwin gives further examples of habit-anomaly on the same page.

The New Zealand Parrot (*Nestor notabilis*) (Buller, 1888, pp. 244–5) was originally insectivorous, but relatively recently began to attack sheep.

The Barbet (*Trachyponus emini*) (Loveridge, 1928, p. 41) nearly always nests in burrows, but was once found nesting in a tree.

Mammals.—The African Buffalo (*Bubalis caffer*) (Elton, 1927, p. 145) used to be a diurnal feeder, but after the rinderpest epidemic of 1890 became a much more nocturnal feeder.

In a highly adaptable mammal like the Grey Squirel (*Sciurus carolinensis*) (see Middleton, 1931) almost endless variations in habit are recorded, *e.g.* in food, use of burrows instead of trees, etc.

These data suggest that the fundamental genetic basis of behaviour is very easily modified by the environment. It also appears to be subject to spontaneous change, though the origin of this change is obscure. It is similarly difficult to distinguish the various rôles of heredity and tradition. Some authors have suggested that 'traditions' ultimately become hereditarily fixed.

(e) **Summary of Data on the Inheritance of Induced Modifications.**—Much of the experimental evidence is unsatisfactory, but it is difficult to avoid the impression that some types of impressed modifications are in certain circumstances inherited.

The indirect evidence appears to require one of three possible hypotheses :

(*a*) That the modifications are all mere fluctuations. This is scarcely tenable.

(*b*) That where the modifications are inheritable, it is due to the selection of adapted variants.

(*c*) That acquired modifications, long impressed, have become inherited.

A serious objection is brought forward by those who hold that in any particular case the correlation between the variation and the environment may be due merely to the selection of variants best suited to that environment. This objection is, quite literally, unanswerable, but it assumes what can never be proved, at any rate with our present knowledge. It is a very large assumption to maintain that a graded series of variations in a species corresponds to a parallel gradient of adaptation to the altering environment, if only because of the extraordinarily discriminative selection required. It appears to us that neither of these rival theories can be dismissed by *a priori* argument. Both are possible, both are at present incapable of final proof and must in each case be judged by the balance of the evidence. The extent to which the discriminative power of Natural Selection is developed is discussed in more detail elsewhere (Chapter VII). We shall merely record our opinion that an adaptive explanation of much of the data on pp. 44–50 is unconvincing. At the same time we do not pretend that the evidence available suggests that any ' Lamarckian ' process is very important as a source of new heritable variation, except possibly in the matter of habits. There is certainly a very large body of evidence (Chapters IV and VII) suggesting that the bulk of the morphological differences between species and races is not in any way correlated with a particular environment ; and conversely that many species and subspecies range widely without any modification. Although this seems in conflict with the evidence for geographical trends (p. 46), yet such trends are relatively uncommon (*i.e.* compared with the number of races and species not arranged in trends) and further usually only some of the characters of a species exhibit the trend.

CONCLUSIONS.

In this chapter we have considered the origin of the various types of variation that may be encountered in a natural population. Fluctuations certainly form a large element, but quantitative data as to the importance of these are hard to obtain. Genetically determined variations include (in addition to gene-mutations) changes due to fragmentation, etc., of chromosomes, polyploidy and recombination. The first two phenomena seem to be of minor importance in animals. Recombination is certainly responsible for much of the normally wide range in phenotypes. We have not much evidence yet whether species in nature are often heterozygous for more than a few characters. If they are not, the results of recombination are strictly limited, especially in any particular direction. In any case Lotsy's theory of evolution by crossing cannot have much application in the animal kingdom, where successful interspecific crosses are relatively uncommon. Gene-mutations are certainly a very important source (or, as some would have it, the only source) of new hereditary material. The real cause of gene-mutations is quite unknown, but it is theoretically improbable that they are in any real sense spontaneous. The rate at which they occur has now been influenced by X-rays, radium-rays and high temperature. Even under these influences the rate is still relatively low.

The problem of the inheritance of induced modifications appears to be ultimately reducible to the question whether there is a process by which the hereditary basis handed on to the next generation may be *gradually* altered, as opposed to the apparently *sudden* induction of mutants. The actual experimental evidence is not very conclusive, except in so far as it shows that lesions and mutilations are *not* inherited. The problem of the degeneration of disused organs requires further consideration. There is no positive evidence that disuse has a direct effect, but the alternative selectionist explanations are equally unsatisfactory.

In a few cases there is experimental evidence which suggests that induced modifications are inherited, but confirmatory experiments are much to be desired. There is also a considerable body of indirect evidence which may be held to support the experiments. In a number of instances alternative adaptational explanations of the data have been (or could be) put forward. Such explanations depend on very large assumptions as to the closeness of the adaptation of the organism to its environment. The prime difficulty of the assumption that induced modifications are inherited lies in explaining how the modified character comes ultimately to be represented in the germ cells.

CHAPTER III

BIOLOGICAL inquiries in general involve recognising that individual animals may be grouped in various ways, and in investigations of variation, heredity and evolution the characteristics of such groups are the subject of inquiry and the measure of divergence. Investigation of the nature and status of these groups and their relationship one with another is an indispensable preliminary to the study upon which we are engaged.

The levels of evolutionary divergence most usually indicated by the species and variety have been subjected since Darwin's time to a careful scrutiny from divers points of view and numerous categories have been proposed to designate groupings of individuals other than the traditional species and variety of taxonomy. Historically we may date the commencement of serious analysis to Alexis Jordan's publication of his work on elementary species, and to such pioneer work as Waagen and Neumayr's studies of ' Formenreihe.' The conception of geographical races may be dated to earlier workers (Kant, Pallas, Gloger (*cf.* Rensch, 1929)).

An admirable study of the lowest systematic categories has been published by du Rietz (1930), who discusses critically the status of the various groups proposed and the synonymy of the terms used. du Rietz's list is defective in one or two important respects. He discusses neither palæontological categories nor physiological differentiation, nor does his survey, which is mainly based on botanical data, include such divisions as colonies, etc.

The most commonly recognised categories are, of course, those used in taxonomy. In addition there are a number of others in regular use in various branches of zoology, which either have not been absorbed into the hierarchy of systematic terms or are only rarely used by systematists. But, although the majority of systematists still maintain the traditional Linnean categories, many feel impelled to supplement them with other terms devised to fit special groups revealed by systematic analysis or to attempt to substitute for the older categories of species and varieties fresh ones designed to bring systematic procedure into line with new methods of analysis, (*e.g.* Linneon and Jordanon (Lotsy), ' Formenkreise ' and ' Rassenkreise ' (Kleinschmidt, Rensch)).

The following appear to be the chief types of category that have been proposed :

Taxonomic.

Palæontological (lineage, gens).

Geographical (local race, colony, ' Rassenkreis ').

Genetical and Reproductive (*e.g.* pure line, biotype, clone, syngameon, sibship).

Physiological (strain, physiological race).

Although for the purpose of convenient discussion we have adopted the above distinctions, it will be noticed that a hard and fast division between, *e.g.*, genetical and geographical categories is fundamentally arbitrary. All we wish to imply by these distinctions is that various methods of research have led to the adoption of various categories which we have to define and relate one to another.

Over and above these we have the various terms which perhaps could be classed as genetical by which heritability, partial heritability or non-heritability is implied, such as *forma, alteration, Dauermodifikation,* genotype and phenotype. There is also a category of groups, partly of geographical, partly of habitudinal significance such as the *school, rookery, shoal,* etc. Some categories are based on more than one concept, *e.g.* the *ecotype,* and *ecospecies* are groups recognised on account of genetical behaviour and ecological relationship. Lastly we may point out that some categories are strictly classificatory, *i.e.* they form part of a system and designate a more or less closed group, though they are not all in current taxonomic use, while others, such as *lineage,* are taxonomically neutral, *i.e.* they involve no recognition of a classificatory system. Of the same order is the term *population* or *natural population,* which is used to designate any number of closely related and interbreeding individuals occupying a given area, without any taxonomic specification of the status of the variants it contains.[1]

We are thus presented with very many different kinds of groups, which seem to reflect various modes of divergence in nature and it is desirable to ascertain what is their relationship one with another, and what light they throw on the actual process of divergence itself.

du Rietz in the paper mentioned above suggests (p. 337) that the most elementary unit of taxonomy is the individual. He points out that the limits of the individual are not always easy to define, but he thinks that the soundest definition involves the recognition of physiological autonomy. We believe, however, that the analysis might be pressed further. To suggest that the character is the most fundamental unit is to open the door to all kinds of complications, chief among which is that the limits of characters are usually very hard to define ; but the suggestion has a particular value from our point of view. Evolution is essentially a matter of character-changes. Individuals are bundles of characters which have each a history of their own, and the divergent groups manifest a progressive accumulation of character-divergences. It is a matter of more than academic or formal interest to keep the individual character before our minds throughout this discussion (*cf.* lineages, p. 65) and to remember that the individual may be resolved into its constituent elements (' structural units '—Swinnerton, 1921, p. 358). The organism has its peculiar autonomy and ' wholeness,' but each of its structural units has an individual history of change which, though related to the needs of the whole organism, can be treated as a separate evolutionary episode. It is also of very great importance to remember the individual character in considering the processes by which we recognise groups of individual organisms such as species, etc. It is not perhaps sufficiently realised how much variation is attainable, if all the possible characters are taken into account. A. Agassiz (1881, pp. 18–19) pointed out that in the Echinoids the number of variable structural items is at least twenty and that the permutations and combinations of the most restricted

---

[1] ' Population ' is sometimes used in the sense of ' sample ' in describing local collections made from a larger assemblage. Thus Schmidt (1930, pl. 1) alludes to the population of the Atlantic Cod, though he uses the word ' sample ' in the text.

types of variation are 2^{19}. Henry (1928, p. 65) has shown that the chance that two human individuals will have the same finger-print pattern for a given digit of one hand is of the order of over 1,000,000 : 1 (*cf.* p. 24, *supra*).

I. Taxonomic Categories

The Linnean hierarchy of morphological groups of which the species and variety are members is still the system by which we express an animal's relationships. We do not wish to discuss the general principles according to which this system is constructed and its capacity to express animal relationships. We may suspect with Bather (1927, p. ci) 'that the whole of our system is riddled through and through with polyphyly and convergence,' and we may agree that the chief and most philosophic duty of the systematist is to ' free it from this reproach ' (Bather, *l.c.*), even if this task presents difficulties which may be occasionally insuperable (Robson, 1932).

Nevertheless the species and the variety or subspecies are the most frequently used categories, and they are the reference points round which all the data as to habits, distribution and variation have been assembled. It will be as well, therefore, to commence our survey with them. The status of the species has, of course, been subjected to long and painful inquiry. It has been challenged on two principal counts—(*a*) that it is an arbitrary abstraction from a number of individuals which vary so much *inter se* that any grouping must do violence to the natural divergences that are found both in *time* and *place* ; and (*b*) that it is not a group having regularly definable properties and a standardised status *vis-à-vis* other groups. The first of these objections questions the capacity of the systematist to designate any part of a more or less continuous natural assemblage, the second criticises the status of the species in a hierarchy of classification.

Most biologists are now agreed that the latter objection is valid and that the species has no standardised attributes by which it can be distinguished from the variety and the genus. Such a standardisation, it is true, might be defined by the acquisition of some qualities constituting critical upward and downward limits in the process of evolutionary divergence (*e.g.* at the lower limit, the intervention of mutual infertility). But, as organisms diverge in many characters, and as these are not correlated in any universal scheme of divergence, any attempt to fix a downward limit fails.

The first objection is far more cognate to our problem. The universal occurrence of individual variation has led certain writers to assert that the individual is the only real unit and that species and similar groups are devoid of any significance. This view is worth dwelling on for a moment, as its importance is not fully recognised. Finding agreement between the members of his species in a limited number of characters the systematist has perhaps given undue prominence to them. When the term similarity is introduced into the definitions of systematic units, we may well ask if any two individuals, even of a moderately complex phylum, are ever alike in all their characters (*cf.* p. 60, *supra*). If this is never the case, we may also ask how it is that any discrete groups, such as species, have come to be recognised and what may be the value of a classification that recognises such crude groupings. The answer to this may be given briefly. In spite of very extensive individual variation (a great part of which is of unknown hereditary status and may be non-heritable), the systematist tends to find certain regular correlations, associations of a limited number of characters that occur regularly in individuals, and it is this correlation that, amid a very great amount of individual variation, constitutes the basis of species-diagnosis. Such correlations are, of course, of very varying intensity and can involve a greater or less number of characters of various kinds ; but, though they cannot be standardised as a universally recognisable grade, the taxonomic procedure is justified. It is necessary to make the proviso that a number of species in each group are founded on inadequate statistical data. Indeed so great is the disparity between the number of species described by the systematist and the knowledge of natural variation of the populations from which species are abstracted, that some systematists (*e.g.* Ramsbottom, 1926, p. 28) have been impelled to draw a distinction between ' the natural species ' and ' the taxonomic species,' and one of the authors of the present volume has suggested that forms which, by reason of the poverty of material, imperfect preservation, or the lack of adult specimens, are of uncertain status, though seemingly distinct species, should be referred to by a symbol rather than by a specific name.

It must be remembered that not a great deal is known concerning the hereditary stability of species. It has always been assumed, since the contrast between hereditary and non-hereditary characters was realised, that the characters of the species were hereditarily stable. Naturally few taxonomists have had the time or opportunity to breed out the members of groups which they have confidently described as species. A substantial number of described species are forms of dubious hereditary stability. 'Environmental forms' are often given distinct specific names, as in the case of *Artemia salina* and *A. milhauseni* and in various groups of Cladocera and Mollusca (*e.g. cf.* Miller, 1922). Finally, in claiming a general validity for taxonomic procedure in the treatment of species as distinct groups, we recognise that this claim must be limited by the admission not only that such groups are of various degrees of distinctness in the number of divergent characters, but also that sometimes intergradation between the various elements in a population may be so complete as to render the limits between species purely arbitrary.

Within the species itself systematists are accustomed to recognise certain subdivisions—the subspecies, the variety, and less frequently the form and the race. At the present time the terms *variety* and *subspecies* are both used for the major subdivisions of the species, but speaking generally they have a different connotation. The subspecies is a term in regular use among mammalogists and ornithologists, and it is used essentially to denote a geographical entity, the major subdivisions of the species of birds and mammals having usually distinct geographical ranges. The term variety,[1] on the other hand, though it is used for a major division of the species of invertebrate animals, has no such geographical implication. In many invertebrate groups the subdivisions are types which occur sporadically throughout the range of the species, and though in morphological status they correspond to the subspecies of birds and mammals, the accidental

---

[1] Rothschild and Jordan (1903) have used the term variety not for any particular category of the components of a species, but for 'all the members of a species indiscriminately.' The different categories of varieties are given special names or symbols.

difference in terminology conceals a real difference in the type of variation (*i.e.* in distribution).

Below the level of varieties and subspecies the ordinary task of the systematist is not pursued. All that we have said concerning the validity of the species-concept applies with equal truth to the subdivisions of the species itself, viz. the uncertainty as to their genetic status and the difficulty of standardising the concepts.

It remains for us to notice the various attempts that have been made to incorporate the results of population-analysis into taxonomy. A good account of this is given by du Rietz (*l.c.*), who reviewed and attempted to harmonise all the various terms proposed. It is enough to state that intensive population-analysis (dating from Alexis Jordan's pioneer work) has revealed the presence within systematic species of various subordinate elements which are imperfectly represented by the old terms variety and subspecies. It is clear that there is a basic distinction, now generally recognised and described in detail by du Rietz (*l.c.*, pp. 349-354), between a population forming a local (variety) as opposed to a regional (subspecies) element in a species. The extent to which the Jordanon (Lotsy), microspecies and elementary species (Jordan), natio (Semenov-Tian-Shansky), etc., are merely synonymous with one or the other of these is an academic point, and it is similarly obvious that the line between ' local ' and ' geographical ' race is quite arbitrary. The differentiation of populations into a large number of intercrossing ' biotypes ' and the way in which such subordinate elements are distinguished by isolation lead to a very finely graded hierarchy of local groupings (*cf.* Crampton, 1916-1932 ; Gulick, 1905 ; Heincke, 1898), and it would be undesirable to attempt to define these by a rigid terminology. Some taxonomists have recognised a finer distinction under the name ' forma ' to designate a purely fluctuational type (= ' modification ') or, with a more non-committal connotation, to designate a type ' occurring sporadically in a species-population and not forming a distinct local or regional facies in it ' (du Rietz).

Finally, we would draw attention to the attempt which has been made by Fenton (1931, p. 30) to remodel the traditional Linnean system so as to suit the findings of palæontology. His definitions of ' subspecies ' and ' form ' are not to be commended, as they introduce fresh connotations for terms which are beginning to acquire a fairly regular meaning.

II. Palæontological Categories

Perhaps the most important principle to which we should refer under this heading is the palæontological ' time-character ' concept. The status of the species in time is as significant as it is in its modern relationships and is often neglected by neontologists. Of recent years some noteworthy studies have been made on series of fossils in which evolutionary change can be studied intensively through successive horizons. The technique of this study was formulated by Neumayr and Waagen ; but its application to series of closely allied forms has been developed by Carruthers, Rowe, Swinnerton and Trueman in this country. The essence of the procedure is the study through a series of successive horizons of series of closely related forms *in terms of their individual characters*. The result of such studies is the concept of the *lineage* and the *bioseries*. The first is a racial complex of lines of descent, which on account of crossing and biparental reproduction must, as Swinnerton (1930, p. 387) points out, prove to be not a series of parallel evolutionary lines, but a finely meshed network. The *bioseries* is the historical sequence formed by the changes in any one character and relates to the modification of any single heritable feature. Each line of descent and each lineage will be composed of numerous bioseries evolving at different rates, just as each individual is composed of different characters. In such developmental series ' transients ' (*i.e.* individual modes) at stages remote from one another are as distinct as taxonomic species, *e.g.* in one such lineage the Cretaceous sea urchin *Micraster* has a stage *M. praecursor* which could be rated as a distinct species from its successor *M. coranguinum*.

There exists some ambiguity as to the relationship between the ordinary systematic concept of species and the lineage. But this much is clear—that although within a given lineage the concept of species is difficult to apply (Trueman, 1930) because of the difficulty of disentangling the series of ' anastomosing ' lines of descent, yet a given horizon will contain discrete entities corresponding to systematic species, each of which represents a stage in a particular lineage. Thus at the stratigraphical level of the Millstone Grit, Carruthers found two distinct species of coral, *Zaphrentis constricta* and *Z. disjuncta*, though each of these at this horizon represented a stage in an individual lineage in which the individuals cannot be specifically delimited from individuals that occur in earlier and later horizons. It seems that the character-complexes, in which the individual characters in any one lineage are modified at different rates and so afford no regular correlation by which species may be recognised, do in fact diverge so that one lineage may differ from another *at a given moment* in the same way as the species of the neontologist differ. In other words, the investigations of lineages have revealed distinct divergences equivalent to species, but these divergent groups show no discontinuity *in time* from their predecessors or successors. The criticism that the forms on which such studies have been carried out are peculiarly plastic (Robson, 1928) and therefore apt to be misleading has, we think, been sufficiently answered by Trueman (*l.c.* p. 307), although there must always exist some element of doubt as to the relationship between groups diagnosed on certain plastic characters of the shell and those founded on more stable characters. Finally, it must be observed that the existence of lineages could be suspected from the distribution of variants in modern populations (*cf.* p. 176, Chapter VI).

III. Geographical Categories

The subordinate units within the species recognised in taxonomy and associated with the intensive study of geographical distribution are somewhat diverse and no standard usage obtains. There are some outstanding works on the geographical variation of single species or on allied forms, such as those of Heincke (1898), Duncker (1896) and Schmidt (1918–1930) (fishes) ; Sumner (1932) (*Peromyscus*) ; Crampton (1916–1932) (*Partula*). Alpatov (1924, 1929), Semenov-Tian-Shansky (1910), Rensch (1929) and others have attempted to define the terms used.

Mammalogists, ornithologists and, to some extent, herpetologists regularly subdivide the species into subspecies or smaller units such as races, all of which are characterised by their members occupying a more or less clearly delimited geographical area. Among the students of invertebrate groups no such regularity of usage obtains and there is evidently no general tendency, easily detected, for the subordinate groups to be spatially segregated. We discuss at some length in Chapter IV the question whether there are any real grounds for this difference in procedure and its implication. For the moment we are concerned only with the categories themselves. How different the procedure among students of invertebrate groups may be will be seen from the following extracts.

Pilsbry (1919, p. 277), in treating of the subordinate divisions of species of African land snails, distinguishes between ' those of racial value or *subspecies* in the sense of forms characteristic of geographic areas or habitats,' and ' the different forms (mutations of de Vries (?)) occurring together in the same colonies and doubtless interbreeding.' These he calls *mutations*. This usage of ' subspecies ' is found largely among lepidopterists (but *cf.* Wheeler, 1913 (ants)).

Bequaert (1919, p. 11), who evidently feels that it is not possible to recognise geographic units of the same status as those in other groups, uses the term variety for his subordinate divisions in a ' neutral ' sense, *i.e.* without any presumption as to their true status as *geographical races* or *individual aberrations* or *elementary species*. His varieties of *Eumenes maxillosus* (African wasp ; p. 59) seem to occupy separate parts of the range of the species (p. 60), but they are not to be considered geographical races, as they ' do not inhabit a given country to the exclusion of all others.' Here we see geographical units less distinctly segregated than in other cases, but still perhaps deserving that status.

The term variety is generally used in dealing with invertebrates in the ' neutral ' sense of Bequaert for anything from a single rather distinctive individual in a limited number of specimens representing a species to the kind of group seen in *Eumenes maxillosus*. It is given regularly to clearly marked and distinctive groups numerically well represented, the individuals of which occur as a certain percentage in any part of the range of a species, but are not restricted to a particular locality (colour-classes of land snails). There seems to be a fairly well-established practice of distinguishing between subspecies and varieties in the sense outlined above according

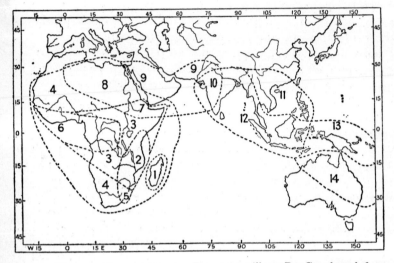

FIG. 3.—MAP OF DISTRIBUTION OF *Eumenes maxillosus* DE G. adapted from Bequaert (1919). FOURTEEN AREAS CAN BE DISTINGUISHED ACCORDING TO THE COLOUR-VARIANTS PRESENT, AS SHOWN IN THE FOLLOWING LIST :—

AREA 1. *Maxillosus, reginus.*
2. *Maxillosus, pulcherrimus, fenestralis.*
3. *Maxillosus, fenestralis.*
4. *Maxillosus.*
5. *Maxillosus, pulcherrimus.*
6. *Maxillosus, fenestralis, tropicalis.*
7. *Maxillosus, fenestralis, dimidiatipennis.*
8. *Maxillosus, dimidiatipennis.*
9. *Dimidiatipennis.*
10. *Dimidiatipennis, conicus, xanthurus, circinalis, petiolatus.*
11. *Conicus, petiolatus.*
12. *Conicus, xanthurus, circinalis, petiolatus.*
13. *Xanthurus, petiolatus.*
14. *Petiolatus.*

to whether intergrades occur between the groups. Sub-species are groups between which intermediates occur only rarely or not at all (see Dice, 1931 ; Merriam, 1919, for conflicting views on this subject).

We have thus quite clearly established the recognition of more or less distinct geographical groups on the one hand and groups or types not spatially segregated, but appearing either as individual variants sporadically throughout a population or as larger local elements not segregated into geographical units. We have now to inquire concerning other subdivisions of this kind.

Races.—The term *geographical race* is used as a complete synonym for *subspecies* by several authors (*cf.* Alpatov, 1929). But it is also used for a smaller unit not of the same dimensions as the subspecies. *Local race* and *local forms* (*cf.* Duncker, 1896) are used in the same loose way. In fact it will be readily recognised that such a hierarchy might exist within the species, that the boundaries of the various groups would be difficult to draw and there would be some confusion of terminology.

That such a hierarchy of local or geographical groups does exist is, we think, quite clear. This is perhaps best seen in the work of Schmidt (1920), who finds that the *Zoarces* population is divided into numerous ' races ' and each of these can be again split into still smaller elements. In this case (p. 114) the averages of the smaller groups combined give the average of the race. A similar example is seen in Duncker's studies of the Flounder and Plaice (1896).

In Sumner's investigation of the local variation of *Peromyscus maniculatus* it is quite clear that the local populations within the three chief subspecies are not identical (1920, p. 388, fig. 2), but exhibit significant statistical differences. He says (1917, p. 173), ' subspecies themselves are far from being elementary.' They are composite groups comprising in numerous cases a number—perhaps a great number—of distinguishable local types. Similar groups which are the result of intense localisa-tion in segregated populations are recorded by Gulick (*l.c.*), Crampton (*l.c.*), Mayer (1902), Boycott (1919), Aubertin, Ellis and Robson (1931) for ' colonies ' of land snails (general discussion of the problem in the last-named paper). Many of these colonies are found in valleys or on ridges. A still more acute form of local differentiation is seen in the ' forms ' of rats found in different houses in India by Lloyd (1912) and the statistical differences between communities of ants found in different nests (Alpatov, 1924) and in the ' races ' of *Partula* found on single trees by Pilsbry, Hyatt and Cook (1912). For such ' besondere kleine lokal geographische Einheiten ' Semenov-Tian-Shansky (1910) has proposed the name ' *natio*.' We might even include here such groups as are produced by a gregarious instinct and appear as centres of attraction in populations not broken up by topographical obstacles (' schools,' shoals and rookeries). In the majority of cases the groups under discussion represent mere statistical divergences from the mean of the population, such as are seen in the percentage-difference of colour- and band-classes of land snails and in the different combinations of ear-, tail- and foot-length of *Peromyseus*.

How far the groups which we have been discussing are hereditarily stable it is impossible to say. Experimental proof is available to show that the races of *Zoarces* and *Lebistes* (Schmidt), *Peromyscus* (Sumner, 1915), *Cerion* (Bartsch, 1920), moths (Goldschmidt, 1922, 1923) and bees (Alpatov, 1929) are stable. We would, however, surmise that a good many alleged racial distinctions are of the nature of ' fluctuations ' (*cf.* Woltereck on non-inheritable racial characters of the Cladocera, 1928). Much valuable work remains to be done in this field. Crossing experiments have been undertaken by Sumner (1917), who finds that some subspecies of *Peromyscus maniculatus* can be successfully crossed, while others are sterile *inter se*.

The fact that populations are divisible into distinct geographical groups such as we have been describing and that some taxonomic species are constellations of geographical forms has led certain students to seek some means of distinguishing such composite groups. They were first called ' Formenkreise ' by Kleinschmidt ; but Rensch (1929) has recently proposed the term ' Rassenkreise ' for them and has thoroughly examined the subject. He suggests that the term ' species ' should be restricted to groups of mutually fertile and structurally similar individuals which exhibit only individual, ecological or seasonal variation, having heritable differences but not divisible into geographical races. Rensch's definition (*l.c.* p. 15) has to be taken in conjunction with that of his geographical race which ' geht gleitend in die Nachbarrassen über.' He suggests that groups of geographical races which may or may not correspond with taxonomic species should be called ' Rassenkreise.' [1] Now Rensch's Rassenkreis, as far as we can see, can scarcely be treated as a classificatory unit, but rather as the name of a principle of divergence. It denotes the tendency to form constellations of geographical races. At times the Rassenkreis appears to us to be clearly conterminous with the taxonomists' species. Rensch does not hesitate to give some of his Rassenkreise binominal names (*e.g.* p. 29, the Rassenkreis of *Troglodytes troglodytes*). The suggestion is of value in pointing the differences between groups of races connected by transitional forms and more homogeneous and geographically undiversified groups ; but it has a disadvantage in that two terms are applied to what are in practice equivalent degrees of morphological divergence.

We are left, in short, with the general result that there is a principle of geographical divergence manifest within the systematic species, and at all early stages in evolutionary divergence, of such a nature that groups very slightly different in structure (often only in a single character, *e.g.* coat- or plumage-colour) are also distinct in their topographical range. That such divergence is, according to our present knowledge, more clearly seen in some groups than others is quite apparent. But we would point out (*a*) that it is by no means a universal feature in mammals and birds and (*b*) that we are a little uncertain as to how far it may not be exaggerated in those groups by the relatively low numbers used in the discrimination of mammalian and bird races. Finally, it is uncertain to what extent many of the subspecies and geographical races described by taxonomists are hereditarily stable.

IV. GENETICAL AND REPRODUCTIVE CATEGORIES

It is convenient to consider here not only the strictly genetical categories, such as the biotype, pure line and the ' petite espèce,' but also the clone and the syngameon which depend on the type of reproduction (whether sexual or asexual, interbreeding or not), and the *aberration, form, modification* and

---

[1] In all probability the Rassenkreis corresponds to Waagen's ' Collectivart ' and the gens of certain modern palæontologists (*cf.* Bather, 1927, p. lxxxviii).

exotype which depend on the recognition that a given form is non-heritable. Perhaps we might also include the *ecotype* and *ecospecies* (Turesson, Alpatov), which are combinations of genetical and ecological concepts. Even in motile animals such as ants Alpatov (1924) has been able to recognise analogous ' subspecies ecologicae truncicolae ' in the European and Japanese subspecies of *Formica rufa*. We are dealing here, however, with a category having primarily an ecological basis, some members of which are physiologically differentiated (*cf.* Chapter IV, p. 119).

In categories such as the *clone* and the *pure line* one may say that the logical classificatory ideal of a category having standardised characterisation is attained. These units are defined not by their degree of morphological divergence, but by their mode of reproduction and degree of genetical homogeneity.

Some of the genetical units are obviously subdivisions of the species. It has long been realised that taxonomic units may contain numerous intercrossing strains (? = petites espèces), just as, considered in the time-relationship, the lineage consists of interwoven and anastomosing lines of descent which at any one horizon seem to have a similar status. Other such categories have less to do with the content of the species. The *pure line* is indeed an expression of differentiation within the species, but as it is (*sensu stricto*) the result of a particular mode of reproduction (autogamous), it is only of importance in certain groups. It must also be noticed that a pure line may consist of individuals homozygous for only one pair of allelomorphs. The term *pure line* is sometimes inaccurately given to a genotypically homogeneous group, without reference to the mode of reproduction, *e.g.* a homozygous biotype. Cloneformation, on the other hand, seen in the Protozoa will be characteristic only of such parts of a species-population as are reproducing asexually.[1]

The term *biotype* (' a population consisting of individuals with identical genotypical constitution ' (du Rietz)) is a recognisable entity among both autogamous and allogamous forms, but, as du Rietz (*l.c.* p. 340) points out, there is little chance that in regularly allogamous forms any biotype will

[1] The term *clone* is sometimes applied to the broods of parthenogenetic animals.

be represented by more than one individual on account of the great number of possible gene-combinations.

Just as Rensch attempted (*l.c.*) to reconcile the systematic and geographical concepts by a new terminology, so Lotsy has attempted to synthesise systematic and genetical results. He pointed out that the homozygous biotype is the only real fundamental taxonomic unit (1916) and therefore the only unit worthy of being called *species*. He proposed the term *Jordanon* to denominate the smaller character-groupings that Jordan had detected within many Linnean species, and *Linneon* for the larger composite groups. A considerable literature has accumulated around Lotsy's suggestion. We do not venture to discuss what is primarily a feature of plant populations. But there seems to be this much of common ground between botanical and zoological results. As we have seen in discussing Rensch's proposal, there are homogeneous and heterogeneous species ('simple' and 'compound,' Cockayne and Allan, 1927) and the lines between a group consisting of a single biotype and a Jordanon and between the latter and a Linneon are quite arbitrary. What we seem to be dealing with is the progressive formation of groups differing in more and more characters.

Genetical analysis has revealed a process of differentiation partly produced by the mechanism of heredity, partly the result of some other factor or factors. At the lowest level, populations have their characteristics determined by the processes of heredity and methods of reproduction—they are homozygous or heterozygous, pure lines or heterogeneous assemblages. Some characters may keep together in pairs according to the amount of linkage. Imposed on this fundamental character-distribution is the process usually recognised by the taxonomists by which larger and more substantial character-groups are formed, either with or without geographical or ecological differentiation.

V. PHYSIOLOGICAL CATEGORIES

Of recent years it has been increasingly apparent that in certain classes taxonomic species are subdivided into races, characterised by slight or no morphological differences, but by marked differences of habitat, food-preference and even of function and occupation. Such units are generally known as biological or physiological races. They have, of course, been for a long time familiar to bacteriologists and have been detected in Protozoa among which structurally indistinguishable strains are found in different hosts. Similar ' host-specificity ' accompanied by morphological differentiation is a well-known phenomenon in various groups of parasitic Metazoa. The whole problem of physiological differentiation involving such phenomena as immunity, certain aspects of interspecific sterility and graft-specificity has been recently reviewed by Robson (1928, Chapter III), and Thorpe (1930, p. 177) has given a survey of the special phenomenon of biological races in insects, nematodes, etc. It should be noted (a) that it is not always easy to distinguish ' physiological races ' from those separated by habitat-preferences which may be determined by other factors than physiological idiosyncrasy, and (b) that ' physiological ' is sometimes used in a very broad sense. Thus Fulton (1925) and Allard (1929) allude to the stridulation of Orthoptera as *physiologically* differentiated.

How frequent this phenomenon is it is not easy to say. It may be that in every phylum the species are composed of subordinate groups diversified in regard to their ' physiological ' characters. The ground has not been sufficiently explored from this point of view. A list of the features of this order that seem in one group or another to be the basis of racial diversification is sufficiently impressive to lead us to believe that it must be of very frequent occurrence.

While in practice it would be undesirable to give separate names to the various physiological races within a species, it should be noted that some botanists have definitely adopted the practice of naming ecological subspecies and that Alpatov (1924) has recognised similar subspecies (' truncicolae,' etc.) in ants.

Just as the taxonomist's species may contain divers structural, geographical and genetical subdivisions, it also seems to contain elements that are diversified by habit, habitat-preference, physiological reactions, food-preference and so on. Such differentiation may or may not be accompanied by structural differentiation and its occurrence must always constitute an interesting starting-point for evolutionary inquiry, as it invites the obvious query—do initial differences in food, habits, etc., lead to structural change? The demonstration by Nuttall (1914), Bacot (1917) and Sikora (1917) that the human head-louse could be transformed into the body-louse by transference from the head to the arm is interesting in this connection.

The physiological race presents no special difficulty in our scheme of categories. How far they are (*a*) regularly distinguished as discontinuous populations and (*b*) hereditarily fixed are more difficult questions, and there are not sufficient data to answer them. Races habituated, *e.g.*, to different food-plants will obviously be discontinuous, but some contrasted types of habitat-preference are certainly not. As regards the hereditary fixation of such racial characteristics little can be said at present. The experiments with *Pediculus* (*antea*) and Thorpe's experiments (1929) with *Hyponomeuta* seem to suggest that physiological preferences are not germinally fixed. Harrison's claim to have induced a new germinally fixed habit of oviposition in *Pontania* (1927), involving the acquisition of a preference for a new host-plant, does not seem to be justified (see p. 41).

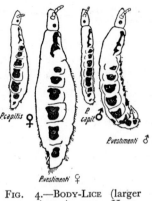

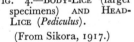

FIG. 4.—BODY-LICE (larger specimens) AND HEAD-LICE (*Pediculus*).

(From Sikora, 1917.)

Different methods of analysing the variation of natural populations have shown that it is not without order and the most obvious tendency is for individual variants to form groups of various kinds. These groups are aggregates of individuals resembling each other usually in a number of correlated characters. The simplest and most fundamental manifestation of this tendency is seen in the homogeneous stocks produced by vegetative or autogamous reproduction. The mechanism of heredity produces another kind of group in the biotype and combined with autogamous reproduction, the pure line. A third kind is produced by topographical and other barriers to intercourse, and here it is customary to indicate the degree of divergence by a hierarchy of grades beginning at the colony and passing through the local race to the subspecies.[1] In this system we see groups progressively diverging either in more characters or in the amplification of individual differences. So far the bulk of our knowledge of these processes is concerned with structural divergence, but there is strong evidence for the occurrence of ' races ' which differ from one another in single features of habit, food-preference and physiological activity. Still further divergence is seen in the groups usually recognised as species which contain a number of distinct but intergrading subordinate elements of the various kinds described above. Species may be more or less homogeneous or they may be markedly diversified by sharply cut constituent elements (Rassenkreise). Palæontological evidence suggests that historically considered the various individual character-sequences within a group do not develop at the same rate. This principle can probably be harmonised with the results of neontology by reference to the observed fact that different elements (*e.g.* colonies) exhibit different proportions of the same stock of variants and the theoretical assumption that new mutations occur at different parts in and spread slowly through a population.

---

[1] Sometimes a form is given subspecific rank because it covers a wide area, although it differs from its nearest ally in very minute details. On the other hand, a well-marked variety with a very restricted range might not be given the same rank, chiefly because, on the whole, fewer workers will be interested in a form found only in a small area.

CHAPTER IV

THE DISTRIBUTION OF VARIANTS IN NATURE

IN this chapter we propose to consider the manner in which variations are distributed in nature. As indicated in Chapter I the distribution is not purely random. Groups of various kinds are manifest on the most superficial inspection, and it is our object to describe the various kinds of aggregates found and the mode of their occurrence, and to indicate any general inferences which may be drawn from the latter.

As a preliminary to this inquiry we have to discuss certain general principles and facts which have an immediate bearing on this subject.

1. In Chapter II we have given certain data relating to the susceptibility of the living organism to its environment and have discussed how far we can form an opinion as to the likelihood that the effect of such susceptibility is heritable. Apart from the latter all-important question, it is clear that some part of the variation (both in individuals and in populations) in nature is causally related to the factors of the environment. How far we are entitled to consider the characters of any variants and groups as heritable and how far our knowledge is embarrassed by ignorance in this respect will be discussed in 3.

In addition to the significant and universal occurrence of groups already noted (Chapter I), it is known (Chapter II) that there is another broad principle of distribution of which the essential characteristic is the correlation of some progressive modification or series of modifications with a climatic or environmental ' trend ' or ' gradient.' Such a series is often represented by a number of subspecies or races, as in the subspecies of the Fox Sparrow (*Passerella iliaca*) of N.W. America (Swarth, 1920). Many cases of single-character modifications are seen in the data brought forward in support of the so-called 'Laws' of Allen, Bergmann and Gloger. In some instances these 'trends' are not obviously correlated with environmental gradients (Swarth, *l.c.* pp. 98–100; Hewitt, 1925, p. 263; Snodgrass, 1903, p. 411). The two last-named writers attribute the series (in scorpions and birds) to successive waves of migration. Hewitt (*l.c.* p. 274) specifically states that the series he studied are phylogenetic. Hutchinson (1929, p. 444) records an interesting trend from west to east in South Africa among the Notonectidae, in which three subspecies of *Micronecta piccanin* form a series, though the typical form *M. piccanin piccanin* is found unmodified along the whole trend. Swarth (*l.c.* p. 92) notes that a trend may be composed of successive areas of subspecific or racial stability separated by narrow areas of intergradation.

2. The very general occurrence of local and geographical races is discussed later on (p. 104). It should, however, be pointed out here that into the formation of some groups more than one factor probably enters, viz. differentiated environments (the effects of which may be inherited or not), isolation, mode of reproduction and inheritance. How far adaptation to local conditions enters into their formation is considered in Chapter VII.

3. It has been shown (Chapters I and II) that there is a great lack of knowledge as to how far the variation of animals in nature is heritable or not and whether the very obvious plasticity of form and habit is of any moment in evolution. It has also been noted that there is among taxonomists and other students a rough-and-ready acceptance of the distinction between fluctuations and heritable variation, though there is no criterion for deciding between them other than the very small number of experiments and rather dubious analogies (Chapter I). All generalisations based on the facts of local and geographical variation labour under this initial disadvantage. There have, it is true, been cited a number of instances in which the heritable or non-heritable nature of variants has been satisfactorily determined. But it is reasonable to ask—what inferences are to be drawn from perhaps 20 or 30 experiments, when our generalisations should cover the whole range of recorded variation? If modern Biology elects to stand by the criterion of experiment in what, after all, constitutes one of its most important fields of evolutionary research,

it is obviously thrown back on a relatively small number of experimentally tested cases and the great bulk of the data on local divergence (often associated with valuable ecological and bionomic data) is worthless !

We have given in Chapter II a general survey of the facts concerning fluctuations ; but it is desirable here to define how far the deficiency in experimental evidence may be remedied by other means. The following means of inferring whether we are dealing with fluctuations seem to be available.

A. Certain characters such as size and colour are sometimes determined by the amount and type of food available and, though the non-heritability of such variation is only very rarely demonstrated, it is a fair inference that they are not inherited.

(*a*) *Size.*—The adult size of insects obviously depends on the food available for the larvæ. In forms with a fluctuating food-supply, such as carrion-feeding flies, adaptability in this respect is very marked (*cf.* Salt, 1932). Mickel (1924, pp. 15–16) has given a summary of a number of cases, in addition to his own definite evidence that in the wasp *Dasymutilla bioculata* adult size is dependent on the quantity of food available for the larva. Especially significant is the experiment of Wodsedalek (1917), who was able to vary the size of the larvæ of a Dermestid (*Trogoderma tarsale*) from large to small by starving them and from small to large by feeding them again. Amongst molluscs, Hecht (1896) records that *Elysia viridis* grows to a much larger size when its diet is changed from *Codium* to *Cladophora*.

(*b*) *Colour.*—Pelseneer (1920, p. 485) gives a long list of colour-changes in molluscs wrought by differences in diet. In insects which feed on different plants the colour likewise varies with the food. Thus Waters (1928) notes that the moorland form of the moth *Coleophora caespititiella*, which feeds on *Juncus squarrosus*, can be distinguished fairly easily by its darker colour from the specimens bred from *J. communis*. Eisentraut (1929*a*) attributes the darker colour of certain littoral forms of the gecko *Hemidactylus* to their feeding on Halophyta. In general it may be noted that there is a traditional suspicion among taxonomists that colour is an unsafe systematic index. This is partly because it is extremely plastic. In some instances, however, experiment is against this view.

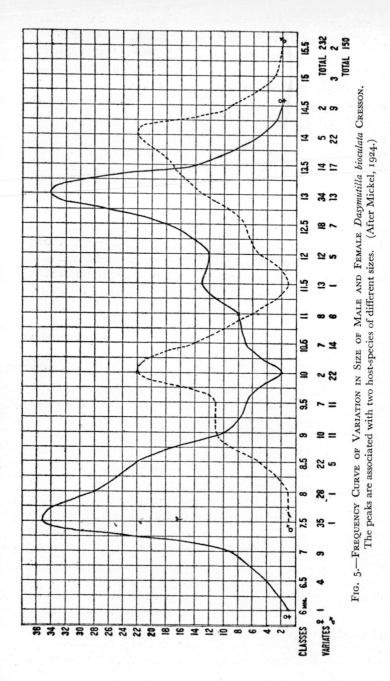

FIG. 5.—FREQUENCY CURVE OF VARIATION IN SIZE OF MALE AND FEMALE *Dasymutilla bioculata* CRESSON. The peaks are associated with two host-species of different sizes. (After Mickel, 1924.)

Sumner (1918) says that in *Peromyscus* ' it [colour] is less subject to erratic local influences than the length of body parts.'

B. Certain mechanical stresses, such as wave and current actions, produce on forms with hard external parts (*e.g.* corals and molluscs) modifications of a particular type which we may fairly infer are not hereditary. Thus we find that *Limnaea andersoniana* of N. India (Annandale and Rao, 1925) exhibits a still-water form, a stream form and a current form recognisable by the shape of the shell. Similar habitat-forms of corals are described by Wood Jones (1910). We may include here such modifications as are imposed on sedentary organisms by the character of their substrate (sponges (Burton, 1928) ; *Anomia* (Jensen, 1912)). There is no direct evidence that these forms are not inherited ; all we can say is that they seem to show that accommodation to external stresses which we have come to associate with non-heritable plasticity. It is known that certain variations in mollusc shells less obviously related to environmental conditions (*e.g.* dwarfing in *Crepidula* (Conklin, 1898) and the ' *abyssicola* ' form of *Limnaea palustris* (Roszkowski, 1912)) are non-heritable.

C. A good number of variations associated with other external factors are probably of a fluctuational nature. These include (*a*) the effects of the chemical differences in the medium (soil or water) (*e.g.* modifications of the shell of molluscs in brackish water (Bateson, 1889), the stunting of marine molluscs in water of low salinity (Pelseneer, 1920, p. 565), and the modification of the shell of terrestrial forms on soils deficient in lime-salts (*id. l.c.* p. 577)), (*b*) the action of humidity and dryness, (*c*) of temperature and (*d*) of sunlight.

In all the cases enumerated in A–B it is necessary to make a distinction between the action of intermittently changing factors and long-sustained environmental pressure, as we have already suggested the possibility that the time-factor cannot be altogether disregarded in the induction of heritable variants.

We ought to consider the converse question—to what extent are natural variations known to be heritable ? A very considerable literature is, of course, available on this subject. The experimental results are, however, very unequally distributed among the various phyla, largely because all animals do not lend themselves to experiment with equal facility. A great deal of work has been done on Protozoa and insects, a less amount on Mollusca, and still less on birds and mammals (wild), fishes and Crustacea. Among the other groups our knowledge is defective. No general inferences can be made from these results as to what characters are especially prone to be heritable nor as to the likely incidence of such variation in the vast number of described species. As regards the heritability of the characters which distinguish local races it is still more difficult to generalise. From the work of Sumner (mammals), Schmidt (fishes), Harrison, Tower, Goldschmidt (insects) and Woltereck (Crustacea) it is evident that some races tend to breed true, though the racial complex is dissociated and broken up on crossing.

4. There are certain special types of local variation which are more properly considered in relation to the causes which are presumed to have encouraged or given rise to them. Prominent amongst these is the occurrence of special insular forms. These include not only normal divergences from the adjacent continental forms, but also certain abnormalities, such as melanic, dwarf and giant types, which have repeatedly been noted as characteristic of insular faunas (see Chapter V).

5. In the intensive study of local variation involving the comparison of distinct races or subspecies there is sometimes available data for estimating the relative size of local groups. Such data have often given us the impression that in a group of closely related groups (races or subspecies) one particular group will tend to occupy a larger area or otherwise tend to predominate over the others. This is usually recognised in taxonomy as the *typical form*. The means for judging how frequent this predominance of one or more forms within a species may be, are not very extensive, as the appropriate data are not often given. If it is, as we suspect, of general occurrence, it is a phenomenon of some consequence and might conceivably be adduced as evidence for the operation of selection. Instances are seen in the distribution of the subspecies of American marmots (Howell, 1915) and *Glaucomys* (*id.* 1918) and also in the races of *Partula* (Crampton, 1916–1932).

It may be pointed out here that the suggestion put forward by Willis (1922) that the size of the area occupied by a species is an index of its age (more recent species occupying smaller areas) has been in some measure confirmed for

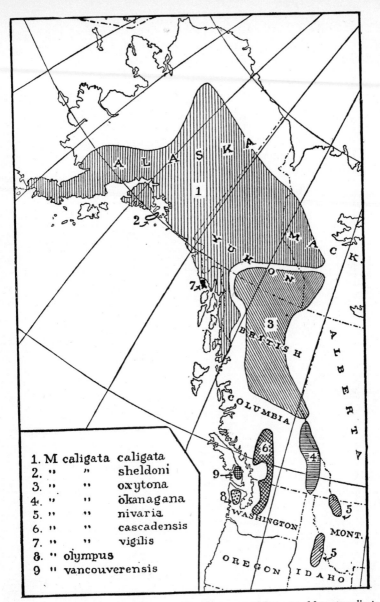

1. M caligata caligata
2. " " sheldoni
3. " " oxytona
4. " " okanagana
5. " " nivaria
6. " " cascadensis
7. " " vigilis
8. " olympus
9 " vancouverensis

FIG. 6A.—MAP OF DISTRIBUTION OF RACES OF THE MARMOT, *Marmota caligata.*
(Fig. 3 in Howell, 1915.)

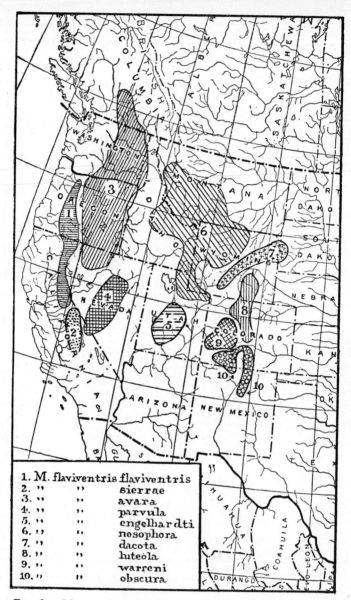

1. M. flaviventris flaviventris
2. ,, ,, sierrae
3. ,, ,, avara
4. ,, ,, parvula
5. ,, ,, engelhardti
6. ,, ,, nosophora
7. ,, ,, dacota
8. ,, ,, luteola
9. ,, ,, warreni
10. ,, ,, obscura

FIG. 6B.—MAP OF DISTRIBUTION OF RACES OF *Marmota flaviventris*.
(Fig. 2 in Howell, 1915.)

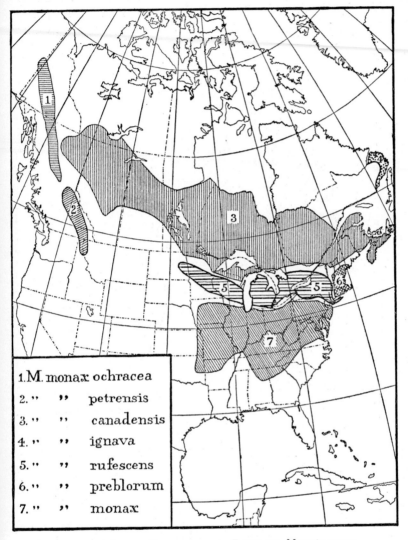

1. M. monax ochracea
2. " " petrensis
3. " " canadensis
4. " " ignava
5. " " rufescens
6. " " preblorum
7. " " monax

FIG. 6C.—MAP OF DISTRIBUTION OF RACES OF *Marmota monax.*
(Fig. 1 in Howell, 1915.)

animals by Riley (1924, p. 77). We hardly believe it feasible to test that hypothesis with reference to the area occupied by related subspecies. Willis's theory seems to have a partial validity ; but, as Robson (1928, p. 114) has suggested, we are not justified in dealing with it as of prime importance in explaining differences in distribution.

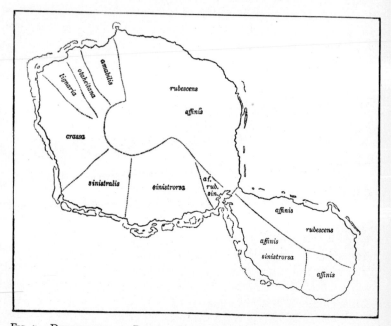

FIG. 7.—DISTRIBUTION OF PRIMARY VARIETIES OF *Partula otaheitana* ON TAHITI.
(Text-fig. 7 in Crampton, 1916.)

6. All taxonomists and probably very many other students know that closely allied species are frequently united by 'intermediates' or, to put it in another way, that they have different means but overlapping ranges of variation in some characters. Other closely allied forms appear to be sharply distinguished in all the characters investigated, though, of course, the analysis is rarely pushed far enough to enable us to say if such distinctions are found in every character.

That all species have a certain, if sometimes very limited, range of 'continuous' variation is too well known to require documentation. The notion of 'continuous' variation is largely an arbitrary one and in practice merely implies that the differences between individuals are sometimes so slight that they can be arranged (in a graph or diagram) in a more or less imperceptibly graded series. Similarly ' discontinuity ' merely implies that there is a more or less perceptible break in such a series of variates. The sizes of the steps in a continuous series and of the breaks in discontinuous series are of course incapable of standardisation. It is largely held that differences of environment (*e.g.* the amount of nutrition received by individuals) contribute very largely to ' continuous ' variability, though it is now known (*e.g.* from the work on *Drosophila* or that on *Ephestia kühniella* (Kühn and Henke)) that the smallest and least sharply distinguished variants may have a discontinuous hereditary basis.

One of the most important applications of elementary genetics to the field of taxonomy is to break down the distinction between ' continuous ' and ' discontinuous ' variation. This is still insufficiently realised by taxonomists. When we are dealing with a single character, the occurrence of continuity or discontinuity is determined by how two contrasting characters happen to interact in a particular species. It is well known that the *expression* (as opposed to the *inheritance*) of hereditary characteristics may depend on the environment to which the individual is exposed. Thus with a given heritable basis deciding the main lines of, *e.g.*, colour-pattern, its actual degree of development may depend on the environment, heredity determining only the mean. This principle is doubtless very important in considering the numerous examples of pairs of species having a different mean but overlapping range in some character. Where a complete gradation can be found over a certain range of variation, it is not sufficiently realised by taxonomists that very simple statistical treatment will often demonstrate that the continuous range of variation really masks a fundamental discontinuity. Taxonomists usually content themselves with saying either that ' intermediates are rare ' or that ' the forms are connected by all intergradations,' in each case deciding summarily to separate or ' lump ' together the two forms. If one makes a table showing the frequency with which the character appears in different degrees of development (*e.g.* as prepared by Sumner, 1923), the true nature of the variation-range may become apparent. The same method may be applied to discontinuity in a complex of characters, by means of a table showing the extent to which they are correlated with one another. In simple cases it may not even be essential to apply actual statistical calculation. It is hardly necessary to point out that discontinuity may be found between single characters and between groups of characters and that, as Robson (1928, p. 11) has shown, the attempt to formulate an exact standard of specific distinctness based on the degree of discontinuity in structural characters breaks down on account of the very varying number of characters which may show discontinuous differences.

The question which really affects our present discussion is the cause of this continuity and discontinuity of variation and its usual mode of occurrence in nature. These two subjects have been discussed by Bateson (1913) and Robson (*l.c.* p. 28 and foll.), and the following brief statement of their views may be given with some expansion.

Intermediate forms may be of two kinds—(i) ' mid-inter-mediates,' which are a blend of the characters of two divergent groups and represent a condition half-way between the two, and (ii) various combinations of the characters of the two groups. The former may be due to environmental causes or to such genetic phenomena as imperfect dominance. The latter are almost certainly due to genetic causes. Where a genetic basis for intermediacy between species is involved, it must arise from crossing or the intermediates may represent the residuum of a stock from which distinct groups are being evolved. It should be noted that between two species which occupy the same area there may be intermediacy in one region and none in another. This is noted for *Cepea hortensis* and *nemoralis* by Coutagne (1895) and for *Notonecta* by Delcourt (1909). It is even seen in such a restricted area.as a single lake, as has been recorded in the pond snail *Vivipara* of Lake Garda by Franz (1928). The extent to which intermediacy in nature is brought about by crossing is very uncertain. That a great deal has the appearance of being due to this cause is undoubted, and many systematists (*e.g.* Pictet, 1926, p. 399 ; Ruxton and Schwarz, 1929, p. 571 ; Lowe, 1929, p. 29) are of the opinion that particular intermediate populations are produced by this cause. Crampton (1932, p. 160 and *passim*) evidently holds that there is good evidence that much of the interracial intermediacy in *Partula* is due to crossing. In a later chapter we give an account of the factors that make for isolation between species in nature, and it will be seen that they are many and varied. Though it may amount to a truism, we must content ourselves with the conclusion that, wherever opportunities for crossing are available, a good part of the intermediacy (notably in respect of recombinations of characters) found in nature, is due to this cause.

Although all degrees of intermediacy are found in nature there are certain broad lines which can be recognised in their mode of occurrence.

Observations in nature suggest that there are three main tendencies recognisable at the meeting-point of allied species or races occupying distinct areas.

(1) The groups occupy distinct areas with few or no intermediates—Lepidoptera (Clark, 1932, p. 8), *Peromyscus maniculatus* and *P. blandus* (Dice, 1931), *Eumenes maxillosus typicus* and *tropicalis* and *fenestralis* (Bequaert, 1919). This may occur either with topographical discontinuity (Thomas and Wroughton, 1916 (squirrels)) or without (Dice, *l.c.*).

(2) There is a narrow area between the two groups occupied by an intermediate type—*Tisiphone* species (Waterhouse, 1922), *Passerella iliaca* (Swarth, 1920), *Peromyscus albifrons* and *P. polionotus* (Sumner, 1929). It is interesting to note that the area of intergradation is very narrow in the last-mentioned case, although the species in question are known experimentally to be quite fertile *inter se* (Sumner, *l.c.* p. 114). In the case of *Passerella* the subspecies mentioned may be broken up into separate populations (*i.e.* there may be no continuity of population).

(3) A number of subspecies may occur over a larger or smaller area with complete intergradation between the various groups—*Troglodytes musculus* (Chapman and Griscom, 1924), *Heodes phlaeas* (Ford, 1924). It is of importance to note that these tendencies may be observed in one and the same group. Thus Clark (1932, p. 8) states that ' while some species pass by a series of minute intergradations from one geographical form to another, others do not, the N. and S. form occurring together with one or perhaps two well-marked intergrading types.' So, too, one may note the sharp

contrast between *Peromyscus polionotus* and *albifrons* and the gradual transition between *P. leucopus* and *noveboracensis* described by Osgood (1909).

It is also worth while, from the genetical point of view, to summarise briefly at this point some of the data with regard to intergradation in specific characters.

(*a*) If two species meet but do not interbreed, then there is no tendency for their character-complexes to break down more frequently in the area where they meet than elsewhere.

(*b*) When the intervening area is inhabited by a more or less definite intermediate form, there is considerable breakdown in correlation. But the breakdown is of a predictable sort and not altogether at random, some of the more strongly correlated characters remaining in association.

(*c*) When there is complete intergradation, correlation between specific or racial characters is completely broken down over an area of varying size. Specimens can be given only a conventional taxonomic name on the basis of the majority of the characters exhibited. Numerous instances of such intergradation are noted in our examples (pp. 102–119).

Grinnell and Swarth (1913) also recognise these three types of intergradation and see in them, probably correctly, three stages in the fixation of specific type.

7. Darwin (1884, p. 42) was the first to point out that there is a relationship between the extent of the range of a species and its variation. Most zoologists probably believe that 'widely ranging species vary the most' (Darwin, *l.c.*). By 'widely ranging' Darwin clearly meant 'having a wide distribution' (as species) and not 'having a wide individual range,' a distinction of some importance. Obviously, if we take 'variable' to involve merely the number of mutations Darwin was at least theoretically correct, because there will be a larger chance of mutation in a large population than in a small one. If he meant that such forms tend to throw more numerous varieties or regional forms, the statement is only true in a very general way. We shall see later on (p. 105) that the amount of regional variation is determined by a variety of factors, among which habits play a very large part, and that there are many cases of widely ranging species (*e.g.* the Common Heron) which show very little or no regional differentiation.

We now proceed to consider the actual mode of occurrence of variants in nature, in so far as they form recognisable parts or assemblages within natural populations.

As we have stated (p. 8), all stages can be traced from a variant which occurs sporadically in a population or occurs in a small local enclave to a well-marked local or geographical assemblage. Any attempt to isolate and classify particular types of occurrence must necessarily be arbitrary ; but it seems to us that the following scheme illustrates the chief stages in the process :

I. Sporadic individual variation usually involving a single character.

II. The local combinations formed from a stock of variable characters.

III. The emergence of qualitatively distinct groups involving large sections of a population. This embraces all the divergences usually alluded to under the terms polymorphism and geographical variation.

Of these three stages the phenomenon usually known as polymorphism includes both II and III, while geographical variation illustrates III.

These differences are seen in physiological as well as structural characters, and the former will be discussed at the end of this chapter.

It will be understood that precise knowledge as to the local distribution of variants (either in single characters or in several) ought to be based on a very large array of specimens collected at all points over the range of the species. Such intensive studies are unfortunately uncommon. Population analyses have been conducted on a large scale upon commercial fishes, though it is at present uncertain to what precise extent the characters studied (size, number of vertebræ and fin-rays) are influenced by the environment. The population analyses of Sumner (*Peromyscus*) are not sufficiently intensive and are more concerned with the causes of local divergence. By far the most valuable data are those based on the population of land snails (Crampton, etc.), to which allusion is made under II.

It should finally be noticed that practical experience as well as a more refined study of natural populations has revealed that they are often broken up into small self-contained communities such as ' schools,' colonies, rookeries and shoals. The statistical constitution of such communities is very little known and only the colonies into which the populations of land snails are divisible are at all well studied. Some progress has been made with the study of the shoals of commercial fishes (Schnakenbeck, 1931). The distinction between such intimate subdivisions of a population and, *e.g.*, the races of *Zoarces* described by Schmidt, is not easy to draw.

A. **Sporadic Individual Variation.**—There seem to be two main tendencies to be recognised under this head according as a sporadic variation occurs throughout the range of a species or is more restricted in its occurrence. The most obvious and commonest type of individual variation of this kind is seen in colour-phases of various sorts. We ought also to include certain pattern-forms which occur rarely and sporadically, *e.g.* in populations of land snails, in which the main pattern-types show local statistical differences.

The following are the principal ways in which individual variants are distributed :

(*a*) A typical form and a variation occur sporadically throughout the range.

1. *Albinism.*—The majority of species of mammals which have been adequately investigated are found occasionally to produce albinos in nature. Twenty-one out of the forty-three British mammals dealt with by Barrett-Hamilton and Hinton are known to have produced albinos sporadically within the British Isles. Similar sporadic variation is widespread in birds and in some Lepidoptera. Though it is rare in fishes, Norman (1931, p. 227) says that it is common in flatfishes.

2. *The variety* caeruleopunctata *of the Small Copper Butterfly*, Heodes phlaeas.—Ford (1924) shows that this variety, in which the upper side of the hind wings has marginal blue spots, occurs sporadically through the greater part of the range. It tends to occur in different proportions in different places ; the ratio may remain constant over a number of years.

3. *'Xanthochroism' in fishes.*—The black and brown pigment is lost more or less entirely in certain groups and the golden and yellow is left. The Goldfish is, of course, a cultivated variant of this type. This condition is found in nature in the Trout and Eel (Norman, *l.c.* p. 227).

4. *Variation in sculpture in the water beetles*, Dytiscidae (*Kolbe, 1920*).—In many species two forms of the female occur, a smooth form and a sculptured form. The latter may have deep striæ or merely denser microscopic sculpture, according to the genus and species. In most cases the proportion of the types varies locally and one or other form may be found almost exclusively in certain parts of the range.

5. *Colour and pattern forms of land snails.*—Many species of *Helicidae* are extremely variable in colour and pattern. It seems at present that the variation is subject to some measure of local statistical divergence ; but certain pattern combinations are rare and occur in single individuals in most local assemblages.

6. *Sinistral varieties of normally dextral snails* (*Crampton, 1916, 1925 and 1932*).—These are somewhat similarly distributed, but are normally rare, while areas of high frequency are very localised.

7. *Colour variation in the wasp*, Synagris cornuta *L.* (*Bequaert, 1919, p. 204*).—The species is practically confined to Engler's Western Forest Province of Africa. There are eight distinct colour forms. Many of these occur together in any one district and several of them have been found in a single nest. Many intergrades occur. The ground colour is black with black wings, and variation consists in the presence or absence of varying amounts of orange on the thorax and base of the abdomen. These occur in all combinations.

(*b*) There is a typical form and a variety or varieties are localised in definite parts of the range, where they occur with the typical form.

8. *The black variety (var. nigra) of the Rose Chafer*, Cetonia aurata (*Blair, 1931, p. 1212*).—In Great Britain this

is confined to the Scilly Isles, where it is rare. It is also known from Corsica and certain parts of the Mediterranean. The type-form ranges all over Europe.

9. *The greenish female variety (var. valesina) of the Silverwashed Fritillary*, Argynnis paphia.—Goldschmidt (1922) has shown that the variety is the expression of a single dominant sex-limited gene. In England the variety is confined to the New Forest, though the species has a much wider range. The variety also occurs sporadically on the Continent.

10. *The ' blue ' and ' white ' phases of the Arctic Fox (Elton, 1930, p. 80 and foll.).*—These two forms often exist together and interbreed with perfect fertility. The proportions in which they occur are subject to much local variation. In certain areas one or the other form is found exclusively.

11. *Colour phases in birds.*—Stresemann (1925) records in birds a type of variation much like that seen in the Arctic Fox. Thus the Indo-Australian *Accipiter novaehollandiae* occurs in a white and a dark form. In Tasmania, however, only the white form is found.

B. **Polymorphism.**—This term has been applied, as we have shown (p. 11), to variation in general and also in a more restricted sense to the occurrence of strongly marked phases within a species, whether they are geographically distinct or occur in the same habitat. We propose to use the term in the latter sense and to use ' Geographical Variation ' for the occurrence of geographically isolated groups.

1. *Colonial divergence in land snails.*

A great deal of intensive study has been devoted to the statistical investigation of ' colonial ' divergence in land mollusca. As the results are of considerable value we give a more detailed analysis than usual and provide a summary of the results.

(*a*) Alkins (1928) studied two characters (altitude and major diameter of shell) in *Clausilia rugosa* and *C. cravenensis* in 19 loci distributed over an area of 8 × 4 miles.

(i) Each colony has a rather wide range of variation in the two characters, rather more in respect of altitude. In altitude the 'spread' is very wide, *i.e.* no one class is very frequent. In diameter there is a distinct tendency for a high grouping about one phase. This is very well seen in the figure of 'polygons of variation' (*op. cit.* pp. 59 and 61).

(ii) In general the series from neighbouring loci are more or less alike, but the converse is not true. No two loci have exactly the same mean. The shell-characters are not correlated with the ecological characters of the various loci.

(b) Boycott (1919, 1927) also studied the shape of the shell in *C. rugosa*. He found the same amount of variation in each locus and that there was no relation between the former and the character of the locus, though he suspected some relation between shell-altitude and environment. 'Significant' differences were found in 5 out of 6 pairs of *contrasted characters*.

(c) Aubertin (1927) studied a number of colonies of *Cepea nemoralis* and *C. hortensis* both for shell-colour, etc., and anatomical characters. The former only are considered here. The number of specimens used is rather low.

(i) *C. hortensis.*—Each colony has a wide range of variation and in three out of four 'adjacent colonies' there was good 'spread' for ground colour. In one ('Hedge Lane') yellow was 90 % of the total. For three types of banding the spread as between type 12345 and 00000 was equal. Some colonies lack a particular ground colour-class altogether.

Adjacent colonies tend to be different significantly in ground colour, less so in banding. A Buckinghamshire colony closely resembles one Wiltshire colony, though it differs in the absence of a colour-class found in the latter.

(ii) *C. nemoralis.*—In colour some colonies lack certain classes altogether, as in (i) ; but this is far more marked in *nemoralis*. The 'spread' of variation is more limited; actually two out of the four colour-classes only are represented, though a few 'brown' occur at three colonies. In one colony (Maiden Castle) one class is 77 % of the population. In banding the spread was fairly wide, though usually one or two classes tend to be more highly represented.

(*d*) Rensch (1932) calculated the percentage frequency in 16 colonies of *Cepea nemoralis* (mostly remote from each other) for 7 colour- and band-classes. The statistical significances of the differences were not worked out. From his table we may give the following results on 'spread.' In four colonies one class was found in over 90 % of the specimens; in four, one class was over 70 %, and in one a class was over 80 %. In the rest the tendency was for two classes to be well represented and the others to be numerically inferior. Very often three or four classes are entirely absent. Two classes, yellow 00000 and yellow 12345, have a very high frequency and are about equal in frequency, and the others are all very low.

(*e*) Crampton's work (1916, 1925 and 1932) is on a much larger scale than the rest. It is, in fact, so extensive and the details are so manifold that one awaits a summary and analysis by the author and only the following points can be noted here :

   (i) The spread of variation tends to follow the same lines as in (*d*), *i.e.* there is a tendency for one or more classes to be preponderatingly frequent and some colonies may lack a whole series of classes.

   (ii) Adjacent colonies tend to be alike, but the same percentage of a given class may be found in remote colonies. Abrupt change in the number of classes and their percentage frequency is found between adjacent loci, and the latter may differ in the absence and presence of whole classes.

LOCAL DIFFERENCES IN FREQUENCY OF COLOUR- AND BAND-CLASSES IN *Cepea hortensis* (RENSCH, 1932, p. 100).

Locality.	No. of Specimens.	% Frequency of Varieties.						
		Yellow 00000	Reddish 00000	Yellow 00305	Yellow 10305	Yellow 10345	Yellow 12045	12345
Sassnitz, Rügen	82	32·9	—	—	26·5	1·2	—	40·3
Stubbenkammer, Rügen	238	36·2	—	0·4	23·5	1·7	0·4	37·8
Warnemünde	76	77·7	—	—	—	—	—	22·3
Ratzeburg	74	70·3	14·9	2·7	5·4	—	—	6·7
Berlin-Buch	73	10·9	—	—	—	—	1·4	87·7
Fauler Ort, S. of Prenzlau	146	48·6	—	—	—	—	—	51·4
Kuhhorst, near Kremmen	79	64·6	—	—	—	—	—	35·4
Pfiffelbach, near Weimar	73	52·0	5·5	—	—	—	—	42·5
Eisenach	55	58·2	—	—	38·2	1·8	—	1·8
Stuttgart	67	65·7	—	—	—	—	4·5	32·8
Doksy, Bohemia	1,069	0·1	22·2	—	—	—	0·5	77·2
Hyčice, Bohemia	204	—	—	—	—	2·9	—	97·1
Siegenfeld, Vienna	87	97·9	1·1	—	—	—	—	1·1
Rohrerhütte, Wiener Wald	54	77·8	1·9	—	—	—	—	20·3
Kahlenberg, Vienna	798	98·6	—	—	—	0·3	—	1·1
Stammersdorf, Vienna	539	93·7	—	—	—	0·4	0·6	5·3

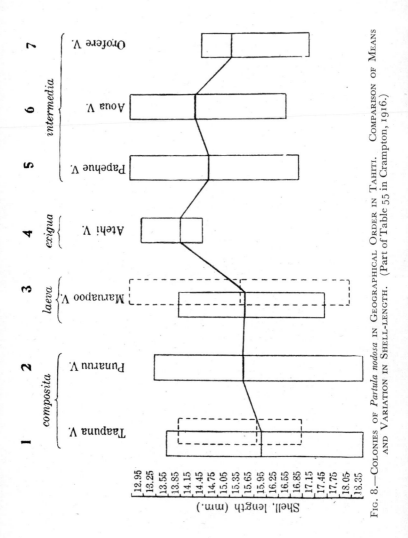

FIG. 8.—COLONIES of *Partula nodosa* in GEOGRAPHICAL ORDER in TAHITI. COMPARISON OF MEANS AND VARIATION IN SHELL-LENGTH. (Part of Table 55 in Crampton, 1916.)

(*f*) Aubertin, Ellis and Robson (1931) studied colonies of *Cochlicella acuta* in W. Sussex in respect of three main types of shell-colour.

(i) 21 comparisons were made (*l.c.* p. 1042), and of these 2 only showed equal distribution of the types. In the rest no regularity of incidence was found, but either one class or two tended to preponderate at the expense of the third. In each colony, however, all three types are usually well represented, and in 63 cases there were only 7 instances of a colony having less than 20 % of any one type.

(ii) The various colonies differ significantly in 36 % of the possible comparisons. The authors say that on the whole (p. 1047) very little relation exists between the distance separating the colonies and the differences in shell-pattern. But this is not quite true, as nearly all immediately adjacent colonies tend to show very little difference one from another. Nevertheless it is true that some adjacent colonies may differ significantly and distant ones may be alike.

From these summaries we may form the following conclusions.

(1) Populations of land snails tend to occur in colonies having a different facies, the differences having little correlation with differences of environment (Alkins, Crampton, Aubertin, Ellis and Robson) except perhaps in size (Boycott).

(2) Continuous populations (*f*) may be divisible into subordinate areas with a statistically different composition.

(3) In two cases ((*b*) and (*f*)) these differences are maintained with a tolerable degree of uniformity over a limited number of years (up to ten).

(4) While each colony tends to show a fairly wide range of variation, certain classes of variants tend to preponderate and often whole classes may be absent. One gets the impression that colonies exhibit the results of *obligatory selective mating*.

(5) That certain classes tend to occur in a high percentage might suggest that selection may be at work ; but we think that this is unlikely, as (*e.g.* in Rensch's observations) we find

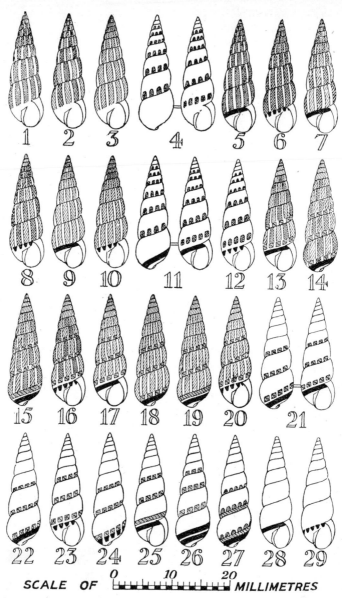

SCALE OF |IIIIIIIIIIIIIIIIIIIIII| MILLIMETRES

FIG. 9.—VARIATION IN THE POINTED SNAIL IN ITS COLONIES IN SUSSEX.
(From Toms, 1922.)

reversal of frequency, *e.g.* yellow 00000 is very numerous at the Viennese locus, very rare in the Bohemian, 12345 is numerous at ' Berlin-Buch,' very rare at Ratzeburg.

(6) (*a*) In populations intensively studied over a limited area (up to 15 × 15 miles) there is an initial tendency for adjacent colonies to be alike, but

(*b*) the converse is not true.

(7) 3 (above) suggests that colonies once they have diverged might give rise to races.

(8) The extent to which boundaries are broken down (*e.g.* by specimens being carried about by birds, wind, etc.) is unknown.

(9) It is indeed a little surprising how much community there is over wide areas, and this suggests that homogeneous races and colonies differing significantly in several characters are not likely to be very often produced in such populations.

2. *Polymorphism throughout the range of the species.*

(*a*) *Slugs.*—The variation of the commoner European slugs is not completely known ; but it has been recorded in sufficient detail to enable us to state that in polymorphic species such as *Limax maximus* and *Arion ater* some of the colour varieties are widely spread over the range and certainly occur together very frequently.

(*b*) *Spiders.*—Bristowe (1931) has described the colour-variation of the spider *Theridion ovatum*, on which there are three types of abdomen-colour, viz. : white, striped and red. Details are given of the various proportions of these characters in different parts of England.

(*c*) *Fishes.*—Norman (1931, p. 220) states that the fish *Epinephelus striatus* has eight colour-phases, none of which can be called more normal than any other. Some of the forms are strikingly different.

(*d*) *Beetles.*—Hauser (1921) has described the extraordinary variation in the Asiatic beetles of the genera *Damaster* and *Coptolabrus* (Carabidae). In most of the species-groups, the characters which elsewhere define species and races are variable. Thus in one local race of a species—*e.g.* in the *coelestis* group—very plump, moderately short-legged and very long, long-legged forms are found ; the elytra may be parallel-sided with strongly marked shoulders, or elliptical or egg-shaped with no shoulders. The pronotum and other parts vary in the same way. There are about forty-six types of variation (such as long- and short-legged ; long-, short- or a-mucronate-forms, etc.), which are liable to turn up in the races of any species. The colour also varies, but may be directly correlated with climatic conditions. In most European *Carabus* variation within the species consists of many local races, each of which is pretty constant. In *Coptolabrus* each race is very variable and not nearly so sharply defined.

(*e*) *Lepidoptera.*—Doubtless some of the most remarkable cases are complicated by the phenomena of mimicry, but many non-mimetic species are quite sufficiently remarkable. In the mimetic forms the discontinuity between the various types tends to be more marked. Of mimetic butterflies *Heliconius melpomene* (Eltringham, 1916) is one of the most remarkable. Eltringham united ten reputed species and 60–70 named colour-forms, all of which are structurally indistinguishable. Some of the forms are geographically limited, but often several are found in one restricted locality.

Fryer (1928) has studied the variation in England of the moth *Acalla comariana* Zeller (Plate II). At Wisbech there are six main forms which differ sharply from one another in colour, the fundamental pattern being the same. Genetical investigations suggest that there are probably three allelomorphs for ground colour and a factor for the colour of the costal blotch which is strongly linked with the ground colour. The proportions of the various forms were of the same order in 1926 and 1927 at Wisbech, but in Lancashire the proportions were quite different and an additional type was discovered. Other species of the genus are even more polymorphic, but have not been investigated genetically. Sheldon (1930–1931) has shown that there are almost innumerable varieties, many of them sharply distinct from one another, in *Acalla* (*Peronea*) *cristana*.

3. *Polymorphism combined with constancy in particular areas.*

Probably most polymorphic species are really of this character. We rarely have enough data to show that all the various forms occur throughout the range. There is always a tendency to form non-variable colonies or even larger populations.

Polymorphism in the moth, *Acalla comariana* Zeller
(From Fryer 1928)

(g) *Humble-bees.*—Many species of humble-bees, besides geographical variation, show marked polymorphism in parts of their range. Certain species, such as *Bombus solstitialis* and *B. soroensis*, which are extremely variable in Central Europe, are almost constant in England.

(h) *The Coccinellid beetle*, Harmonia axyridis.—Dobrzansky (1924) shows that this species varies in colour from yellow to black, the colour-pattern of the elytra falling into eight main classes. Most of the variations can be found all over the range in different proportions, with the exception that in the western part of its range (Russia to Japan) there is a tendency for a single form, *H. axyridis* (typical), to dominate the others.

(i) The previous type of variation may be compared with instances of local specific intergradation, which give rise to a similar distribution of variants. Thus von Schweppenburg (1924) notes that the sparrows *Passer domesticus* and *P. hispaniolensis*, in various subspecific forms, inhabit most of Europe, N. Africa and Asia without interbreeding, but in large areas of Algeria, Tunisia and in Malta they interbreed so much that it is hardly possible to find specimens true to either type.

Barrett-Hamilton and Hinton (1915, pp. 545–6) record that the mice *Apodemus flavicollis* and *A. sylvaticus*, which occur more or less commonly together in England, occupy different habitats in Norway. In the latter country the lowland mice of the south are nearly all *sylvaticus*, while those of the high upland pastures are *flavicollis* ; in intervening areas intermediate forms occur, almost certainly as a result of cross-breeding.

(j) Fernald (1906) shows that the American sand-wasp *Chlorion cyaneum* and its race *C. c. aerarium* differ in average size and in colour. The typical form is mainly southern and *aerarium* mainly northern, but they overlap over a wide area and occasional specimens of *aerarium* are found very far south. He records the same type of variation in *C. thomae* (with var. *bifoveolatum*), and Porter (1926) found a similar relation in *Sceliphron cementarium* between the forms *servillei* (southern) and *flavipes* (northern). In other species of *Chlorion* Fernald found more complicated variation. Thus in *C. ichneumoneum* there are three forms, one found in U.S.A. between Maine and

Mexico, one found in Florida, Mexico, Cuba and Venezuela, and a third found in Florida and the Greater Antilles. In *C. flavitarsus* there are four forms, which overlap in a rather similar way, but there is a main type in U.S.A. and another in S. America.

C. **Geographical Variation.**—Under this heading we propose to deal with instances illustrating the tendency seen in the species of certain groups to be divisible into subordinate groups occupying separate or overlapping areas. Such groups are usually alluded to as subspecies (p. 63).

We have already had occasion to contrast the frequent occurrence of this kind of geographical variation in Vertebrates with the irregular and more complex distributional phenomena in the Invertebrates. This point required some further discussion. So far as we are aware Rensch (1929) was the first to point out and to stress the fact that species of certain groups are more obviously divisible into geographical races than those of others. Admitting the inadequacy of taxonomic study and the slight amount of attention paid so far to the study of geographical variation in some groups, he considers that mammals, birds, reptiles and Amphibia, Coleoptera, Lepidoptera, Hymenoptera and Orthoptera display this tendency markedly. The other insect groups, Arachnids and Myriopods, probably show the same tendency, but the available knowledge is defective. The tendency is seen in land molluscs, but is largely masked by individual and ' ecological ' variation. Freshwater and marine groups show it in some measure ; but it is less marked here. Rensch's actual survey of the chief groups of the animal kingdom is not exhaustive, but it includes the more important groups.

He explains (p. 79) the difference in the incidence of geographical variation by pointing out that in certain groups the habits, size and mode of reproduction are of such a nature as to prevent the establishment of barriers and so of isolation between the parts of a population. Migratory habits, as in many seabirds and fishes, small size which facilitates accidental transport, as in land snails, Tardigrada, Nematoda, etc., and the occurrence of ' resting eggs ' as in Cladocera (but *cf.* Lowndes, 1930 ; see on p. 135) are all factors which make for the homogeneity of a population.

Rensch contrasts the uniformity of the widely ranging

heron [1] with the acute local differentiation of the sedentary wren. Schmidt (1918, p. 112) in the same way contrasts the homogeneity of the Common Eel population with the acutely diversified races of the localised Blenny (*Zoarces*), and Burckhardt (1900) shows that the cyclic and acyclic species of Crustacea in Swiss lakes exhibit analogous differences in the degree to which they form local races.

It will at once strike the critic that, if Rensch's theory is correct, the proneness or inability to form local or geographical races must be the resultant of a number of conflicting tendencies. Thus animals like land molluscs by their sedentary habits should be especially prone to form local races, yet this factor may be more than counterbalanced by a marked liability to accidental transport arising from their small size and mode of life. Small mammals, on the other hand, which are more or less localised and have a limited range, are less prone to be transported, so that they should form conspicuous local races. Finally, large mammals and certain kinds of birds, though they have a wider range, are obviously not prone to wide accidental dispersal, so that they should form larger, but still distinct (geographical) groups. Probably Rensch would hold that the greater range of the last two groups is set off by their localised breeding habits. It will be noted that the contrast is not between, *e.g.*, birds and molluscs, but between widely ranging and sedentary forms even of the same group. It will also be seen that wide-ranging habits in the Mammalia should have the same effect as small size in the Mollusca, viz. the restriction of local variation. As the distinction between forms which vary geographically and those which do not must be based on a resultant of the kind just suggested, we would expect to find very considerable differences in the degree in which local or geographical races are formed, according as one or another of the conditioning factors is paramount. We must also take into account a tendency to which little attention has been given, viz. the inherent tendency of a species to vary. We will now review some of the salient facts from these points of view.

[1] The example chosen is perhaps not very fortunate. The Common Heron has a remarkably wide range, is migratory and shows little or no regional variation. Nevertheless, it is a bird of otherwise sedentary habits and evidently conservative in its breeding habits, as many of the English heronries date back to an 'immemorial antiquity' (Nicholson, 1929, p. 270).

In birds there is a very noticeable tendency to form geo- ✗
graphical races (cf. *Troglodytes musculus*, fig. 12), and this is
probably connected with the tendency of migratory species to
return to the same spot to breed. Exceptions occur to Rensch's
rule that habits condition race-formation. Thus Chapman
(1923, p. 252) states that *Buarremon brunneinuchus*, though it
ranges from Mexico to Peru and is essentially sedentary in
habits, ' shows no appreciable variation which can be correlated with any given area.' This is all the more striking when
it is realised that a species, *B. inornatus*, has been evolved in and

FIG. 10.—VARIATION IN THE FINCH, *Buarremon*. *a* and *c*, *B. brunneinuchus*; *b* and *d*,
B. inornatus FROM THE CHIMBO VALLEY AND LOS LLANOS, ECUADOR.
(After Chapman, 1923.)

is restricted to a single valley in Ecuador. The case of the
Common Heron (p. 105) has already been discussed. We
believe that these instances must be referred to some inherent
inability to vary.

As far as the recorded facts go, Rensch's rule holds for
mammals, though some exceptions should be noted. Roosevelt
and Heller (1915, p. 570) show that the Steinbok (*Raphicervus
campestris*) is remarkably uniform throughout its range and
is not separable into geographical races. Christy (1929)
finds that the African Buffalo (*Bubalis caffer*) is undifferentiated
over all its range, while the Congo Buffalo (*B. nanus*) has many
local races. The remarkable differences in local variation

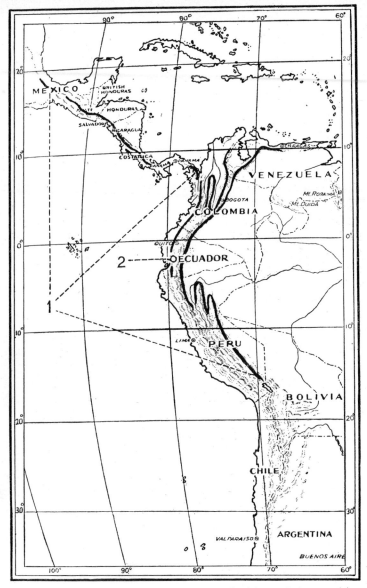

FIG. 11.—DISTRIBUTION OF *Buarremon brunneinuchus* (1) AND *B. inornatus* (2).
(From Chapman, 1923.)

of the species of *Dicrostonyx* (Hinton, 1926, p. 148 and foll.)
should be noted. Grinnell (1918, p. 241) points out that,

in spite of their powers of flight, bats are as much prone to form subspecies as other mammals. Possibly this is explicable on the grounds of localised range, though no facts can be produced to support this suggestion. Among reptiles the common African tortoise, *Testudo pardalis*, ' extends practically over the whole continent . . . and is everywhere uniform as regards its colour-pattern ' (Duerden, 1907, p. 74).

Land molluscs tend to fall into well-marked local races in spite of Rensch's statement. These are especially well marked if the terrain is favourable to isolation (Gulick, Crampton, Bartsch, Mayer, Sarasin, Simpson). Even when these conditions are absent, races may be formed as in *Murella*, *Helicogena* and *Iberus* (Kobelt), *Otala* (Boettger), and in sundry African species (Pilsbry). On the other hand, certain forms such as *Carychium* (Thorson and Tuxen, 1930) show no such tendency. Again, in such forms as *Cepea* and *Cochlicella*, though statistical differences occur in the percentage incidence of colour-patterns in various colonies, there is no regional differentiation worth mentioning. In contrast with the acute local polymorphism of *Achatinella* and *Partula* in the valleys of the Sandwich and Society Islands, the land snails of the valleys of Valais (Piaget, 1921) show no such variation, and although numerous insular races are found in *Liguus* on the Florida Keys (Simpson, 1929), *Amphidromus* in the Philippine Islands (Bartsch), etc., the land snails of the Hebrides and Scilly Isles are, as far as they are known, quite like the mainland forms.

Amongst insects, taxonomy is still, as a rule, insufficiently advanced to allow certain conclusions to be drawn. It is probably significant, however, that in the minute, wingless Collembola the species often have a very wide range without any apparent signs of local differentiation. Uvarov (1924) records an interesting example in the grasshoppers of the genus *Cyrtacanthacris*. *C. tatarica* is found over the whole of South and Equatorial Africa, including Madagascar, Seychelles, Comoro Is., Khartum, Massourah, Sokotra, India, Siam and Ceylon. There is no geographical variation and the species is extremely constant, though very common. On the other hand, *C. aeruginosa*, which is purely African, has three races, a southern, a western and an eastern race.

It is a remarkable fact (and one which might seem to be easily explicable on the grounds that there are no barriers

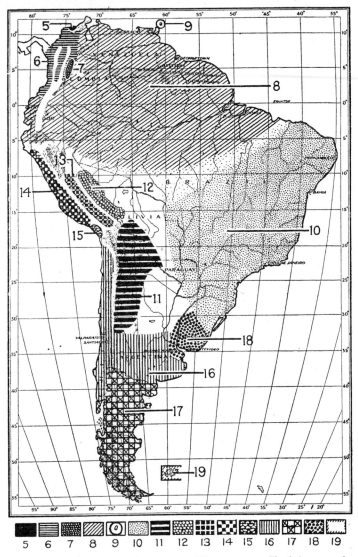

Fig. 12.—Distribution of S. American Wrens of the *Troglodytes musculus* Group. 5, *Troglodytes m. atopus* ; 6, *T. m. striatulus* ; 7, *T. m. columbae* ; 8, *T. m. albicans* ; 9, *T. m. tobagenis* ; 10, *T. m. musculus* ; 11, *T. m. rex* ; 12, *T. m. carabayae* ; 13, *T. m. puna* ; 14, *T. m. audax* ; 15, *T. tecellatus* ; 16, *T. m. chilensis* and, from the valley of Copiapo northward, *T. m. atacamensis* ; 17, *T. m. magellanicus* ; 18, *T. m. bonariae* ; 19, *T. cobbi*.

(From Chapman and Griscom, 1924.)

to intercourse) that many species of marine Crustacea (Copepoda—Scott, 1909 ; Euphausiacea—Hansen, 1911) are homogeneous throughout very extensive areas and pass practically round the world within certain isothermal limits.   It is perhaps curious that there is no gradual regional differentiation of such species and that such mutations as occur are so rapidly and effectively extinguished or spread throughout the population.

Doubtless many of these exceptions may be ultimately explained by reference to differences of habit, etc., which so far are unknown.   In some cases this seems to be very unlikely. The contrast between the Oligochaeta and the land Mollusca is a case in point. We are indebted to the late Lt.-Col. J. Stephenson, F.R.S., for pointing out many facts in connection with the slight variability of earthworms. He informed us that undoubtedly many species are ' peregrine ' and are carried round the world either as cocoons or adults, probably in agricultural and horticultural produce. Michaelsen (*fide* Stephenson) also postulates the action of winds in dispersing the cocoons, but Benham criticises this view. Peregrinal species like *Allolobophora caliginosa* are remarkably constant and exhibit very slight or no variation over an enormous range, and it would seem that the means of intercourse must be fairly regular if local differentiation is so easily effaced (*cf.* marine Crustacea). But there are also many species of earthworms which are not thus peregrine and have a more localised range, and these are invariably homogeneous.   Lt.-Col. Stephenson did not think that these species are accidentally transported from place to place. Moreover the means of transport either of cocoons or of adults (human agency, birds, winds) should be also similarly operative in the case of land snails.

It remains to notice some theoretical considerations which have a bearing on the interpretation of these facts. In the first place we must emphasise the difference between small local assemblages having a distinct statistical expression and larger ' geographical ' groups. The greater average size of Vertebrates must be of importance here, as it tends to involve a wider range and less isolation. Small size, on the one hand, facilitates accidental transport (Nematoda, Tardigrada), and on the other makes for a homogeneous local population. In the majority of cases the former influence seems to have been paramount.

Certain other facts are also relevant. In the first place the relatively small number of species in birds and mammals has enabled much greater advance to be made in the study of subspecific differences ; the definition of a large number of geographical races does not of itself prove that this type of variation is more common in these groups than in others in which the number of species is very much greater. Again, where the number of species is small, the systematist will tend not to hesitate to introduce a new name for any apparently stable local form. In such groups as the insects the species are already so numerous that considerable evidence is needed before definite named races will be published. In the Lepidoptera, in dealing with which authors have been less cautious, considerable confusion has resulted. The local variation is so great that it is a difficult and lengthy task to deal adequately with even a single species, and, where species are numerous, it is unlikely that more than a few have been sufficiently studied for so-called ' races ' to be very clearly defined.

Secondly, a geographical race is commonly defined by the average size, proportion or colour of certain parts. No one (p. 69) supposes that geographical races are normally uniformly homozygous for merely a single differential factor, so that the variation within the race cannot be regarded as purely somatic. This implies that the race could be broken up into a number of varieties differing slightly from one another in the diagnostic race-characters. The average of these varieties gives the race, because, being quantitative, these characters can be given a mean value. But, in other cases, as often in insects, a species consists of several rather sharply discontinuous varieties. If these differ qualitatively, they cannot be averaged : it is possible only to give the proportion in which the different varieties occur in different parts of the range. Difference in these proportions evidently defines a race of exactly the same nature as described in the last paragraph. But in normal taxonomic procedure the race described there would receive a name, whereas in the second case each of the distinct forms would receive a name, but there would be no name for the various populations defined by consisting of different proportions of the named forms. The example of *Harmonia axyridis* ((h), p. 103) exhibits this difficulty.

Thirdly, we are a little doubtful if the data for various groups are really comparable and whether samples of populations consisting of a few individuals, such as are used in mammals and birds, afford a sound basis for distinguishing local races. Sumner (1918, p. 292) seems to express this doubt concerning the races of small mammals. We do not as a matter of fact think this vitiates the general principle, for there are groups (*e.g.* the Cephalopoda) in which the numbers used are equally low and yet few races are recorded. What we feel is that comparable data are required and that some modifications of the alleged incidence of race-formation might result, if large numbers were regularly used.

In conclusion, it seems likely that geographical variation will ultimately be found to be as frequent in groups like terrestrial arthropods and molluscs as in vertebrates. Where all the present evidence is against the likelihood of such races being discovered, it will be usually found that special habits and other factors that prevent isolation and colony-formation are mainly responsible. Again, in some species we must look to the *inherent capacity for variation* as a cause. It must always be recalled that our knowledge of variation is at present very unequal in its incidence in the various groups and is less easily obtainable in some than in others.

Examples may now be given of the occurrence and distribution of geographical variation in various groups.

1. *Geographical variation in* Lygaeus kalmii (*Hemiptera, Heteroptera*).

Parshley (1923) has shown that there is a clearly marked eastern and western race in the United States. These meet at a line joining Winnipeg to Brownsville, Texas. Along this line intermediates occur, which cannot be referred to either race. Since the species is, in addition, highly variable in colour, it is only possible to recognise the geographically significant characters by careful study.

2. *Geographical variation in water beetles.*

Omer Cooper (1931) summarises the evidence for two examples. The extremes in each case are treated as species, but they correspond to what are called geographical races in other groups. Thus in *Deronectes depressus* and *D. elegans* there are differences in size, shape, colour, tarsal claws and width of penis. In the south of England only *elegans* is found, while in the north of Scotland only *depressus* and in Ireland only *depressus* or approximating intermediates. But in N. England and S. Scotland a completely intergrading series is found. There is a similar relation between *Gyrinus natator* and *G. substriatus*, except that the overlap appears to be wider.

3. *Geographical variation in butterflies.*

In this group geographical races have been more studied than in any other order of insects. Frequently, however, races have been described from too little material and their geographical limits are often very uncertain. A well-studied example is described by Waterhouse (1914, 1922), who deals with the races of an Australian butterfly, *Tisiphone abeona*. This species is found on the S.E. coast to the seaward of the main dividing range. Five races follow one another in succession down the coast. Two of the races have been proved to be interfertile with a third, which is not in direct contact with either of them. Another two races appear to interbreed and produce peculiar forms not known elsewhere. A similar outburst of peculiar forms where two races meet is recorded by Harrison and Carter (1924) in *Aricia medon* in England. Doubtless a variety of genetic conditions will determine whether the recombinations resulting from an interracial cross shall produce an intergrading series or an unexpected new type.

4. *Geographical variation in fleas.*

Jordan (1931) gives an interesting example in the variation of the common mouse flea *Ctenophthalmus agyrtes*. This species is represented in Western Europe by five races—one in England and N.W. France, one in E. France, Germany and Switzerland, three in Switzerland and N. Italy (separated by various mountain ranges). There are several peculiarities in this distribution. First, the presence of the English Channel has not led to the formation of a peculiar English race. Secondly, the environment of fleas is unusually constant and wide differences in external conditions do not appear to affect them (*e.g.* in the Alps they occur without modification right up to the tree limit). It is difficult, therefore, to see why races

should evolve where there are no very definite barriers, *e.g.*
races of E. and W. France. On the other hand, the existence
of several races in Switzerland, where mountain barriers are
numerous, suggests that isolation alone may account for the
changes observed. The identity of the English and W. French
races, however, is in disagreement with this view. Possibly
a survey of the hosts most commonly affected in different
areas might be important, though the variety of hosts appears
to be unusually great.

5. *Geographical variation in fishes.*

Examples are available of intense ' local race formation '
in the sedentary *Zoarces viviparus* (Schmidt, 1918) and in
species, such as the Atlantic Cod (*id.* 1930), which have a
wider range. The latter is split up into ' a mosaic of populations,' each of which has a peculiar statistical facies in respect
of the two characters (number of vertebræ and fin rays)
studied by Schmidt.

6. *Geographical races in squirrels and mouse-deer.*

It is well known that the squirrels of the Old World tropics
provide examples of some of the most extraordinary racial
complexes. The data are worth some consideration, since
they raise the question how far the variation of other
animals would prove equally refractory to schematic treatment if more material were available. The races in squirrels
are largely separated by colour-pattern, differences in which
are sharply marked and easily studied. In such forms
as the smaller Muridae, where the study of each individual
requires a far more tedious technique and the characters
cannot be seized at a glance, a similar complexity might more
easily be masked.

Evidence as to the African squirrels (*Heliosciurus*) may be
found in Ingoldby (1927) ; certain Burmese forms are dealt
with by Oldfield Thomas and Wroughton (1916), and Banks
(1931) discusses the Bornean races of *Sciurus prevostii*. The
last-named species has numerous races in Malaya, Sumatra
and Borneo. The latter island has about eight races, one of
which is also found on Sumatra or at least represented by a
closely similar form. Where the races overlap, intermediates
are found, almost certainly as a result of intercrossing. Some

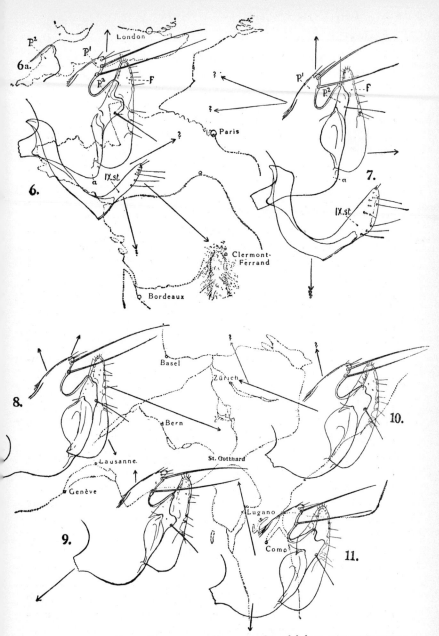

FIGS. 13A AND 13B.—MALE GENITALIA OF RACES OF *Ctenophthalmus agyrtes* DRAWN ON A
MAP OF WESTERN EUROPE TO SHOW DISTRIBUTION OF RACES.

6 and 6a, Race *celticus*; 7 and 8, *agyrtes*; 9, *provincialis*; 10, *oreadis*; 11, *verbanus*.
(From Jordan, 1931.)

of the races, however, are sharply isolated from one another by rivers. Oldfield Thomas and Wroughton also note the importance of rivers as barriers to the Burmese forms. Banks, further, finds that individual variation within the races is extreme and appears partly to produce forms which might be called races were it not that they do not form definite populations. Thus in *S. prevostii borneensis*, according to Banks (*l.c.* p. 1336)—'No two specimens are alike, and the variation is endless.' Both colour and pattern are affected, and Banks shows it is very difficult to correlate the characters of the races with any known feature of the environment. Apart from one mountain race, most of them appear to live under very similar conditions, the island being tropical throughout. It is also interesting that certain races appear to have a discontinuous distribution, such as has already been noted in the flea *Ctenophthalmus agyrtes*. A similar example of discontinuous geographical groups is found in the Carrion Crow (Kirkman and Jourdain, 1930, p. 2). An E. Siberian form of this species is separated from the main area of the species by the whole distributional area of the Hooded Crow. It cannot, of course, be proved without elaborate genetic experiments that apparently similar forms are really identical, but the formation of similar races in different areas within a larger patch of uniform conditions is strongly suggestive of the convergent establishment of the same chance combinations of genetic factors. It may be mentioned that Bequaert (1931) has shown that the geographical race of the Hornet (*Vespa crabro*) inhabiting the British Isles, resembles a Chinese race far more closely than it does the adjacent continental form.

In the African *Heliosciurus*, Ingoldby has shown that similar races tend to be found on each side of the equator, with races of a different type lying between them. Here there is a greater possibility of a direct environmental effect and, according to this author, the races in two localities with identical ecological conditions are the same. It is not difficult, however, to find instances where there is no obvious correlation with the environment; in fact such correlation appears to be the exception rather than the rule. Thus Miller's study of the Malayan mouse-deer (*Tragulus*) (1909) shows that numerous races have been developed under conditions as nearly uniform as possible. In this genus races are more often developed on the smaller islands than on the larger ones and on the mainland, suggesting that isolation has been the most important factor. It is curious that some of the races occur on more than one small island. Admittedly these islands are usually close to one another, but not always closer than other islands which bear distinct races. Further, the most similar races do not usually inhabit the closest islands. Taking the islands as a whole we see a progressive change in colour from the mainland form, but, as the various changes are scattered at random amongst the islands, it is unlikely that the series represents the actual line of evolution, which was probably polyphyletic.

In considering geographical races it is a matter of some importance to examine the normal size of the racial population. Many races of course exist over enormous areas and include millions of individuals, but in the case of smaller units taxonomic practice becomes somewhat arbitrary. It is evidently convenient to have a name for any race which covers a large area, even if structurally it is little differentiated from its closest allies. But in more localised races a higher degree of divergence tends to be demanded. Thus a statistical examination of the populations of a species inhabiting a number of small islands might show that each had a different mean character, but it might be taxonomically very inconvenient to give a name to each. On the other hand, unnamed variations tend to be ignored, and in making any such survey as the present only the most general information about such forms can be obtained.

We may give examples. Perhaps a record for smallness of racial area is held by *Lacerta simonii* (Cott, 1932), which inhabits a small rock with a surface of perhaps 1,000 square yards in the Canaries. Cott estimates the total population at not more than a few scores of individuals. The Skomer Vole is confined to an island only a few square miles in extent, and the same is true of many other island races. Isolated colonies of the Rabbit (*Oryctolagus cuniculus*) are known which are quite distinct in colour, *e.g.* a mouse-coloured race on Sunk Island in the Humber (Barrett-Hamilton and Hinton, *l.c.* pp. 196–9). The Skomer Vole is given a name because it is a relict form whose nearest allies live in the Hebrides, while the Rabbit is unusually variable and there are too many trifling local variants for a name to be given to any one. In the moths of the genus *Zygaena*, particular colonies have often

FIG. 14.—AFRICAN SQUIRRELS OF THE GENUS *Heliosciurus*.
1 and 2, Forest forms; 3 and 4, Grassland forms.
(From Ingoldby, 1927.)

a distinctive pattern ; possibly in some of them the mean of the colony would not actually be repeated anywhere else in the range of the species. But such colonies are so numerous, and so often show a considerable range of variation, that it is useless to name them all. Thus, while taxonomic procedure has very good practical arguments in its favour, it tends to exhibit geographical variation more distinct from other types of variation than it really is.

Physiological Races (see also Chapter III, p. 73).—There is no theoretical reason to suppose that the physiological (instinctive, psychical, ethological, etc.) characters of species should be less variable than the morphological except in so far as variation in the latter is less likely to impair viability. In the Protozoa, strains differing in various physiological properties (immunity and virulence) have long been known. The literature of entomology, ornithology, etc., is full of descriptions of individuals with aberrant habits or instincts. In most cases, however, the previous history of the individual was unknown, so that little can be concluded except that instinct is capable of modification. It is easier to study the phenomenon when a whole population exhibits such a change. Such populations are termed ' biological races ' or ' physiological strains ' of the species concerned. If physiological characters are inherited in the same way as morphological, the same tendency to group-formation and subdivision of the species might be expected in them, some groups being characterised mainly physiologically, others mainly morphologically. A very much more complete knowledge of animals than we possess might perhaps break down the distinction.

Some of the data as to biological races are considered elsewhere (Chapters II, III and VII), so that we shall endeavour here mainly to establish that physiological differentiation occurs in all degrees. As an instance of the association of minute physiological differences associated with almost equally small structural ones, we may mention the work of Bodenheimer and Klein (1930), who deal with three subspecies of the ant *Messor semirufus* in relation to temperature. It was found that each race had a different optimum temperature for normal activities (viz. 18·4°, 19°, 20·3° C.). This and similar evidence that is now accumulating show that at all grades of morphological differentiation physiological differences are likely to be present as well, even if requiring refined methods for their detection. Food- or host-selection is the feature in which physiological differentiation has been most studied, but Thorpe (1930) also notes differences in the susceptibility of scale-insects to fumigation, and differences in song may also be mentioned. Owing to the difficulty of the investigation not very many examples have been really exhaustively examined, but it is clear that various stages can be traced from forms which differ only in physiology to those which also differ morphologically, eventually to such an extent that they are regarded as closely allied species.

Hachfeld (1926) records that in the bee, *Trachusa byssina*, different individuals use different plant-leaves with which to build their nests. In different localities different plants are the main source of material.

Hackett and Missiroli (1931) have investigated factors leading to the reduction of malaria in various areas in Europe. It is practically certain that the disappearance of this disease in some localities (*e.g.* parts of Italy) is due not to preventive measures but to the establishment of definite zootrophic races of *Anopheles* which attack domestic animals but not human beings. Another instance of purely physiological races may be found in the wasp *Tiphia popilliavora*. This is being imported into the United States from the East to control the introduced Japanese Beetle (*Popillia japonica*), which has proved a serious pest. Holloway (1931) finds that the forms of this wasp found in Korea, China and Japan respectively cannot be separated into geographical races on the basis of their structure, but that they are so different physiologically that three strains must be recognised if economic measures are to be successful. The strains differ principally in their temperature-relations and their consequent fitness to survive in the climate of the United States. The strains differ, for instance, in their length of life, developmental period and in the minimum temperature for mating. As a result of such differences the Chinese race is able to maintain itself only at the extreme southern border of the area now infested. For control in the greater part of eastern U.S.A. the Japanese race is alone suitable.

Fulton (1925) finds races of tree-crickets, *Oecanthus*, which differ in song, method of oviposition and habitat, but not in structure, while Myers (1926) states that the song is the most stable single character in the cicadas, though here morphological differences are also fairly conspicuous.   In grasshoppers, taken as a whole, structure would appear to be more distinctive than song, though the latter is difficult to define owing to environmental effects (temperature, presence of other individuals, etc.).   Promptoff (1930) records statistical local differences in the song of the Chaffinch in two different areas of Russia.   Again Kinsey (1930), in his valuable revision of the genus *Cynips* (*Spathegaster* and *Dryophanta*, auctt.), finds several pairs of species or races which are only to be distinguished by their galls.   His actual summary for the genus (p. 38) is as follows : 52 species have structure more distinctive than the galls ; 24 species have galls more distinctive than structure ; 17 species have the two equally distinctive.   The formation of the galls is known to be due to the action of the larval gall-wasp.

Thorpe's account (1929, 1931) of the races of the Small Ermine Moth (*Hyponomeuta padella*) shows that structural and physiological differences are about evenly balanced, neither being very great.   There is a distinct food preference, indicated by oviposition-response of the female and even more by larval choice ; members of one race cross with one another more easily than they do with members of the other, and there are slight overlapping colour-differences between the adult moths ; the larvæ construct different types of cocoons.   The two forms of the Human Louse (*Pediculus*) are somewhat more distinct and crossing is liable to lead to abnormalities in the hybrids.

Unfortunately data as to selective mating between races are very scanty.   If we knew more it might be possible to regard species differing only in the male genitalia as a special type of biological race.   In a number of forms (*Lucilia*, the blow-fly ; *Chironomus*-midges, etc.) the females are morphologically indistinguishable and the maintenance of the species must depend on the reactions of the male, perhaps to a scent emitted by his mate.

In connection with biological races it is interesting to consider the differences which may be found in the developmental stages of animals, especially in larval forms.   If we eliminate species which are still imperfectly known, it is probable

that of the remainder the majority are more easily recognised as
adults than as larvæ. But this is not always true. Thus Edwards
(1929) points out that a number of Chironomid midges are

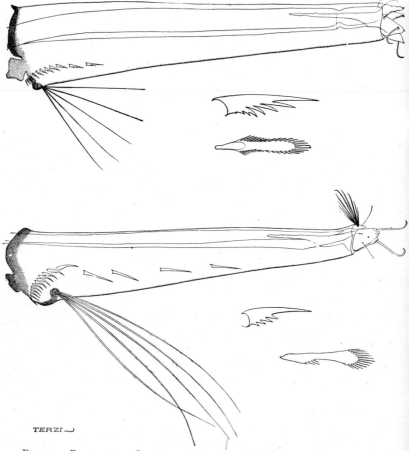

TERZI

Fig. 15.—Respiratory Siphons of Larvæ of *Culicella morsitans* (above) and
C. fumipennis, of which the Adults are almost indistinguishable.
(From Lang, 1920.)

almost indistinguishable as adults but have totally different
larval habits or structure. In some mosquitoes two different
types of larvæ have been found to produce identical adults
(Lang, 1920; *Culicella morsitans* and *C. fumipennis*). In this
case the larvæ are said to be dimorphic, because it is usual
to lay most stress on adult structure. The egg-rafts of some

mosquitoes are similarly dimorphic. The common British moths *Acronyctapsi* and *A. tridens* may also be mentioned. The larvæ differ sharply in colour, though the adults are separable only by the genitalia. In all such cases it is logical to claim that evolution has progressed further in the larvæ than in the adults, just as in biological races evolution has been in the direction of physiological rather than structural divergence. It is of some interest to show that the tendency to form local populations does not affect only structural characters. The existence of biological races evidently provided partial proof of this, but we may add a number of other instances of local segregation of what may be called ' non-taxonomic ' characters.

Local variation in the extent of sexual dimorphism is not at all rare, but is best considered a special case of normal group-formation in structural characters. There is much variation in seasonal occurrence in most insects with a wide range. It is usually unknown to what extent this character is due to the direct action of the environment. Probably the genetic element is larger than is commonly supposed. While often the number of broods gradually increases as one goes south, in other cases closely allied forms have a different life-cycle in the same district. Sometimes the effect of temperature is reversed. Thus, in gall-wasps, Kinsey (1930) finds that the species emerge earlier in the north, and Willey (1930, pp. 79–80) records a comparable condition in Copepods, in which growth is faster in the north. Many butterflies which have more than one brood a year show marked differences between the spring and summer broods. Such seasonal change is much subject to local variation and may be almost absent in some parts of the range (*cf.* Ford, 1924).

Gurney (1929) shows that some Copepods are locally dimorphic in size, while elsewhere this character is distributed in a normal curve. In some species one sex alone shows the dimorphism. This may be compared to the dimorphism in the males of the Common Earwig (*Forficula auricularia*). Bateson and Brindley (1892) showed that in some localities high males were much more prevalent than in others. Stephenson (1929) records various methods of reproduction separating species of *Sagartia*. Amongst eight species there are five methods.

Local variations in the sex-ratio are also well known. The subject has been dealt with at some length by Vandel

(1928), who finds that in many Hymenoptera there is a tendency for the species to be parthenogenetic in the northern part of their range, but to reproduce normally in the south (*cf.* also Brues, 1928). Poulton (1931) described similar local anomalies in the sex-ratio in the Fijian butterfly, *Hypolimnas bolima*. There appear to be a good number of instances of insects which possess two types of females, male-producers and female-producers, but the two types are not often geographically segregated.

SUMMARY

Any account of variation is unfortunately limited by the inability to present more than a small selection from the vast mass of available data. It has been usual in the past (and the practice is difficult to avoid) to construct all-embracing theories on the basis of selected species or genera which supply favourable data; the theories based on the genetics of *Droso-phila* or of *Oenothera* are cases in point. Obviously the best method would be to treat all doubtful points statistically and to state definitely that a particular type of variation occurred in such-and-such a percentage. In the present state of taxonomy no numerical statement of this sort is possible except perhaps for a few well-worked groups. For, in the absence of experimental investigations, it is often quite uncertain whether particular variations are inherited, and moreover the diverse types of variation encountered are very numerous and difficult to classify, so that statistical treatment might in any case be liable to serious errors. In the preceding account we have tried to choose our examples fairly and not to pick out merely those which support views we already hold on other grounds.

Up to the present we have not considered the effects of isolation and the different ways in which it can be brought about. Evidently isolation of one sort or another is a prime factor in the process of group formation. Geographical isolation is the type most easily recognised, and it is on this account that taxonomists have evolved the conception of the 'geographical race,' a term applied to minor categories, whose ability to interbreed with their closest allies is held in check only by more or less marked spatial separation. Other categories, of a similar structural grade, have been termed 'subspecies' by some entomologists.   These subspecies, unlike geographical races, live side by side ; but they can be called species only if we give up all attempts to indicate (in any one group) the same degree of divergence by the latter term. It is probable that these subspecies occur in some groups more than in others owing to differences in the mode of reproduction, particularly in the length of the breeding season, in the way in which the sexes find one another and in the degree of development of gregarious habits.   Subspecies tend to occur in any group in which non-geographical methods of isolation are easily effective.   The great possibilities of such isolation have often not been sufficiently realised and undue weight has been given to geographical effects.

The following are the more important general results which emerge from our survey :

1. We have discussed at some length the antithesis between individual and regional and geographical variation.   In some cases the antithesis stressed by Rensch and others between populations broken up into clearly defined regional or geographical groups and those in which the variants are more universally distributed is clear and can be shown in some instances to be due to differences in habits, size, etc.   We believe, however, that the distinction is more apparent than real and that no particular significance is to be attached to it. To begin with, there seems to be a likelihood that geographical variation will be found to be less clearly cut when the relevant forms are more exhaustively studied and knowledge of their distribution is based on more material.   Series of geographical races are easy to demonstrate when the samples are not too large.   Secondly, while we admit that clearly-cut qualitative divergences on a geographical basis are not so typical of groups such as terrestrial molluscs and arthropods, it is quite evident that the proportions of the variant types in these groups define populations quite as definitely as average dimensions, colour, etc., define those of vertebrates.   It is of secondary importance that the regional divergences among, e.g., populations of land molluscs tend to be smoothed over as a result of the size and habits of these animals and in certain (but by no means all) of their characters by reason of their plasticity.   When many characters of vertebrate populations

are examined statistically (Sumner, Schmidt), the same quantitative local divergences are discovered as those observed in populations of land snails. It seems to be true on the whole that there is a lack of innumerable individual variations in vertebrates that requires explanation, though the observations of Fowler and Bean (1929) on variation in fishes of the order Capriformes must prepare us to realise that individual variation is far more frequent than Rensch has allowed ; but perhaps the wider range and consequent less susceptibility to minor isolating influences render their populations more homogeneous. It is also possible that a more highly evolved physiological control makes them less susceptible to external factors. A study of the variability of sedentary mammals (such as small rodents) contrasted with that of more widely ranging forms (carnivores and ruminants) is much to be desired.

2. The very frequent occurrence of variants established as a small percentage of a population and at the same time living along with the typical forms seems to us of some importance. Many more examples are available of this phenomenon than those which we have cited.

3. The frequent occurrence of statistical divergences calls for attention. It is not without significance that, when populations are broken up by divergences of this kind (p. 99), the latter can be maintained over periods of about ten years, at least as far as the admittedly imperfect records allow us to judge. As to the origin of these divergences it seems most unlikely that they are due to selection. They sometimes occur under identical ecological and bionomic conditions and, unless we appeal to the *argumentum ad ignorantiam*, are most unlikely to be produced by selective adaptation to local conditions. For a similar reason they do not appear to be produced by the direct effect of the environment. We are thus forced to conclude that they are produced by the effects of local isolation or obligatory preferential mating working on available stocks of hereditary material.

4. We have introduced somewhat cautiously the idea that certain species have a more marked proneness to local and regional variation than others, apart from any habits, etc., which might promote this feature. The contrast between the South American Wren and *Buarremon* (p. 106) is an

instance of this.   It seems evident that all animals are not equally prone to receive the impress of their environment nor in the same state of mutational activity.

5. The general impression that one gets from a survey such as the foregoing is that groups are formed by the spread of individual variants rather than by mass transformation. What we find is a gradation from single variants, or variants represented only by a low percentage in the population, to larger and more distinctive assemblages and eventually to distinct regional geographical groups.   We do not know, of course, how many of the smaller groups may not be on the way to extinction ; but we may assume that at least half of them are not and that this possibility does not vitiate the general conclusion that there is a process at work in nature which facilitates the multiplication of single variants.   If the latter were spreading from single loci the mosaic of poly-morphism is exactly what one would expect to find.   Rensch's attempt to show that variants are distributed in ' Rassenkreise ' under the influence of differentiated environments seems to us to break down on three counts :

(*a*) The very general occurrence of polymorphism is a proof that the environment is not the direct trans-forming agency.   The only way in which those who favour that view could explain the occurrence of differentiated forms living side by side in the same habitat is to suggest that they acquired their differences elsewhere and have subsequently met.   But, as Robson (1928, p. 174) has pointed out, this involves explaining (1) the frequent lack of epharmonic con-vergence and (2) the means of spreading.

(*b*) In numerous cases variants are not arranged with reference to environmental gradients and many races range unmodified through a variety of environments (*cf*. Sumner, 1932, etc.).

(*c*) To argue that many of the observed changes that are correlated with environmental differences may only be somatic is but a negative objection ; but it is a great weakness of Rensch's case that there is so little experimental evidence that local races, etc., are of a fixed heredity.   We do not wish to ignore the many and striking cases of structural and en-vironmental trends.   We would even admit that in such cases mass transformation of populations may be possible.   But we hold that the occurrence of the various grades of poly-morphism is far more widespread and far more significant, and whether we are considering groups such as colonies of land snails which are distinguished by the varying proportions of a number of characters or the statistical differences in the occurrence of single characters, we cannot fail to be impressed by the evidence for a process of multiplication of certain types rather than their production *en bloc*. Nevertheless, if the evidence from the facts of distribution suggests such a process, it does not justify any conclusions as to how it took place.

CHAPTER V

ISOLATION

THE importance of isolation in evolution was first strongly insisted on by M. Wagner (*cf.* summary of his work, 1889). Darwin also allowed its influence to be considerable, as, for instance, in the production of island races. Both these authors regarded adaptation to the local conditions as of fully equal importance (*cf.* Wagner, *l.c.* p. 401). In Chapter I it was indicated that isolation may be regarded as playing two opposing rôles in the process of group-formation, viz. the maintenance of the identity of groups and the splitting up of large groups into smaller ones. In the present chapter this matter is considered more fully.

The more general problems of geographical distribution need not be given special attention. They have been discussed at length in many works wholly devoted to the subject. For the same reason actual dispersal mechanisms are only of secondary interest. These also have been much discussed, but well-authenticated data are somewhat meagre and scarcely sufficient to enable us to formulate any general relation between powers of dispersal and race-formation. Allusion has already been made to this difficulty in Chapter IV (p. 104), and it may be added that any such relation might be obscured by innate tendencies to race-formation which appear to be independent of dispersal. Two main types of isolation itself may be recognised. *Geographical* or *topographical isolation* is operative when two populations are separated by uninhabitable country. Sections of a species isolated by such a barrier would, for some time after their separation, be able to interbreed if they could be carried across the barrier. (Isolation of this kind is temporary, since without changes in the animal itself it is always liable to break down as a result of modification of the barriers themselves (*e.g.* movements in the earth's surface). Jordan (1896, p. 442) indeed states that, if in the course of divergence a point is reached after which it is impossible for the diverging form to coalesce with the parent stock, we are given by this point a definite means of distinguishing *varieties* from *species*.)

The changes in animals themselves which make inter-breeding actually impossible form the second or permanent type of isolation. *Permanent isolation* may be the result of a variety of factors, and an important consideration is to determine whether it can ever be developed in the absence of some degree of geographical separation. The establishment of geographical isolation might often be due to geological changes within the area of a widely ranging species, but we must also recognise the importance of the wanderings of the animals themselves. The continual invasion of all countries and habitats, however apparently uncongenial, is a commonplace of natural history. Where the invaders have to overcome great difficulties, we usually find the formation of isolated colonies, as in oceanic islands.

Permanent isolation may arise frequently from ' accidental ' changes in the structure and habits of populations no longer in a position to eliminate or assimilate the variant individuals by free intermixture. The actual mechanism which prevents allied species from interbreeding is rarely understood in detail, but very often there seems to be a great difficulty in explaining how the mechanism can have been perfected, since the charac-ters on which it depends appear to be of little use to in-dividuals or even to the species as a whole.

Although we now suspect that some measure of permanent isolation may be developed amongst individuals inhabiting a continuous area, yet it is probable that geographical isolation is more often than not a necessary preliminary. The temporary nature of the latter type of isolation makes it important for us to examine the rate at which topographically isolated populations diverge from one another. It may be admitted that the degree of permanent isolation is only very roughly correlated with that of the resulting morphological divergence, but in so far as the latter is likely sooner or later to entail permanent isolation, the rate of divergence under geographical separation becomes relevant. We shall therefore digress to consider the available evidence as to the time necessary for the establishment of a new species or subspecies.

In this inquiry we are obliged to depend on the relatively few groups which both provide suitable material and have been subjected to sufficient taxonomic study. We are not so much concerned with the maximum as with the minimum time which such a change may take. We can never know whether a fossil form which is identical in structure with a modern one would, in fact, be able to interbreed with it. But even in the majority of living species we do not know whether interbreeding is possible, and we are endeavouring rather to estimate something which has a meaning in present-day taxonomy, viz. how long it has taken to evolve differences which would be considered sufficient to separate races or species, if they characterised recent forms.

Modern species known to have persisted since pre-Tertiary times are rare. An interesting example is the shark *Scapanorrhynchus owsteni*, which was first described from fossil teeth in

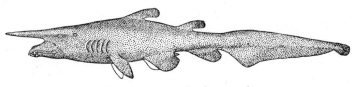

FIG. 16.—*Scapanorrhynchus owsteni*.
(From Norman, 1931.)

the Upper Cretaceous but has since been found living off the coast of Japan (Norman, 1931, p. 124). In other instances, as perhaps in the Brachiopoda, the characters available for study in the fossil state are so few that the comparison with recent species could not be expected to be very enlightening. But it appears that, just as some species with discontinuous range soon form numerous races while others remain relatively homogeneous, so the rate of evolution, judged by palæontological evidence, must be variable from group to group, and probably depends on innate potentialities.

Wheeler (1913, chapter x) has discussed the fossil history of the ants. Many of the amber fossils are perfectly preserved and are as capable of exact study as recent specimens. In the Sicilian Amber (Lower Oligocene) nearly 69 per cent. of the genera are still living. Three species, belonging to different genera, are not separable from well-known living forms. There is some evidence that even the main features of the habits of ants were established at this early date, though it appears that the polymorphism of the workers was not developed till the Pleistocene. Apparently the species and genera of ants were established at a much earlier date than those of several other groups. If such a species as *Ponera coarctata* (Wheeler, *l.c.* p. 174) has really existed with little change from the Lower Oligocene, then only the most permanent geographical barriers would have any effect on its divergence. Unless permanent biological isolation was set up, there would be ample time for two isolated races to be joined together again in the course of so prolonged a specific history.

Lapouge (1902) has given some account of the beetles of the genus *Carabus* found in the Mid-Pleistocene of Belgium. In this genus the surface sculpture of the elytra is highly distinct and provides some of the most important characters for separating species and races. The fossil elytra could all be referred to existing species, except in one case ; but the sculpture was nearly always somewhat different, to an extent which in a modern form would be considered deserving of a varietal or racial name.

Borodin (1927) has published some data on the Clupeid fishes of the Caspian Sea and a neighbouring lake. Certain subspecies have probably been isolated from one another since the second interglacial period (*ca.* 350,000 years). The changes they have undergone are not yet very great. Analogous data are recorded of another fish (*Cottus*) in the Swedish lakes (Lonnberg, 1932) and of the prawn, *Limnocalanus* (Ekman, 1913).

The British mammals provide perhaps the best material for an inquiry of this nature. The evidence for each species is given by Barrett-Hamilton and Hinton (1911–1921). Two main types of evidence are available. First, in numerous instances, an existing species is found fossil in the Pleistocene as an identical or a scarcely different form, and we have some idea as to the length of time the species has remained unaltered. Secondly, in a few specially valuable instances, a species which is now represented by a purely British race does not occur in the British Pleistocene, and must have evolved to the extent to which it differs from its continental representative since that period.

The following data for British insectivores and rodents are derived from Barrett-Hamilton and Hinton (1911–1921).

(1) Adequate fossil data not available : 9 species.

(2) Species not known in the Pleistocene, but now represented by a distinct British race : 3 species (Common Hare, Field-mouse (*Microtus hirtus*), and Water-rat (with two races)).

(3) Form apparently identical with the modern representative known from at least Late Pleistocene : (*a*) No British race : 4 species (*Epimys rattus*, Shrew, Pigmy Shrew, Rabbit). (*b*) With a British race : 3 species (Irish Hare, Northern Field-mouse (*Microtus agrestis*), *Apodemus flavicollis*).

(4) Late Pleistocene form racially distinct : (*a*) No British race : 2 species (Mole, ? Water-shrew). (*b*) One or more British races : 4 species (*Apodemus sylvaticus* (2 races), Skomer Vole (3), Bank Vole, Orkney Vole (5)).

The examples under (2) are particularly instructive, since it is almost certain that fossils would have been found had the animals been present in the Late Pleistocene. On the other hand, since there is now a distinct British race, or, in the Water-rat, two races, we can say that this degree of evolution has taken place since the Pleistocene.[1]

In the six species included in (4) evolution has been rapid enough to produce new races since the Late Pleistocene, while in the seven species under (3) there has probably not been much change since the Pleistocene.

Evidently the data are not sufficient to support much speculation, but they do at least suggest that in the rodents and insectivores, of which at least the former group appears to evolve very rapidly, the evolution of a new race normally takes an interval of time not much shorter than that intervening between the end of the Pleistocene and the present day. This period of time is well known to have been sufficient for considerable changes in geographical barriers and we may surmise that, with evolution working at this rate, intrinsic methods

---

[1] An alternative hypothesis would be that the British form had remained unaltered, and that it was the continental representatives that had changed.

of isolation are a very necessary supplement to any purely topographical isolation.

With this preliminary conclusion, we shall now return to the main theme of the chapter and consider first topographical isolation in somewhat greater detail, before passing on to the intrinsic factors. The mere fact that most species have a more or less extensive range automatically introduces a measure of isolation between the more widely separated individuals. We have already reviewed this question in Chapter IV, where we came to the conclusion that, while habits and mode of reproduction may predispose a species to race-formation, the latter process is not a very good index of the extent to which the species-range is broken up by topographical barriers. Intrinsic factors exert an important effect, which is at present largely unpredictable. Possibly some of the anomalies might be explained away if we knew more of the minor migrations of individuals that occur within the range of many species.

An important point is that relatively slight barriers often appear to be sufficient to determine the limits of races or species. Thus in the Central Arabian desert, two races of the rodent *Meriones syrius* (Cheesman and Hinton, 1924) inhabit different stream valleys separated by only a mile of bare limestone plateau. The intervening area is inhabited by two quite distinct species. The habitat barrier is here much sharper than would be normal in ordinary temperate regions. Again, Wagner (1889, pp. 53–7) gives some instances, in various groups of animals in N. Africa and Syria, of rivers acting as the boundaries of races or species. In Chapter IV we have also noted this in the case of squirrels (p. 116).

Probably far more ecological knowledge of particular species is required for a profitable discussion of topographical isolation on continuous areas. It is possible, however, briefly to review the problem of ' island-races,' since here the same difficulties arise but in a more clear-cut form.

When once a population has been cut off or immigrant individuals have succeeded in reaching an isolated area, there is much evidence in favour of the view that sooner or later the fauna will undergo larger evolutionary changes. Probably the oceanic islands, such as the Hawaiian or the Galapagos groups, are the best examples of a high degree of geographical isolation. Under these conditions it is well known that the proportion of endemic species is very high, and often what was probably a single immigrant species is at the present day represented by a large genus (*cf.* Perkins, 1912).

The effects of isolation in these extreme cases appear sufficiently striking, but there is a danger of overestimating the part that geographical isolation has played in the evolution observed. The enormous area of continuous tropical forest covering the larger part of northern South America is probably proportionately quite as rich in endemics. The distribution of the fauna of South America is still very imperfectly known, but it appears likely that an enormous number of species have developed under the relatively constant rain-forest conditions without the intervention of any very definite barriers. Some species would appear to occur over the whole area, while others are apparently definitely localised ; but much more information is needed on this point. Again, in the Hawaiian Islands with their singularly stable and relatively uniform environment (especially before the arrival of Man), numerous allied species have often been evolved on one island. Further, while islands as a whole are characterised by the endemism of their fauna, there are a good many exceptions. We may instance the following :

Crustacea. Lowndes (1930) records that, in a collection of Copepods from the New Hebrides, practically none of the species are endemic. Many are identical with British species, though in this group dispersal powers would not be expected to be very effective. The Ostracods, on the other hand, are nearly all endemic, though special dispersal mechanisms (resting eggs, etc.) are developed.

Spiders. No peculiar forms occur on the Scilly Isles, Lundy Island or Channel Islands (Bristowe, 1929*a*, 1929*b*, 1929*c*). On the whole, dispersal power (by gossamer) is good, but the incidence of this power throughout the order requires investigation (*cf.* Bristowe, 1929*c*).

Hydracarina. Lundblad (1930, p. 24) records only one endemic variety on the Faroes.

Myriapoda. No endemics [1] on the Faroes (Hammer and Henriksen, 1930).

---

[1] *i.e.* definite subspecies.

Fig. 17.—A Group of Endemic Hawaiian Insects. All belong to Large
Endemic Genera (except the *Odynerus*).

A. *Plagithmysus blackburni* Sharp (Cerambycidae). B. *Omiodes anastrepta* Meyr.
(Pyralididae). C. *Odynerus nigripennis* Holmgr. (Vespidae). D. *Anomalo-
chrysa blackburni* Perk. (Chrysopidae). E. *Megalagrion blackburni* Macl.
(Agrionidae). Photo W. H. T. Tams.

Mollusca. No endemics [1] on the Scilly Isles (Richards and Robson, 1926). Probably no endemics on the Hebridean Islands (Robson, MS.). This may be contrasted with the high degree of endemism in the mammals.

A somewhat similar phenomenon is the capricious occurrence of endemism in archipelagoes. We have already given a few examples (*e.g.* mouse-deer, p. 116). Simpson (1929), in his study of the species of *Liguus* (land snails) on the Florida Keys, finds that they are broken up into numerous varieties, but that there is no regular localisation on particular keys (contrast with ' ridge ' forms of *Partula* (Crampton)). A given variety may occur on several keys, and a given key may have only one or else several varieties. There appears to be no obvious correlation between topographical isolation and varietal differentiation.

Similarly Riley (1929) finds that the birds of the Sumatran Islands are on the whole more differentiated on the remote islands than on the less remote. But this is not invariable, and in the W. Sumatran Islands the relation between differentiation and spatial separation is not nearly so obvious (*cf.* Robson, 1928, p. 139 (Hebridean mammals) ; also Aubertin, Ellis and Robson, 1931 (colonies of *Cochlicella acuta*)).

We are led, therefore, to inquire as to the circumstances in which some species change or remain stable ; and, secondly, as to whether numerous smaller factors tending to produce isolation on a small scale are not just as important as the high degree of isolation produced by marked geographical separation.

The relative stability of some species and the high degree of variability in others provide one of the most curious and baffling problems in biology (*cf.* p. 106, Chapter IV). It is remarkable to what an extent certain species of a genus may vary, when others are quite constant. The same differences are found in the frequency with which geographical races are formed. It might be supposed that such differences in variability depended on whether a species was exposed to constant and homogeneous or varying and heterogeneous conditions. But in fact all who have analysed such cases agree that no such detailed relation can be found. With one

[1] *i.e.* definite subspecies.

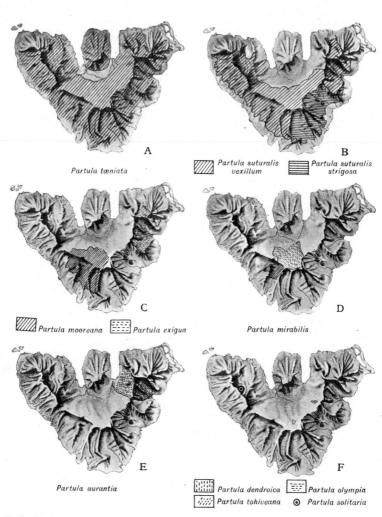

A

Partula tœniata

B

▨ *Partula suturalis*
vexillum   ▤ *Partula suturalis*
strigosa

C

D

▨ *Partula mooreana*   ▦ *Partula exigua*

Partula mirabilis

E

F

Partula aurantia

▦ *Partula dendroica*   ▧ *Partula olympia*

▨ *Partula tohiveana*   ◉ *Partula solitaria*

FIG. 18.—DISTRIBUTION OF THE SPECIES OF *Partula* ON THE ISLAND OF MOOREA.
(From Crampton, 1932.)

exception (see below) there appears to be little really convincing evidence that differences in rate of evolution are
determined by the environment. In this matter, however,
one positive example is probably worth several negative ones.

The exception referred to above is provided by island
races. We have already noted that endemism, though not
uniformly developed, is considerable. Not only are endemics
numerous, but they are sometimes of a peculiar type. Rensch
(1928, p. 174) has already noted that on small islands there
is a ' Neigung zu Excessiv-Bildungen in Grösse, Form und
Farbe.' We may note particularly :

Dwarfing. Birds. (Rensch, *l.c.* pp. 174–5 ; Dwight, 1918,
              p. 269.)
          Tiger. (Pocock, 1929, p. 505.)
          Mollusca. (Sturany, 1916, p. 137.)
          Lizards. (Kammerer, 1926, p. 88.)
Giant forms. Lizards. (Kammerer, *l.c.*)
          Mollusca. (Rensch, *l.c.*)
              (Not observed by other describers of
          insular variation, *e.g.* Bristowe, Lundblad,
          etc.)
Melanic forms. Reptiles. (Kammerer, *l.c.* ; Mertens, 1931,
          p. 205.)
          Spiders. (Bristowe, 1929*a*, p. 164.)
          Hydracarina. (Lundblad, 1930, p. 24.)
          Mollusca. (Pelseneer, 1920, p. 561 ;
          Aubertin, Ellis and Robson, 1931, p.
          1049 ; Kammerer, *l.c.*)
          Mammals. (Kammerer, *l.c.*)

These rather striking consequences of life on islands require
further investigation.

Another factor, viz. the numerical abundance of the species,
has been supposed (Darwin, 1884, pp. 42–3 ; Fisher and Ford,
1928 ; Ford, 1931, p. 100) to be important. Abundant
species are or tend to be more variable. A good example of
this is given by Fisher and Ford (*l.c.*) in the species of British
Noctuid moths. Greater variability will on the whole mean
quicker evolution. According to this idea evolution will
proceed by the fission of a few common, widespread variable
species, while the rarer, less variable species will become

extinct, and will not contribute to the evolution of the group. It seems doubtful whether this principle is very helpful, except in comparing fairly similar forms, and it can scarcely explain the anomalies of differentiation in archipelagoes, etc.

Apparently much more importance must be ascribed to innate differences in species, which we have to allow for but cannot at present explain. When once we admit that some species may have an innate tendency to unusual variability, we make it very difficult to study the effects of isolation. A high degree of innate variability will increase the chance that any isolated parts of a population will have a composition differing from the norm of the species. If permanent isolation depends on the cumulative effect of various small accidental disharmonies, then geographically isolated populations of a variable species may be expected to reach a state of permanent isolation more quickly.

Later in this chapter there is a discussion of whether permanent isolation is most often gained by the accumulation of numerous small differences rather than by one substantial change. It can be shown that relatively slight differences sometimes maintain a significant degree of isolation, and it is much easier to imagine the evolution of the isolatory mechanism by several small steps than by one big step. In larger animals, on the other hand, geographical isolation may be very important, but, as body-size is reduced, it becomes progressively less significant. This is probably a natural result of large animals [1] wandering over extensive areas, which often include numerous types of habitat, while smaller animals can maintain themselves in a population of efficient size, within the much smaller limits of perhaps a single restricted habitat.

Our argument, then, runs as follows : in large animals geographical isolation is probably an important factor, though the degree to which the inherent variability of the species is developed is no less important. Unless a population changes enough to become *permanently* isolated, it will be liable to be recombined with the parent stock by subsequent topographical changes. We do not know how long it takes to evolve permanent isolation, but, at least in some species, evolution is

---

[1] von Schweppenburg (1924, p. 143) says he knows of no clear case in birds in which subspecies are in the least likely to have arisen in one place. Where there is considerable overlap it is likely to have arisen by spread since the races originated.

slow enough to allow considerable land-changes to occur during the establishment of a race. In small animals geographical isolation becomes, on the whole, less important, for even on continuous areas there are numerous ways in which populations can be isolated from one another. While it might be thought that none of these ways was sufficiently absolute to allow permanent isolation to set in, the recent studies of biological races point to another view.

Methods of permanent isolation.

These have been analysed by Robson (1928, pp. 122–33). We recognise a primary division into two chief methods, each of which may be subdivided.

I. Indirect methods :
> (*a*) Seasonal occurrence.
> (*b*) Time of breeding.
> (*c*) General habitat.
> (*d*) Differences in breeding habitats.
> (*e*) Loss of means of dispersal.

II. Direct methods :
> (1) Prevention of copulation.
>> (*a*) Psychological or physiological.
>>> (i) Differences in specific recognition marks.
>>> (ii) Differences in epigamic characters (scents, courtship behaviour, secondary sexual ornaments).
>> (*b*) Mechanical.
>>> (iii) By differences in the mechanical relations of the copulatory apparatus.

> (2) Prevention of effective fertilisation.
>> (*c*) By failure of the sperm to reach the egg.
>> (*d*) By disharmonies in development, including and leading up to sterility in hybrids.

In sedentary animals and aquatic animals with externa fertilisation only I and II (2) can be effective. In motile animals with internal fertilisation II (1) may also operate. In this respect plants are in the position of sedentary animals.

I (*a*) and (*b*).   *Seasonal occurrence and breeding season.*

In short-lived animals the breeding season of a species is usually almost coextensive with the seasonal occurrence. With longer-lived animals a definite season tends to be set aside for breeding.   In either case, one of the simplest ways in which varying degrees of isolation may be brought about is by specific differentiation of this season.   Besides being simple, separation in this way appears to be important because the seasonal occurrence or breeding period is likely to express the summed effect of the reaction of the organism to its environment.   The various small characters by which we separate species can be regarded as the visible expression of differences in growth-rates and in various physiological processes.   The species must develop in a different way, and the length of the period necessary to complete the life-cycle is one of the most obvious ways in which developmental differences may be expressed.   Where the species live in more or less separate habitats even greater disparities might be expected.   It is, indeed, surprising that species are not more often separated by differences in breeding season, but it may be supposed that the fluctuations of the environment make it difficult for any species to have a sharply defined breeding season, and further that the rhythm is much modified to fit in with other periodic features in the environment, particularly the food-supply. The latter factor becomes more important as species diverge more and more widely from one another.   Where an insect, *e.g.*, depends on one or a few species of plants there is often a very close correlation between their life-cycles.

Specific differences in breeding season or seasonal occurrence are extremely common in insects and are not rare in other groups, though complete isolation by this means is probably rather rare.   We can only mention here a few typical examples. One of the most striking instances is seen in the Seventeen-year Cicada (*Tibicen septemdecim*) of the United States (Marlatt, 1907).   To begin with there are two races, the 17-year race (mainly northern) and the 13-year race (mainly southern). The number of years refers to the time spent as a subterranean nymph.   These two main races scarcely differ in structure, but do not appear to interbreed where they meet.   Almost every year a brood of each race emerges in some part of the range of the species, but some broods are very localised.   Other broods are discontinuous, but the 17- or 13-year period of the broods in any one locality has been well established over the last 200 years.   Occasionally some individuals come out a few years late or early, and it is probably by this process of retardation or acceleration that the different broods originally became established.   This accounts for the discontinuous distribution of some broods and also for the general rule that broods adjacent to one another in space are also adjacent in time.

von Schweppenburg (1924, p. 151) notes that *Lasiocampa quercus* and *L. quercus callunae* scarcely interbreed because their times of emergence are different (May and June in *callunae* and July and August in *quercus*).   There is also a more or less marked difference in larval food and in habitat, but the moths are structurally almost identical.   Tutt (1910) states that the only known barrier between the butterflies *Agriades thetis* and *A. coridon* is that the single brood of *A. coridon* falls between the two broods of *A. thetis*.   Dietze (1913, pp. 134–136) gives an interesting account of the relation between the moths *Eupithecia innotata* and *E. unedonata*.   The larvæ feed on *Artemisia* and *Arbutus* respectively and the moths have a non-overlapping seasonal occurrence, *unedonata* appearing much earlier.   By cooling the pupæ of *unedonata* he was able to obtain a late emergence, and the resulting moths paired freely with the production of fertile hybrids.   Lackschewitz (1930) has recently revised the crane-flies of the *oleracea* group of *Tipula*.   The seven species now recognised were all ' lumped ' together until recently, and even now are distinguishable mainly by minute differences in the male genitalia.   The females are mostly still inseparable.   Of the three species occurring in Western Europe, *T. oleracea* has two broods—one in the summer and one in the autumn.   *T. paludosa* has one brood between July and September, while *T. czizeki* occurs only in mid-September and October.   The Morrisons (T. A. and L.) (1925) have shown that there is in addition a preferential mating reaction between *T. oleracea* and *T. paludosa*.   Peacock (1923) records a difference in seasonal occurrence between the very closely allied sawflies *Thrinax mixta* and *T. macula*. The former emerged between April 29 and May 8, the latter between May 8 and May 17.   The species are exceedingly alike both as larvæ and adults, and the food-plants are identical.

Differences of this type seem to be fairly common in phytophagous insects, but there is usually some overlap between the seasons. Where the female of a species is always impregnated immediately after emergence and the male emerges before the female, very small differences in the total period of occurrence may have considerable effect.

In other cases seasonal occurrence appears to play no part in isolation. Thus Schubert (1929), in his account of the dragon-flies of the neighbourhood of Neustadt, records that all the 18 species (6 genera) have overlapping periods, with the possible exception of the two species of *Orthetrum*. Richards (1930, p. 321), in his account of the British flies of the family Sphaeroceridae, shows that most of the species occur throughout the year, and many of them seem to have no restricted breeding season.

Isolation by means of differences in seasonal occurrence has a special interest because of its relation to the environment. It is a general rule for insects to have more broods in the south than in the north and, although partial broods, in which only a few individuals of a given generation emerge, are often found, there is a natural tendency for a species to fix on a definite reproductive rhythm. The intermediate state, where partial broods are formed, would appear to be one of unstable equilibrium. A species which is single-brooded in the north will be double-brooded in the south and, if the range is sufficiently great, even more broods may develop still further south —e.g. *Agrotis segetum* (Filipjev, 1929), *Pyrausta nubilalis* Hb. (Babcock, 1927).

Owing to climatic conditions there will be a tendency for the single-brooded form to occur between the broods of the bivoltine form in time. If we knew more as to how such rhythms become fixed, we might see a way in which the two forms could remain permanently isolated, even if their ranges came to overlap. This subject has been ably reviewed by Uvarov (1931, pp. 104 ff.), who concludes that rhythms originally induced by climatic conditions are eventually hereditarily fixed. Pictet (1913), experimenting on *Lasiocampa quercus*, obtained results suggestive of such a process. (See also Chapter II.)

In longer-lived animals with a definite breeding season a comparable state of affairs exists, but isolation appears to be much more partial, except sometimes between races of one species, e.g. *Rana esculenta* (Cuénot, 1921), *Sepia* (Cuénot, 1917), *Crangon* and *Orchestia* (Plate, 1913). In addition long-lived animals appear to be largely those which also evolve mainly through geographical races, in which the breeding period is not likely to be an important factor in isolation. When the races have evolved so far that their ranges overlap, and we find two species living side by side, other factors often override any original differences in the breeding period. It may be suspected that any environmental pressure tending to reassimilate two rhythms would sooner or later be effective and, if the two forms were not by that time intersterile or isolated in other ways, they would be reunited. We might, therefore, expect that differences in seasonal occurrence in the breeding season would usually be found as specific only between forms still quite closely allied.

I (c). *General habitat.*

It must be very rarely that two closely allied species have so sharply different habitats that no crossing could occur. In a country like England, where no one habitat covers an extensive area without interruption, this is obvious, but in some continental areas habitat-differences may be much more important, though no clear distinction can be drawn in this case between restriction to one habitat and to one geographical area. Even on a much smaller scale, however, habitat-differences will lead to some degree of selective mating, especially with forms with low powers of dispersal. This small contribution towards the establishment of isolation is important because some degree of differentiation in habitat preference must be regarded as one of the commonest of specific characters. As the general facts are well known to most zoologists, we will give a few instances, confining our attention mainly to pairs of closely allied forms.

von Lengerken (1917) and Macgillavry (1927) record that the tiger-beetle *Cicindela hybrida* L. is restricted to the part of sand-dunes which is fixed by vegetation. The subspecies (or species) *C. maritima* Latr. occurs only on stony places on the actual strand. In Holland, however, a darker race of *maritima*

L

occurs on alluvium inland, where it is associated with *C. campestris*. The two moths *Lasiocampa quercus* and *L. quercus callunae*, already noted as differing in emergence period, also differ in habitat, the former being a lowland species, the latter inhabiting moors and mountains. The two habitats in this case are subject to considerable overlap. Fulton (1925) has described two races of the common N. American cricket, *Oecanthus niveus*. The races differ in song and habits of oviposition and also in habitat, one living on trees, the other on bushes. Myers (1929, p. 50) records that the various New Zealand species of Cicada are strictly confined to different plant-associations. It is probably not usual, however, in England for a species to be strictly confined to a plant-association. Many species have a single food-plant, but few plants are rigidly confined to a single association. Again, allied insect species not rarely feed on the same plant, *e.g.* many Chrysomelid beetles and weevils. It is not easy to find numerous genera in which both taxonomic and ecological studies are so advanced that we can say with certainty which species are closely allied and what range of habitat is occupied. It is certainly quite impossible to give a numerical estimate of the frequency with which allied forms are found together or in different habitats. We only know that both conditions may be encountered.

Amongst the vertebrates, closely allied forms tend to be geographically isolated, so that this method of separation can hardly arise. Amongst more distinct species, of course, habitat-differences are common, but are probably not very important in preventing interbreeding.

I (*d*). *Differences in breeding habitats : minor geographical units.*

Differences of this type are best known in forms with a definite breeding season. In migratory birds, for instance, there is a well-known tendency for individuals to return to breed in the locality where they were reared, and this tendency makes possible the formation of geographical races, since races which may mix in the winter, sort out and return to their own areas in the spring. Though this phenomenon is largely part of geographical differentiation, it must also lead to the formation of smaller units. Thus Schmidt (1931) has shown that species of eel which breed in a single restricted area are relatively uniform and are not separable into subspecific units, while other species which breed over a large area are much less homogeneous, being formed of a number of separate strains. From the point of view of isolation, it is difficult to distinguish between the action of geographical barriers and of differences in migratory instincts.

I (e). *Loss of means of dispersal.*

The examples cited in the previous paragraph lead us naturally to consider animals in which the power to migrate has been lost. Our ignorance of this matter is much greater than would appear at first sight. The high percentage of endemism on islands is well known, as is the tendency for island forms of winged species to be apterous. Evidently, if the species had not been winged originally their chances of reaching an oceanic island would have been small. Once an island has been reached, loss of powers of dispersal will aid the formation of local colonies, though it will not aid in isolation from fresh immigrants. We need not consider at this point the theories that have been put forward to account for the winglessness of island species, but, however produced, apterism will tend to multiply the numbers of endemic species on an island. At the same time very numerous examples of complete or nearly complete loss of wings are known from continental areas. In the beetles these facts have been summarised by Jackson (1928), and for Diptera by Bezzi (1916, 1922). The former author, working on the weevils of the genus *Sitona*, found short-winged, long-winged, and dimorphic species. Wherever the power of flight has been lost we might expect some degree of isolation to arise between colonies that previously were able to interbreed, if only because the ordinary habitat of the animal is not likely to be continuous. But we have to be very careful not to assume that the species with apparently the best means of dispersal are necessarily the most active species in getting about. Thus Richards (1926) points out that the wingless beetle *Helops striatus* is one of the first insects to re-invade heaths after fires. The wide range of many other wingless forms suggests that detailed knowledge of actual methods and powers of dispersal is necessary before we can assume very much about their significance in isolation.

The loss of eyes in cave insects is a parallel phenomenon.

Jeannel (1911 and 1926) has shown how cave species tend to be confined to one or a few adjacent caves. Doubtless blindness is not the only agency confining a species to its own cave (for, just as some apterous species are widespread, some blind species also occur in the open), but it probably plays an important rôle. This subject is discussed elsewhere (Chapter VII, p. 269).

The truth is that we know extremely little about the powers of dispersal of animals, apart from the more sensational migrations, and it is possible that some of the anomalous differences in the variability of different species might become clearer if we knew more. It is especially difficult to trace the minor wanderings which occur within the normal area inhabited by the species. The frequency of such wanderings must largely determine the homogeneity (or the reverse) of the species, and this, in turn, has an important effect on the significance of geographical isolation, since any isolated population has a greater or less chance of differing from the norm of the species. The converse, however, is equally important, viz. that no true random mating can occur in any species, because the chance of an encounter between individuals separated by a few miles of country is relatively low. Even in long-lived and wide-ranging forms this must have some effect, and in small, short-lived species, unless the specific range is extremely small, the results must be very significant.

II (i). *Recognition marks.*

We have very little information as to the function of recognition marks (or odours) amongst animals, apart from structures (or odours) specifically connected with mating. Something of the sort is evidently present in most gregarious animals. Thus Ward (1904) has shown that the bats in certain caves in Mexico roost according to their species. Feuerborn (1922) has given some evidence which suggests that flies of the family Psychodidae recognise the species as well as the sex of other individuals. He suggests that certain glands, present in both sexes, produce odours on which this faculty depends. Seitz (1894) long ago suggested that some Lepidoptera may produce both specific and sexual odours. Colour must also play a part in species recognition, as Eltringham (1919) has shown in certain butterflies in which the sexes are alike. Again, many insects, just prior to mating, form swarms of one sex only : the attraction here cannot be strictly sexual, although it is a preliminary to mating. While we know little in detail as to the influence of recognition marks, we can see that any tendency to form aggregations will lead to some degree of isolation. We cannot yet say whether such recognition marks often come to differ in the early stages of species evolution. In many animals with more than one colour-form the various types all interbreed (*cf.* Elton, 1927, p. 182 *et seq.* ; Richards, 1927). Probably recognition marks grade insensibly over into what must be classed as epigamic characters, but the former would include stimuli not acting only during a brief period before mating.

II (ii). *Differences in epigamic characters.*

The enormous mass of data concerning the epigamic characters of animals is not very helpful from the present point of view. An examination of the literature shows that the greatest number of papers describe the morphology of epigamic structures ; a less number describe the mating behaviour, including the use of such structures ; still fewer provide any evidence as to the significance in isolation of specific differences in epigamic structure and behaviour.

It is well established that species do very often differ in secondary sexual characters. In only a small fraction of the total number of species have these differences been shown to have a significance in mating. In many cases (*e.g.* Saturniid moths (Mayer, 1900)) the characters are probably only indicators of important differences in metabolism. In other cases the female may have been modified in connection with her maternal duties (development of brood-pouches, etc.).

Where the sexual characters are known to play a part in courtship their exact significance is nearly always doubtful. There is not enough experimental work to prove that particular structures or types of behaviour are actually essential if the male is to be successful. Usually the most that is known is that some conspicuous structure is exhibited in a provocative way during courtship. We may give a few examples in which the significance of epigamic structures or behaviour is fairly certain.

Sturtevant (1915) has shown that the wing-waving of male

Drosophila has a significant effect in reducing the time taken by the male to succeed in copulation. Males with their wings removed are able to mate sooner or later, but in them the pre-mating period is longer. In the Lepidoptera the experiments of Fabre, Mayer and Freiling have shown that the scent-apparatus of the female is frequently (probably nearly always) an essential element in pairing. The males are normally attracted to the scent of their own female, who distributes it until pairing has been effected. In some fireflies, different species of a genus emit light of different colours or in flashes of different frequency. Where both sexes are luminescent, each sex may respond only to the signal of its mate (Coblentz, 1911 ; Macdermott, 1910, 1911, 1912a, 1912b). In the Mollusca, Diver (quoted by Robson, 1928, p. 126) has shown that the two common English banded snails (*Cepea hortensis* and *C. nemoralis*) differ in the energy with which mating individuals stimulate one another with their darts. This difference, which appears to have no connection with the actual structure of the dart (which is also specific), is normally sufficient to keep the species apart if they attempted to pair.

Standfuss (1896) was able to show that the females of the Italian subspecies *persona* of *Callimorpha dominula* (Lepidoptera) are scarcely attractive to the males of the normal form. Grosvenor also (1921) has found local variations in the attractiveness of the female in *Zygaena* (Lepidoptera).

In the Orthoptera, where sound-production plays an important part in courtship, Fulton (1925) has shown that two biological races of the tree-cricket, *Oecanthus niveus*, differ in their song. Faber (1928), however, in his study of the German Orthoptera, found that by no means all species could be separated by their song, which, further, was very variable owing to the influence of temperature and the rivalry of other males. Whether a species responds only to the song of its own kind appears still to require much more confirmation.

In spiders, Bristowe and Locket (1926) show that courtship antics and male decorations may have a real value as recognition marks. It appears that unless the female recognises the male as belonging to her species she will often eat him, and the peculiar dances of the males assist the females to avoid mistakes. Tactile stimuli may play a similar part in families where sight is little developed, and it is probable that the dances are also stimulatory in their effect. The female behaviour has two phases, an amatory and an aggressive one, and when the former holds sway she is much less likely to attack the male. Thus courtship dances, besides giving the female a chance to recognise her mate, also put the female into a state in which attack is unlikely. After copulation, when the aggressive phase reasserts itself, she may devour the male, though she can scarcely be said not to recognise him.

Against these examples we may set others in which the epigamic characters are not yet known to play a part in isolating species. Among birds, as Huxley (1923) and others have pointed out, the exhibition of coloured parts and the performance of special antics, flights and songs take place usually after the birds are already mated up for the season. The displays are supposed to have a purely stimulatory effect. It is possible that male epigamic characters may play a minor part as recognition marks, though on this point we have no evidence. The stimulatory function seems likely to be important in many groups. Species which hybridise naturally also provide important evidence, since they show that no single element in the isolationary complex is necessarily and always competent to produce its normal effect.

II (iii). *Differences in the mechanical relations of the copulatory apparatus.*

We may, in the first place, mention a rather exceptional example amongst the fish. In the genus *Anableps* (Norman, 1931, p. 296) the male genital orifice is prolonged into a tube. The genital aperture of the female is covered by a special scale, free on one side only. The opening may be on either the right or the left and the males may have the intromittent organ turned in either direction. Copulation takes place sideways and a right-sided male always pairs with a left-sided female and *vice versa*.

The whole problem becomes much more complex when we consider the more usual type of specific differences in the genitalia, which are so often found, especially in the males, in a number of groups (see p. 296). It is important to discover how far these elaborate structures act as a mechanical means of isolating allied species. When we find that the male genitalia (as often happens in insects) differ sharply in characters whose degree of variation is not enough to make them overlap, in a species in which most or even all other structures intergrade from species to species, it is tempting to assume that we see here the actual agency for permanent isolation in these forms. The essence of this theory, the well-known ' lock-and-key ' theory of L. Dufour (*cf.* Pérez, 1894), is that the females should also differ in some way from each other ; differentiation in the male alone would not be effective. Whether the females do differ and whether the male armature really is effective in isolation have for many years been matters of controversy. The argument has chiefly lain amongst the entomologists, and a decision for the insects would probably also be valid in the case of many parasitic worms, Crustacea and Arachnida.

The chief supporter of the ' lock-and-key ' theory has been Jordan (1896, 1905). Boulangé (1924) has reviewed the subject and takes the opposite view. Jordan, in his first paper, dealing with the swallow-tail butterflies (*Papilio*), showed that the differences in the male genitalia are quite manifest, sometimes in geographical races. The females sometimes differ markedly in their genitalia, though they were much less thoroughly investigated. The actual proof that the male structures coincided so accurately with those of the female that copulation between different species would be difficult or impossible was not very convincing, and the evidence put forward was derived from a few species only. In his second paper the correlation between differences in genitalia and in other characters is examined. His main thesis is that local and seasonal [1] polymorphism in colour and wing-shape is quite independent of variation in male genitalia. In one geographical area the genitalia vary only slightly and at random, but as soon as a distinct geographical race becomes recognisable the variation in the genitalia tends to be correlated with the size and colour characters defining the race. It may be admitted that the male genitalia are easily modified in the evolution of species, but it is much more uncertain what part they actually play in that process.

In the Lepidoptera as a whole interspecific crosses are not

---

[1] Mercier (1929) claims to have demonstrated seasonal variation of the male genital organs in the fly, *Cynomyia*. Jordan also records one case in *Papilio*.

very rare and there is little evidence that differences in the male genitalia are often a very serious barrier between species, except when the structures are extremely different, as between species belonging to different genera or families. In a number of species of Diptera the male genitalia are extremely diverse, and there appear to be no corresponding differences in the female ; sometimes (*Lucilia*) it is only with great difficulty that the females can be distinguished, if at all. In many Hymenoptera the male genitalia differ greatly, with little or no differentiation in the females (Richards, 1927*a*, p. 262 ; Boulangé, *l.c.*). In *Bombus*, where the female genitalia do to some extent vary specifically, it is largely groups of species which differ and the structures showing differences come into contact only with part (and that not the most complicated) of the male armature. Further, in some species the male genitalia, though nearly identical, show certain minute but constant differences, too small to have, with any probability, any functional significance (Richards, *l.c.*). Although there seems to be usually no detailed co-adaptation between the male and female, there are some exceptions. Edwards (1929, p. 40) records a correlation between the length of the male penis and of the female spermathecal duct in the flies of the family Blepharoceridae. A similar correlation is sometimes observed in beetles of the family Chrysomelidae (Harnisch, 1915), but how far this is specific rather than generic requires investigation.

A more rational explanation would appear to be that differences in instinct—possibly (*e.g.* in insects) in the nature of the scent produced—are the first stage in the permanent isolation of species ; later, differences in genitalia may arise and may sometimes, incidentally, make the isolation more perfect. In this way it is possible to explain the occurrence of groups (families, genera, etc.) in which the genitalia are scarcely specifically differentiated. All who have studied insect genitalia agree that the value of these structures to the taxonomist varies greatly in different families, in some providing characters of little more than generic value, in others differing very greatly in species otherwise very similar.

In the preceding paragraph we have advisedly used the phrase ' permanent isolation ' to describe the result of changes in instinct, for temporary isolation may result from geographical barriers. It is a matter of controversy whether some measure of geographical isolation is necessary for divergence to begin. This view has been strongly maintained by Jordan (1896, 1905), and is implicit in the 'Formenkreis' theory of Kleinschmidt and Rensch, according to whom geographical races alone are the starting-point for new species.

In the case of birds and mammals there would appear to be good evidence for this idea. The lowest systematic categories (geographical races) never occur together except in a minimal part of their range (*cf.* von Schweppenburg, 1924, p. 143) and, generally speaking, only rather widely divergent forms live together in the same habitat. It is true that the geographical barriers between the races are not always absolute, but imperfect barriers combined with the usually discontinuous occurrence of suitable habitats may be sufficient to allow divergence. The chief lack at the moment is the accurate study of the distribution and nature of the forms occurring where two races meet.

With insects the necessity of geographical isolation is much more difficult to maintain, as might be expected from the relative complexity of the way in which the sexes are normally brought together. If selected cases are examined (*cf.* Jordan, 1896), it is easy to show the importance of geographical isolation, which in any case must always be operative, even if it is not the only agency responsible for divergence. Thus Jordan found in certain Oriental swallow-tail butterflies that forms differing in colour, shape of wings or seasonal occurrence never differ in genitalia unless they are restricted to geographically separated areas. Since Jordan maintains that mechanical isolation as a result of differences in the genitalia is the chief means of making divergence permanent, he argues that in these swallow-tails it is only the geographical races and not variants which occur together in one locality which will (or may) give rise to new species. It is possible, however, in other groups to find examples which suggest the opposite point of view. Thus species or races with genitalia so similar as to differ from one another no more than do the geographical races of swallow-tails, may occur together over wide areas, as in the butterfly *Satyrus huebneri* (Avinoff, 1929), in many Tortricids (compare male genitalia of species of the genera *Cnephasia* or *Epiblema*, Plates v and xxiii (and p. 68) in Pierce and Metcalfe, 1922) or in some Hesperiids (Warren,

1926, p. 40). While it is possible to assume that these forms evolved in geographical isolation but have since crossed their barriers, it is doubtful whether the evidence for the necessity of geographical isolation is so cogent that it is necessary to make so big an assumption.

We may summarise the outstanding points in this controversy as follows :

1. The male armature differs specifically much more often and usually more markedly than the female.

2. There is often, perhaps usually, no close specific correlation between the male and female structures. At least such correlation has not been established.

3. The numerous interspecific crosses, mostly artificial but some natural, between species with very different genitalia, show that the male and female armatures by no means necessarily impose an insuperable barrier.

4. The vast mass of species with different genitalia probably do not *try* to interbreed. They are in fact separated by other types or combinations of types of isolatory factors (especially those included under I and II (*a*)).

5. As a corollary to (4), large groups of species exist in which the female genitalia differ but little from species to species. There is no evidence that such forms hybridise more readily than those in which the differences are marked.

6. There appears to be no very high correlation between degree of differences in genitalia and the fertility of hybrids if a pairing does take place—*e.g.* Sturtevant (1920) shows that *Drosophila simulans* and *D. melanogaster* have identical mating habits and hybridise freely, but the hybrids are quite sterile. The male genitalia differ, but not those of the females.

We can only conclude that the genital armature may sometimes provide a bar to interspecific crosses, but the bar is by no means universal or incapable of being surmounted. This is particularly true of the smaller differences which characterise very closely allied species. The value of specific differences in the genitalia lies rather in their relative constancy. Thus, while variation does occur (*e.g.* marked variation in the Magpie Moth, *Abraxas grossulariata*, recorded by Kosminsky, 1912), it is not usually of a type to make species overlap.

If small differences in the genitalia are not in themselves enough to isolate species, it becomes a matter of importance to decide whether the degree of difference commonly found between species is likely to have been built up in several stages. One series of observations made by Foot and Strobell (1914) suggests that the specific differences must be due to the action of several independent hereditary factors. In crossing two bugs of the genus *Euschistus* they found that the length of the penis (a specific character) was intermediate in F_1 and only rarely reached either parental type in F_2. This suggests that more than one factor for penis-length is involved, and we may suspect that the first stages in this divergence cannot have been very important as means of isolation.

Apart from the genital armature, difference in size in itself might be expected to play some part in isolation. This would be more important if really closely allied species did more commonly differ markedly in size. We have little very definite information on this subject. Mickel (1924) has shown that the Mutillid wasp *Dasymutilla bioculata* Cress. has a bimodal variation in size owing to its having two main hosts. A male, however, could mate with a female which was only half his size, so that there was not much chance of the size difference leading to isolation. In insects generally size-variation does not appear to be very important. In a sea slug, however, Crozier (1918) has shown that mating individuals tend to be of about the same size. But even in the molluscs this is not universal (Robson, 1928).

II (2). *Prevention of effective fertilisation.*

Some degree of sterility on crossing is well known to be a common type of difference between species. The term ' sterility ' is in fact employed to describe a number of distinct phenomena. Only exceptionally do we know exactly what occurs in a particular case. After an apparently effective pairing, we may distinguish between the following possibilities :

1. The sperm fails to reach the egg.
2. The egg is fertilised, but development ceases at an early stage.

3. Development proceeds further, and a feeble or malformed F_1 may be produced.

4. Well-developed, more or less vigorous hybrids are produced which are sexually abnormal—*e.g.* one sex missing from brood, spermato- and ovo-genesis abnormal, production of intersexes, etc.

5. F_1 more or less fertile—*e.g.* fertile with one sex of one of the parent species.

6. F_1 fertile, but F_2 infertile or weakly.

7. Complete fertility.

In noting this wide range of possibilities, it is important to remember that some degree of intraspecific sterility is always met with. Sometimes sterility between certain types of individuals is very marked—*e.g.* in some Ascidians (*cf.* Plough, 1930, 1932). The nearly fertile interspecific hybrids, therefore, grade over completely into species in which intraspecific sterility is normally present in some degree.

The essential question is whether any of these forms of sterility provides commonly the first important stage in isolation. At least one case is known of extreme sterility between a species and a mutant differing only in a single character, viz. *Drosophila obscura* (Lancefield, 1929), in which a naturally occurring race, with a very large Y-chromosome, will not cross with the normal form. It is difficult to see how a mutant determining sterility could establish itself in the population ; the process is not likely to be very common. On the whole, however, the facts do not suggest that sterility is commonly the initial method by which isolation is established ; at any rate it is unlikely to have been the only important factor. This subject has been discussed at greater length by Robson (1928).

Conclusions

This survey of the factors which promote isolation suggests the following generalisations :

(1) There is no one predominantly important way in which isolation becomes established in the early stages of species-formation.

(2) Geographical or temporary isolation is undoubtedly very important, but it cannot be claimed that this

is the only way in which new species arise. The permanent isolation of geographical races must be established in much the same way as permanent isolation between species inhabiting the same area.

(3) The establishment of isolation is probably due to the interaction of a number of different factors, none of which would be effective by itself.

The third generalisation is the one which appears to be most useful. The study of geographical races is not likely to be helpful, except in the narrow zone where two races meet, and not here if, as often happens, the races interbreed at this point. It is rather in the study of biological races of animals that our hope lies. These closely allied taxonomic groups, differing more in habits than in structure, show us where the fission of species is just beginning. Since the races often occur together without much intercrossing, isolation must have been developed and may be analysed with some likelihood of reaching definite conclusions (*cf.* Thorpe, 1929, 1930). In 1896 Jordan was able to make out a case for the theory that permanent isolation would be developed only between species already geographically isolated. It seemed at that date that a difference sufficient to isolate two forms could not arise at one step without a new species also arising suddenly, and this appeared to contradict the widely accepted generalisation that specific change was gradual. The more recent study of biological races demonstrates that these *a priori* arguments are unsound. Whether it seems probable or not, biological races more or less isolated from one another do appear to arise from an originally homogeneous species.

The occurrence of local breakdowns in a normally effective isolatory mechanism also suggests the complex nature of the process. Delcourt's (1909) study of *Notonecta* shows that species isolated in part of their range may interbreed in a small area. von Schweppenburg (1924) records the same thing in *Passer domesticus* and *P. hispaniolensis*, and Tutt (1909, 1910) in *Agriades thetis* and *A. coridon*. If we take an imaginary example in which two species are separated almost completely by the time of their breeding season, and if we suppose that the onset of the breeding season partly depends on climate, but that the two species do not react to climate in precisely the same way, then it is easy to see that at some point in their range the breeding seasons might coincide. Or again, two species with different habitat preferences might be brought into close proximity in certain areas where only an intermediate type of habitat was available. We are in great need of accurate analyses of actual concrete examples.

The most important conclusion in relation to our more general argument as to the course of evolution is that, in so far as the isolation of *species* from one another depends on the combined effect of *several* agencies, it is likely that the same agencies produce some degree of isolation between *populations within* the species. The likelihood that species are much broken up into populations which are to a considerable extent isolated from one another must be fully allowed for in any theory as to the spread of variants.

CHAPTER VI

CORRELATION

IN a previous chapter we have endeavoured to show that throughout the animal kingdom there is a tendency for individuals to be capable of arrangement in a hierarchy of groups, each group being defined by an association of characters which are more or less correlated together. It is evident that whatever the cause or causes of evolution may be, one of its most characteristic effects is the divergence of groups distinguished by blocks of characters which tend to hang together. Much of this correlation is far from unexpected and calls for little comment. It is not surprising, *e.g.*, that a given mammal of carnivorous habits should have teeth adapted for tearing or crunching, a skull with suitable muscular attachments and limbs appropriate to a raptorial habit. The regular association of characters whose functional significance is far from apparent, such as we see in species and subspecies, is quite another matter and is the main theme of this chapter.

From a restricted point of view the origin of such correlation appears a relatively simple problem, but a full treatment involves the examination of some of the most difficult problems in biology. It is easy to suggest how a group of characters (each regarded as the expression of a single genetic factor) could come to be correlated together, even if we cannot actually verify our hypothesis in any concrete example. There is, however, a tendency to treat the separate characters as something apart from the fundamental organisation of the living animal (*cf*. Chapter IX). While this may be a justifiable simplification for the practical purposes of genetics and taxonomy, as we shall show at the end of this chapter, it comes into conflict with another conception of the living organism.

The term *correlation* has, since Darwin first made the

phenomena an object of study, been applied to a variety of relations which are not of the same nature. The credit of distinguishing them seems to be due to Dürken (1922). He recognised three distinct types of association :

(1) *Relation.*—The ' unilateral ' dependence of a structure for its full expression on an internal factor on which the structure in question itself has no effect (*e.g.* the dependence in development on the optic capsule of the embryonic lens in the Vertebrata).

(2) *Correlation.*—The reciprocal dependence of two associated parts of such a nature that alteration of the one leads to the alteration of the other (*e.g.* the reciprocal dependence of the extremities and nervous system in vertebrate development).

(1) and (2) include all *causal* associations.

(3) *Combination.*—The ' static ' coincidence of variables without any reciprocal or unilateral dependence (*e.g.* specialisation of several parts for the same function ; dependence of several structures or organs on sex hormones or on an external stimulus (*cf.* Sumner, 1915)).

Graham Kerr (1926) distinguished *primary* or gametic correlation from *secondary* or physiological correlation. This is a fundamental distinction of considerable practical value, and forms the basis of our discussion. Robson (1928) discussed the various kinds of correlation in so far as they are contributory to the process of group divergence, pointing out some of the difficulties that are encountered in explaining the origin of groups by the current theories of evolution. In particular he dealt with Pearson's contention (1903, p. 2) that Natural Selection is probably the chief factor in causing correlation. The fact that correlation may be *fluctuating* or *stable* according to the degree in which the variables are affected by environmental factors, was pointed out by Love and Leighty (1914).

Darwin's views on the importance of correlation in relation to selection and the data which he assembled are discussed in Chapter VII. It is true that in the course of his examination of a large series of cases of correlation he touched on the causes of the phenomena—*e.g.* he discussed the correlation of variation in homologous parts (1905, vol. ii, p. 389) and the effects of selection (*l.c.*). He did not, however, take his discussion on the causes very far, nor did he attempt to distinguish the various phenomena to which the name ' correlation ' is given.

The distinctions made by Dürken and Kerr can be harmonised, if we realise that Dürken's ' relation ' and ' correlation ' are *causal* types of association and correspond to Kerr's ' physiological correlation ' ; while Dürken's ' combination ' includes Kerr's ' gametic ' correlation as well as other phenomena. Thus we can include in it (*a*) character associations produced by the mechanism of heredity in its distribution of segregating characters (*e.g.* effects of linkage, strains homozygous for several characters, etc.), and (*b*) equally *fortuitous* association produced by the coincident effects of external causes operating simultaneously on the individual.

It is desirable, before proceeding further, to obtain some general idea as to the extent to which the characters distinguishing species and races, etc., are correlated. Were such a measure obtainable, it would give us an idea as to the extent to which these groups are homogeneous for their diagnostic characters. Taxonomic experience, of course, prepares us for the result that the degree of correlation is very varied, probably on the whole rather low. The value of the available data is rather dubious, as what we obviously want to know about is the correlation of *hereditary* characters, and in systematic data little attention is paid to the discrimination of fluctuational from hereditary characters.

A great deal of statistical information is available as to the correlation of miscellaneous characters, but very little concerning those which distinguish groups. The exact analysis of the variation—*e.g.* of pairs of related species or races—from this point of view has been very little studied, and more work of this kind is desirable. The facts we give are slight in amount, but we believe they may be typical of a larger array. It must be borne in mind that such studies as are available are made on limited sections of populations, and we have no means of saying how far the correlations indicated are characteristic of the groups over their entire range. Lastly there is available, as far as we know, no analysis of *all* the diagnostic features of a pair of allied species.

We will first give (*a*) some data concerning the correlation of characters within species, and then (*b*) examples of the correlation between characters diagnostic of pairs of related species.

(a) :

Species	Authority	Characters	Correlation
Clausilia itala . .	Alkins (1923a)	Length × width of shell	0·39
Ena obscura . .	,, (1923)	,, × ,, ,, ,,	0·36
Rhynconella cf. boueti .	,, (1923b)	,, × ,, ,, ,,	0·86
,, ,, ,, .	,, (l.c.)	,, × depth ,, ,,	0·30
Terebratula punctata .	,, (l.c.)	,, × width ,, ,,	0·94
,, ,, .	,, (l.c.)	,, × depth ,, ,,	0·94
,, ,, .	,, (l.c.)	Width × ,, ,, ,,	0·88
Portunus depurator (carapace)	Warren (1896)	Total breadth × frontal breadth	0·14
,, ,,	,, ,,	,, ,, × R. dentary margin	0·56
,, ,,	,, ,,	R. antero-lateral length × L. dentary margin	0·74
,, ,,	,, ,,	R. antero-lateral length × L. antero-lateral length	0·86
Gryllus sp. . .	Lutz (1908)	Length of body × tegmina	0·61
,, ,, . .	,, ,,	,, ,, posterior femora × tegmina	0·80
,, ,, . .	,, ,,	,, ,, ovipositor × tegmina	0·73
,, ,, . .	,, ,,	,, ,, body × posterior femora	0·53
,, ,, . .	,, ,,	,, ,, ovipositor × posterior femora	0·77
,, ,, . .	,, ,,	,, ,, ovipositor × body	0·70
Carbonicola affinis .	Trueman (1930)	Height × length	0·28

It will be seen that in these examples, which have been collected at random, the average correlation is 0·56, which is a fairly high figure.

In all probability this figure is rather in excess of the general average. Thus, in his analysis of the variation of various groups of invertebrate fossils, Trueman (l.c.) emphasises the tendency for the characters of species to vary independently of each other, and the consequent low correlation.

(b) Alkins (1928) has analysed the variation of the land snails *Clausilia rugosa* and *C. cravenensis* in a study which is particularly valuable on account of its being based on samples taken from different colonies (though from a restricted region). He studied two of the diagnostic characters, viz. length and major width of the shell. He gives no statement of the correlation of those characters in the two species over the whole area investigated, as his work is centred on the analysis of the correlations in each species in each colony. But he states (p. 68) that ' the mean altitude and mean diameter of *C. cravenensis* always exceed those of *C. rugosa* . . . individually their altitude ranges may overlap to some extent, but their diameter ranges hardly ever . . . doubtful cases (shells of uncertain specific identity) are rare.' From this one may infer, though without a definite measure, that the correlations between length and width and between shortness and narrowness are marked enough to render it easy to decide at once to which species a shell must be assigned. Within the range of each species, however, the correlations are low, in a selected series of colonies (p. 68) never exceeding 0·50 and sinking as low as 0·1, the mean being for *rugosa* 0·31, and for *cravenensis* 0·39. This is interesting as showing that, though the two species tend to reveal two regularly contrasted characters, the latter do not maintain an absolute identity of association within the species.

Alkins (1921) and Alkins and others (1921) also studied the correlation of various proportion-indices in *Sphaerium lacustre*, *corneum* and *pallidum*. They find that in all three species the correlation of length and width, length and thickness, and width and thickness has a high value, never falling below 0·9. In *S. lacustre* and *S. corneum* length and width are certainly diagnostic.

We owe to Sumner (see his summary, 1932, and bibliography of a long series of papers) a valuable study of interracial diagnostic characters in the deer-mouse (*Peromyscus*). He states (1928, p. 183) that ' there is no *general* tendency for the elements which distinguish one race from another to vary together within the single race.' He does not state what the figure for the total range of variation is, but from this paper and a later one (1929) we may infer that the distinctive interracial correlations may be fairly well marked : indeed in the forms dealt with in the latter paper the amount of intermediacy is very slight (*l.c.* p. 112). He sums up the situation in his final review as follows : ' Interracial correlations, so far as these concern the length of body parts, are altogether erratic. While within single populations certain parts (*e.g.* tail and foot) tend to vary together in their relative size, such concomitant variation may or may not be encountered when

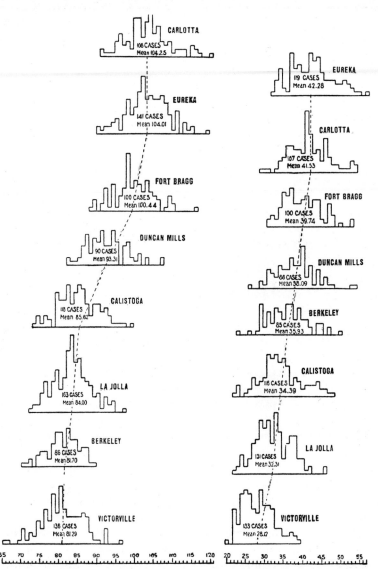

FIG. 19.—*Peromyscus maniculatus*. HISTOGRAMS SHOWING DISTRIBUTION OF FRE-
QUENCIES FOR THE VARIOUS VALUES OF RELATIVE TAIL-LENGTH (LEFT) AND
RELATIVE WIDTH OF THE TAIL-STRIPE (RIGHT) IN EIGHT LOCALITIES. THE
BROKEN LINES CONNECT THE MEANS OF THE VARIOUS SERIES.
(From Sumner, 1920.)

we examine a series of geographic races. Throughout considerable tracts a positive correlation may hold : in other territories the correlation may be entirely dissolved. Intraracial correlations in pigmental characters, on the other hand, are even more pronounced than are interracial ones. Darker races, like darker individuals, tend to have more extended coloured areas in their pelages, deeper pigmentation in the skin of their feet, broader (and longer) tail stripes, etc.'

Other papers of Sumner's (*e.g.* 1918, 1920, 1923) make it quite evident that the character complexes which distinguish subspecies are by no means highly correlated, and certainly his evidence concerning the behaviour of these complexes on crossing shows (1923) that they fail to behave as units. The systematic analysis of species and geographical races has yielded similar results, and there is a good deal of evidence that the characters distinguishing such groups vary independently (*cf.* Swarth, in Linsdale, 1928, p. 257 ; Mertens, 1931, p. 205).

The discussion as to the kinds of correlation (p. 161) shows that they may be reduced to two fundamental types : (1) one in which the characters stand in relation to each other as cause and effect, and (2) one in which their association is coincidental (' combination ').

(1) This includes (*a*) the dependence of one part on another, and (*b*) the reciprocal dependence of two parts on each other.

(*a*) A structure may depend, as we have seen, on another structure on which it has no effect itself. Certain of the phenomena of development have been interpreted as due to various kinds of stimuli (chemotaxis, thigmotaxis) exerted by one part on another. The classical example is the failure of the lens of the vertebrate eye to develop if the optic capsule fails to make contact with it. Other examples are discussed by Jenkinson (1909, p. 273 and foll.).

The dependence noted here affects the main architecture of the parts rather than the characters which distinguish species. But certain characters of proportion are obviously influenced by growth principles, and Huxley (1932, *passim*) in particular has applied the principle of *heterogonic* growth to explain certain differences between species. (See especially the case of the Lucanid beetle, *Cyclommatus tarandus*.) It may therefore come about that correlated specific differences

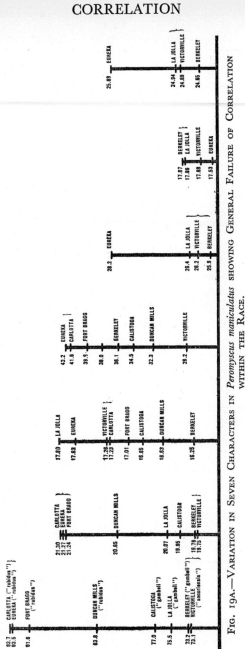

FIG. 19A.—VARIATION IN SEVEN CHARACTERS IN *Peromyscus maniculatus* SHOWING GENERAL FAILURE OF CORRELATION WITHIN THE RACE.
(From Sumner, 1920.)

consisting of proportional differences of parts might arise, if the characters in question were related to the absolute size of the animal and if the latter were of selective value.

Another kind of correlation of this type is seen in the dependence of a structure on the specific activity of a gland—particularly those of internal secretion.

(b) As regards the reciprocal dependence of the parts of the living organism little can be said. There is some evidence that in the course of development various parts are dependent for their expression on each other. This fact was indeed made a prominent feature of Driesch's theory of development. According to Jenkinson (l.c. pp. 75–7), the dependence diminishes with age ; correlation is only high during periods of rapid growth, and there is an increasing power of self-differentiation. That certain relations of this kind persist into later life is seen in the dependence of the extremities on the nervous system in the Vertebrata.

Correlation has often been invoked to supplement the theory of Natural Selection. The modification of apparently non-serviceable structures has thus been attributed to their being correlated with characters influenced by selection. The nature of the correlation has not seriously been studied. It was probably some kind of causal association such as we have been discussing that was in (e.g.) Darwin's mind when he stressed its evolutionary importance. Not only, however, does this kind of correlation require much more study and exploration, but also the efficacy of selection itself (Chapter VII) is open to question. Possibly some differences of size and proportion between species have been produced by selection acting on characters correlatively associated in this way. Whether differences of colour, ornamentation and the arrangement of parts are influenced by it is far more problematical.

(2) We have already seen (p. 162) that we have to deal here with two types of correlation, viz. (a) one due to the coincident effects of various external causes, and (b) another due to the mechanism of heredity.

(a) There is a variety of ways in which such correlations can arise. Thus Hubbs (1926) shows that low temperatures tend to make fish large, small-headed and small-eyed. High temperatures make them small, large-headed and large-eyed. Schmidt (1930, p. 28) finds that in the Atlantic Cod (as in the Salmon and *Lebistes*) external factors (? salinity and temperature) can alter the average numbers of vertebræ and fin rays.

It is probable that the groups of characters employed in diagnosing species are not usually held together by a correlation of this sort. How far the coincident effects of several separate factors or the multiple effects of single factors of this order may have been influential in evolution must be left for a later discussion (p. 172). Theoretically at least groups of correlated specific characters might arise as the direct effect of environmental causes or from simultaneous selective processes. The value of this suggestion depends on the evolutionary importance we attach to these processes. There is, however, some evidence of a convincing nature that characters of the same kind as distinguish taxonomic species are altered in association as the result either of single environmental factors or of several such factors acting concurrently. Thus it is known that in the Baltic *Macoma baltica* and *Mya arenaria* are both smaller (Brandt, 1897) and have thinner shells than usual (Möbius, 1873). Bateson (1889) found that the proportions and shape of *Cardium edule* are modified in the brackish water of the Sea of Aral. Sumner (1915) experimentally induced lengthening of tail and foot in white mice by high temperature, and such differences are known to differentiate the wild races of rodents. Perhaps we should draw attention to Sumner's point (1932, p. 53) that, though in some of his experimental cases we might expect ' parallel modification by the environment, the latter cannot account for correlations which increase in segregating generations of hybrids.'

There is a theoretical possibility that all the characters of a species may be produced by several coincident selective processes or by a single selective process affecting several characters. The wing-pattern of a mimetic butterfly would be an example of the latter. The pattern is composed of several elements, all of which are associated in the mimetic effect and, on the selection hypothesis, must have been produced coincidentally by a single selective process. As an example of the modification of several quite distinct structures in relation to a special mode of life we may cite Hora's (1930, *passim*) demonstration that in torrent-dwelling species several characters may be modified in the same species as a result of adaptation to the particular habitat.

Any attempt to explain such correlation as the expression of single or multiple effects of Natural Selection must, of course, depend on whether Selection is a *vera causa*. The occurrence of correlation should not be held to be a proof of the action of Selection.

It is possible in some cases that isolation may make for correlation, as, for instance, when a few individuals of an aberrant form are isolated on an island, so that an association of characters originally accidental is prevented from returning to the normal distribution (by the lack of facilities for crossing with the parent form). Hagedoorn and Hagedoorn (1921), in particular, have stressed the point that isolation will lead to inbreeding of the isolated stock, with a considerable likelihood of the establishment of a new mean.

(*b*) The occurrence of correlation due to the mechanism of heredity has been discussed by Robson (1928, p. 229), who cites a certain number of instances revealed by genetic experiment in which, on crossing, character complexes tend to hang together, instead of being dissociated as is the usual fate of *independently segregating* characters. The majority of the instances are found amongst plants ; but a more limited number occur in animals—*e.g.* Castle and Wright (1916), Phillips (1921), Harrison (1916, p. 145 ['segregation *en bloc*' of specific characters]). The actual basis of such correlation is obscure. The relation between linkage and correlation has been stressed on several occasions, but Robson (*l.c.* p. 231) makes it clear that it is difficult to attribute the correlation of specific characters to linkage. Sumner (1932, pp. 53–5) had discussed this question in greater detail in connection with his interracial studies of *Peromyscus*, and finds good grounds for preferring the hypothesis of the multiple effects of single genes. According to Haldane (1932, p. 114), 'a number of cases of multiple action of this kind in *Drosophila*' are available. At present very little is known concerning such 'multiple' effects in animal genetics, and certainly we are not in a position to discuss how far they are influential in producing intraspecific character correlation.

In any homozygous strain or pure line all phenotypic characters are more or less strongly correlated together until mutation occurs. The degree of correlation will depend on the susceptibility of the characters to environmental influences. Again, the phenotypic expressions of dominant genes lying in the same chromosome will be more or less strongly correlated, depending on the amount of crossing over. We can even invent a hypothetical case in which two characters would show complete correlation, by assuming that each of the genes responsible was lethal when not associated with the other.

On the whole we believe that the bulk of intraspecific correlations is due to most members of a species being homozygous for their distinctive characters. As Fisher (1930, p. 124) has said, ' the intimate manner in which the whole body of individuals of a single species are bound together by sexual reproduction has been lost sight of by some writers. Apart from the intervention of geographical barriers so recently that the races separated are not yet regarded as specifically distinct, the ancestry of each single individual, if carried back only a few hundred generations, must embrace practically all of the earlier period who have contributed appreciably to the ancestry of the present population. If we carry the survey back for 200, 1,000 or 10,000 generations, which are relatively short periods in the history of most species, it is evident that the community of ancestry must be even more complete. The genetical identity in the majority of loci, which underlies the genetic variability presented by most species, seems to supply the systematist with the true basis of his concept of specific identity or diversity.' Hagedoorn and Hagedoorn (1921) have expressed the same idea in a rather different way. In nearly all species the population is not of constant size throughout the year or from one year to the next. This is particularly obvious in all species which, in temperate climates, have a definite breeding season. The large population existing at the end of the breeding period is gradually depleted till only a relatively small number is available to breed again the next year. The survival of only a small number to carry on the species must mean an enormous reduction in variation each year, probably enough to account for the observed constancy of most species. The chance that any variant represented by only a few individuals will form a part of the next year's initial population is very low, the magnitude of the chance depending (apart from survival value) on the ratio between the numbers of the variant and the total number of individuals in the species.

As we have said already, the actual basis of correlation is in nearly all species unknown, but there are certain methods by which important information may be obtained, indicating that the correlation is often of the second type.

(1) There may be considerable presumptive evidence that the characters are physiologically independent of one another. Thus in insects we should have no reason to suspect a direct physiological relation between the arrangement of the wing-nervures and the structure of the external genitalia, or, in birds, between the shape of the beak and the colour of the tail. How far the mere unlikelihood of a relation is significant has to be decided in each individual case. The somewhat anecdotal instances of correlation between apparently independent parts which are cited by Darwin should be borne in mind.

(2) Some specific characters are unusually variable and cannot, therefore, show a very high correlation with more stable ones. Wherever low correlations are observed, there is a likelihood that the basis is not physiological. More important evidence can be obtained in species in which in some individuals a single specific character is replaced by one normally distinctive of another species. The identity of such aberrant individuals may be reasonably certain, since the other members of its character complex are still associated together. Further, these variant forms may be quite rare, so that the correlation of the character in the species as a whole remains high. Such cases strongly suggest that the character (and, by inference, similar characters in allied species) is capable of independent segregation.[1]

As an instance of this type of evidence we may mention the Tortricid moth, *Euxanthis straminea* (*cf.* Waters, 1926, p. 159). A form has occurred in S. Devon (and elsewhere) which, in its large size and distinct dark wing markings, resembles the allied species *E. alternana*. The aberrant specimens, however, have typical genitalia, and the direction (though not the intensity or dimensions) of the wing fasciæ is normal. Similar

---

[1] Nabours (1929, p. 33) has made the interesting observation that there are differences in the linkage relations of similar patterns in different species of grouse-locusts.

cases are mentioned by Warren (1926) in his account of the
European Hesperidae ('Skippers'). One of the authors has

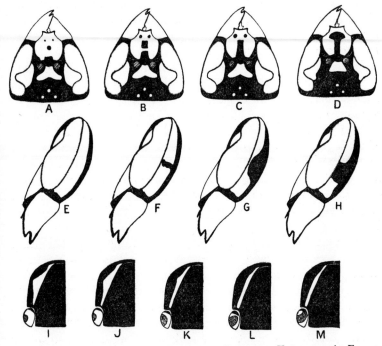

FIG. 20.—SPECIFIC DIFFERENCES BETWEEN THE QUEENS OF *Vespa germanica* F. AND
V. vulgaris L. YELLOW MARKINGS, COMPOUND EYES, AND OCELLI SHOWN IN
WHITE. BLACK PARTS SHOWN IN BLACK. REDDISH-BROWN PARTS DOTTED.

1. Differences in the markings of the head (head seen anterodorsally,
   antennæ removed, antennal sockets cross-hatched). In *V. germanica*
   (A–C) the black marks on the clypeus are variable and the black
   stripe between the yellow supra-antennal spot and the yellow in the
   eye-emargination narrows posteriorly. In *V. vulgaris* (D) there is
   constantly a black 'anchor' mark on the clypeus and the black stripe
   broadens posteriorly.
2. Head seen from the left side (antennæ removed). In *V. germanica*
   (E and F) the postocular yellow stripe is normally continuous. In
   V. vulgaris (G and H) the stripe is normally interrupted. Various
   intermediates (F and G) occur.
3. Left half of pronotum and mesonotum (with tegula), seen from above.
   The yellow pronotal stripe in *V. germanica* (I–K) is more or less angled
   outwardly; the tegula, typically, is yellow with a small reddish
   outer spot and a small black inner one. In *V. vulgaris* (L and M) the
   pronotal stripe is narrow and parallel-sided and the tegula is typically
   reddish-brown with two yellow and one black spot. Figures K and L
   show intermediates.

noted a similar phenomenon in the wasps *Vespa vulgaris* and
V. germanica (*cf.* fig. 20).

(3) A good many of the specific characters observed in a genus may occur in different combinations amongst the various species.　In so far as we are justified in assuming that similar characters in different species can be rated as fundamentally the same, we may use these permutations as evidence of independent segregation.　Lutz (1924) has described a case of this sort in the S. American stingless bees (*Melipona*).　Kinsey (1930) presents convincing evidence that short-winged forms of *Cynips* have been repeatedly produced from long-winged species.

(4) Crosses between distinct species may provide convincing evidence as to the essential independence of characters. Sometimes the hybrids show an extraordinary intermixture of the characters of the two parents.　Less commonly some of the characters tend to remain together and segregate in blocks. It is not actually necessary to assume that the correlation between characters segregating in blocks is of a different nature from that between characters segregating independently. It might be suggested that disharmonies during cell-division in the hybrids make normal segregation impossible.

We have hitherto spoken of specific characters as units without considering their relation to a genetic basis.　This relation is of importance when we try to define the meaning of the term ' independent segregation.'　An initial complication in the discussion arises from our ignorance as to whether apparently similar phenotypic characters in different individuals or species really are the same.　We know from genetical researches that superficially similar mutants are not necessarily due to a mutation at the same locus.　In dealing with the mutant forms of a single species the question can be always answered by making the appropriate crosses.　But in the mass of species such crosses have not been or cannot be made.　An individual aberrant in one specific character is not usually recognised to possess theoretical interest until death has made experiment impossible.　The direct identification of similar specific characters in different species is usually impossible, owing to refusal to cross and to the rareness of hybrids.　The point we wish to make here is that practically no analysis of specific characters in terms of genes is available.　Sturtevant (1921, p. 119 and foll.) has shown that some of the mutations in

Drosophila resemble generic or family characters which distinguish other groups. But even in *Drosophila* there is practically no evidence as to the genetic basis of the characters used to separate species in that genus. The geneticist, naturally enough, has concentrated on the mutations most easily observed and studied. A special search for mutation in characters known to be of specific value seems scarcely to have been attempted.

We are in great need of information as to whether the unit phenotypic characters are really genotypic units. We may discard for the moment the numerous specific characters which are not unambiguously definable as units and consider only such differences as : number of metameric parts, presence or absence of definite spines or bristles, development of definite coloured patches, etc. These are the sorts of characters which appear in different combinations in allied species and are therefore spoken of as segregating independently. Analogy with the results of genetical studies would lead one to expect that a number of these character differences might be due to more than one gene difference. We are seeing here, in the segregation of unit phenotypic characters, the transfer of blocks of genes, and it may be asked how these blocks come to remain as units.

When, on crossing two species, all degrees of intermediacy are found in any character, we have a clear case of the breaking-up of one of the gene blocks referred to. When, however, the character acts as a unit, we do not know enough as yet to affirm that only a single gene is necessarily involved. The possibility of some unsuspected correlation mechanism cannot altogether be dismissed.

The recent emphasis on the idea of the multiple effects of single genes also raises a difficulty. The result of postulating multiple effects is to increase the number of genes which are regarded as contributing to the phenotypic expression of any one character. But, evidently, the more independent genes are concerned in the expression of characters, the more difficult it is to explain the independent segregation of characters as units. At the present moment this point has scarcely more than theoretical interest, but we shall have to return to it (p. 177) in our consideration of the validity of a unit-character analysis of living animals.

It is instructive to compare the correlations between specific with those obtaining between generic and family characters. Some diagnostic characters are 'good' and hold for every member of the genus. Others are variable or only present in some members. The permutations of characters amongst related genera or families are also common. In fact, it would seem at first sight that at all stages in divergence the correlation between characters was of the same nature and depended on the extent to which the different unit characters had succeeded in permeating populations of different sizes. Highly correlated characters seem to be those for which large numbers of individuals are homozygous. The position of a character in the hierarchy would seem to depend on the extent to which it had spread, and this, in turn, approximately on the time that has elapsed since it first appeared.

The study of lineages by palæontologists appears to bear out such a view of evolution. The material studied (Bryozoa, Mollusca, Brachiopods, Echinoids, Mammals) is restricted by certain preliminary requirements. The organism must possess sufficient characters (in the fossil state) to admit of establishing correlations between groups of characters. Indeed, it may be suspected in some phyla (*e.g.* certain Mollusca) that the number of characters involved is actually too small for the results to be very significant. Secondly, abundant material must be available of approximately the same age. Lastly, the forms studied must occur in an uninterrupted succession of strata, so that the fate of the character combinations may be revealed. We do not wish to deal fully with the palæontologists' data in the present chapter, but only to note certain general conclusions, of which the most important are the following.

Each character evolves as a separate unit. In different lineages the same character may evolve at very different rates (*cf.* Trueman, 1930), so that in one case it is associated with one set of characters and in another with quite a different level of divergence. Correlations between groups of characters are often only maintained at one horizon. As we traverse the strata the associated characters alter. These conclusions, derived from the study of actual fossils, are exactly what one would have expected from a study of living species. In the latter, the variation in correlation and the permutations of characters might have allowed us to infer that the history of species in time would be exceedingly complex. Groups of living animals are broken up into hierarchies of divergence isolated from one another to a varying extent. We can, therefore, if we wish, separate any two groups by a single differentiating character, but only at the expense of ignoring all the other features in which they may happen to agree or differ. The palæontological evidence that single characters evolve more or less independently of one another is only a corollary of their failure as group-indicators in living forms. From this point of view evolution is a relatively simple process with two main aspects— (1) the origin, in a relatively small number of individuals, of new characters, some of which spread throughout large populations, and (2) the ' trying-out ' of such material in all sorts of combinations.

It does not require a highly developed critical faculty to see that this is a very simplified and abstract account of the living organism. The picture of species as being built up like houses from bricks is very hard to reconcile with any theory of development. The phenomenon of *regulation* in the individual is so like that of *correlation* in the species, that it is difficult to believe that the modern genetic concept of species as mosaics of gene interaction illuminates more than one aspect of our problem. If the regulatory activity of organisms can determine the development of a single blastomere into a whole rather than a fractional organism, it would be strange if the relations between specific characters were not also in some way controlled.

We may consider first how far it is possible to sum up an organism as a mosaic of unit characters. Such a question might be asked not only with regard to the relatively crude, unanalysed specific characters, but also with regard to the supposedly more fundamental genes of the geneticist. In discussing specific characters as they appear in taxonomy we have not indicated how far the taxonomic definitions are incomplete. Actually everyone knows that specificity is not something superficial and external, like the last coat of paint on a new car, but something which permeates the organism through and through. It may show itself in any part of the organism, whether structural, physiological or psychical. It is seen perhaps most characteristically in the apparently unique character of the proteins of each species. Experimental embryology has shown that this unique character may be maintained even in small fragments grafted into an individual of another species. Perhaps some taxonomists would bring forward certain pairs of very closely allied species that seem to differ only in one or two unit characters. But we think it can be safely said that, even in these cases, the few unit characters are only indicators which the taxonomist finds convenient to use. As soon as a comparison can be made on the basis of a sufficiently large number of individuals studied alive as well as dead, all sorts of other differences begin to appear, sometimes not easy to define, yet statistically significant. Sometimes it is a slight difference in habit that first suggests to the taxonomist that there may also be undetected morphological differences.

Such considerations make it very doubtful how far the abstract concept of species as mere collections of characters really covers all the facts. But we may further recall that many characters, which in taxonomy are conveniently considered as units, actually affect many different parts of the body. Such are size, colour (especially ' ground colour '), hairiness and sculpture. It is possible that these could be reduced to unitary physiological effects, but this is unlikely. As soon as we consider structure in terms of the physiological processes that give rise to it, the whole idea of units becomes more difficult. This is implicit in the idea of the multiple effects of genes. A complete extension of this theory would make every gene responsible in some degree for every part of the whole, and the unit-character conception of heredity would go by the board. Actually geneticists are now more cautious than they were in the past in their theories as to how genes affect development. As Morgan (1932a) has recently stated, ' the earlier, premature idea, that for each character there is a specific gene—the so-called unit character—was never a cardinal doctrine of genetics, although some of the earlier popularisers of the new theory were certainly guilty of giving this impression. The opposite extreme statement, namely, that every character is the product of all the genes, may also have its limitations, but is undoubtedly more nearly in accord with our conception of the relation of genes and characters. A more accurate statement would be that the gene acts as a differential, turning the balance in a given direction, affecting certain characters more conspicuously than others.' This view certainly harmonises better with the data of genetics, but it does not enable us to envisage the process by which complex structures develop harmoniously.

This is the question which has been raised by Russell (1930). He points out that there is no evidence for a qualitative division of the chromosomes at any stage of development. Each cell (in typical cases) has the same equipment of hereditary material. The fact that different cells give rise to such varied structures can only be explained by considering the spatial relations of the cell to the whole. Russell is so impressed by this antinomy that he is prepared to discard the whole unit-character hypothesis of heredity. But this extreme attitude appears perverse. Somehow or other the quantitative predictions which can be based on the chromosome theory must be accounted for. The difficulty here raised has also been considered by Woodger (1929, chapter ix, especially sect. 9). He attempts to visualise development as a process of gradual realisation of spatio-temporal parts, while genes are concerned only with the characterisation of the parts. In order to include those cases in which whole parts may be inherited on Mendelian lines (*e.g.* vertebræ) he suggests that, for the purposes of genetics, the part should be defined rather by its dimensions, so that ' absence ' is merely the end term in a gradual process, rather than something sharply different from ' presence.' This idea of the relation between heredity and development seems helpful in trying to orientate our fragmentary knowledge, but scarcely helps us as yet in the matter of character correlations. The characters do not act as separate units in development, and we cannot help suspecting that whatever controls the orderly unfolding of the inherited organisation must be deeply concerned with the correlation of the characters on which the end result largely depends.

We feel that there is a very real difficulty here. On the one hand we have the obvious and incontestable fact that (p. 163) the characters defining species are rather loosely correlated, we have produced certain reasons (p. 172) for not considering their association as of a ' physiological ' (*i.e.* intimate and causal) nature, and we have definitely suggested that it is in the bulk of cases due to the members of species being homozygous for their distinctive characters. Nevertheless we have shown that ' specificity ' may be a deeply seated property of the organism, and that the facts of development argue a close connection between the parts of the organism and an interdependence from which even the more superficial character expressions could hardly be expected to escape. There is some risk, it is true, in exaggerating the degree of this dependence, and we should remember that progressive emancipation and self-sufficiency of the parts which Jenkinson (*l.c.* p. 168) has described.

The question which we have to face is—are the complexes of specific characters in their ultimate genetic representation simply fortuitous mosaics associated either by the mechanism of heredity or by the coincident effects of selection or environment, or are they bound together more intimately by the organic association seen in development ? It is highly doubtful whether we know enough about the basis of specific characters to come to any decision. Such evidence as we have certainly suggests that the association is, on the whole, fortuitous. If this view is ultimately found to be correct, a general question of some importance is raised, and that is—how does it come about that some parts are more independent of the general organisation ? We might suggest that specific and racial characters, being newly acquired, have not yet been incorporated in the general unity of the organism and have not yet attained that closeness of association and mutual dependence that is found in other parts. How such dependence has arisen, and how exactly the accretions produced by new evolutionary steps have their association transformed from a fortuitous to a permanent basis, is a matter which it does not yet seem possible to discuss (*cf.* Chapter X, p. 370).

CHAPTER VII

NATURAL SELECTION

In this chapter we propose to examine as fully as possible the validity of the theory of Natural Selection in so far as it depends upon zoological evidence. We believe that a final verdict on the efficacy of selection may be arrived at on zoological evidence and that there is no special category of botanical data that is of crucial importance in determining the value of this doctrine.

In the seventy-six years that have elapsed since its first announcement the main framework of this theory has remained unchanged. It has been rejected by many and held by others to have a less universal application than was originally believed. We have obtained a clearer insight into the various natural processes involved and a wider knowledge of the historical facts of evolutionary change. But no material alteration of the basic principles has been introduced and, for those who subscribe to its tenets, it stands very much as it did when it was first announced. Nevertheless, the volume of evidence that may be produced both to support and to undermine it has expanded and it is not inaccurate to say that the accumulation of data on the various issues involved has outrun the synthetic and comprehensive treatment of the subject. It is therefore desirable at the offset to indicate what kind of evidence is now available and to what degree of completeness the field of inquiry has been covered.

1. **Darwin's Statement of the Evidence.**—We may take the evidence as presented in ' The Origin of Species ' (Darwin, 1884) as the chief demonstration by Darwin of the efficacy of Natural Selection. In his letters and other works there is a considerable mass of corroborative evidence and reasoning, but the actual marshalling of the evidence for the operation

of the principle is given in ' The Origin.' As stated in that work the proof consists of four essential parts :

(*a*) A demonstration of the efficacy of selection by Man.
(*b*) A survey of the circumstances in which Natural Selection is assumed to work (numerical increase, struggle for existence, variation, etc.).
(*c*) A consideration of the phenomena of adaptation.
(*d*) A survey of the facts of ' divergence ' in relation to distribution in time and place.

The occurrence of sundry secondary phenomena of importance in the theory (such as correlation and isolation) is also dealt with.

Throughout the work Darwin does not clearly distinguish between Evolution as an historical process and Natural Selection as the effective agent. A large amount of his data merely serves to prove the occurrence of the former. The following quotation from 'Animals and Plants under Domestication' (1905, vol. ii, p. 10) serves to illustrate this. ' The principle of Natural Selection may be looked at as a mere hypothesis, but rendered in some degree more probable by what we positively know of the variability of organic beings in a state of nature, by what we know of the struggle for existence, and the consequent almost inevitable preservation of favourable variations ; and from the analogical formation of domestic races. Now this hypothesis may be tested—and this seems to me the only fair and legitimate manner of considering the whole question—by trying whether it explains several large and independent classes of facts, such as the geological succession of organic beings, their distribution in past and present times, and their mutual affinities and homologies. If the principle of Natural Selection does explain these and other large bodies of facts, it ought to be received. On the ordinary view of each species having been independently created, we gain no scientific explanation of any one of these facts.' To a modern reader, it cannot but occur that any theory of evolution would explain, say, the facts of homology and geological succession : Natural Selection has no particular advantage in this respect.

In Darwin's treatment of the subject no proof is adduced that a selective process has ever been detected *in nature*.

Throughout the work such a process is *suggested* and assumed :
its actual occurrence is nowhere demonstrated. Stated briefly,
the argument is as follows : selection has plainly ' worked '
in domesticated races, analogous results and appropriate
processes and conditions are found in nature, therefore we
may assume that selection works in nature. In short, the
proof is based on circumstantial rather than direct evidence,
and the mainstay of the case is the analogy between Artificial
and Natural Selection.

On the question of variation Darwin's mind evidently
hovered in some uncertainty. He clearly thought of it ' as
indefinite and almost illimitable ' (' Animals and Plants under
Domestication,' ii, 292). In the sixth edition of ' The Origin '
(1884, p. 648) he was still under the impression that to some
extent ' physical, *i.e.* environmental conditions seem to have
produced some direct and definite effect . . . with both
varieties and species use and disuse seem to have produced
a considerable effect.' Nevertheless in ' Animals and Plants '
(*l.c.*) he had doubted whether ' well-marked varieties have
often been produced by the direct action of changed conditions without the aid of selection either by man or nature.'
Bateson (1909, p. 209) points out that Darwin originally held
that ' individual variation ' (*i.e.* mutation) was of high importance, but subsequently abandoned the belief. With
these minor inconsistencies and changes of opinion we need
not occupy ourselves.

It is far more relevant that, though the importance of
Natural Selection is always stressed, Darwin nowhere suggests
that it is the only modifying agency. He always laid stress
on isolation and correlation and, as we have seen, on the
effect of the environment. He even goes so far as to suggest
that the modification of a species may proceed without selection—that species may arise and be perpetuated ' for no apparent reason.' He carefully disposes of a (for him) too rigid
and literal application of the theory—*e.g.* when he shows that
Bronn's objection to it, based on the occurrence of parent
species and their varieties living side by side, may be met by
assuming that, if both had become fitted for slightly different
habitats, they might subsequently extend their ranges and
overlap (1884, p. 264). It is quite clear that he thought that
varieties might arise and species might exist without having

any special adaptive qualifications.   Recent studies have much diminished the value of Darwin's subsidiary hypotheses. Consequently the lack of any clear demonstration that naturally occurring varieties do indeed experience a differential mortality is all the more serious.   Tschulock (1922, p. 290) calls ' The Origin of Species ' ' ein logisches Monstrum,' because it deals with the secondary issue before the primary.   It seems to us to deserve this censure far more because it fails to demonstrate the actual occurrence of the process which it seeks to establish as the cause of evolution.

2. **Subsequent Confirmation and Development of the Theory.**—It is pertinent to inquire whether the theory has undergone any radical modification as a result of the enlargement of the field of inquiry, and whether it needs to be restated in a form different from that presented by Darwin.

It seems to us that the theory has persisted in very much the same form as that in which it was originally presented. There is no need to enlarge on the fact that Darwin's belief in the heritable effect of ' changed conditions ' was abandoned by most students under the influence of Weismann's teaching. Although we do not suggest that the evidence in favour of the environmental origin of mutations impels us to return to Darwin's somewhat vague and naïve belief in the importance of ' changed conditions,' we think that it cannot be summarily dismissed, and that more allowance has to be made for the likelihood that mutations may be due to external causes.   There are, however, two points on which modern investigation compels us to revise the conception of selection itself.

(1) Fisher (1930, chapter i) has very clearly shown the effect on the concept of selection of the discovery that inheritance is governed by a particulate instead of the blending principle which Darwin—perhaps against his better judgment (*cf*. Fisher, *l.c.* pp. 1–4)—had in mind.   The point at issue is that, with a blending principle at work, ' if not safeguarded by intense marital correlation, the heritable variance is approximately halved in every generation,' and ' to maintain a stationary variance fresh mutations must be available in each generation to supply the half of the variance so lost.' On the particulate theory the mutation-rate may be far smaller than that required by the blending principle.

(2) It is implicit in Darwin's presentation of the theory that single variants will be ' swamped ' by intercrossing, and that the swamping of new variants is only avoided if they happen to be serviceable and if there are enough of them to reach maturity and breed together. Though even on the particulate theory of inheritance a character depending on several genes would undoubtedly run the risk of being ' swamped ' by intercrossing, much of the risk envisaged by Darwin is seen, in the light of more exact knowledge, to be non-existent. There is, however, at the present time an increasing emphasis laid on the effects of wholesale elimination, and in particular on the slight chance that a single mutant will have of surviving unless it has some selective advantage. A tendency has thus arisen to stress the importance of selection in serving to multiply or ' spread ' variants, as opposed to its value as a means of preventing the ' swamping ' process. This valuation of selection has gained ground correlatively with the estimation of mutation-rates based on those of *Drosophila*. Whether this estimation has any general application is discussed on p. 220, but in all probability the revised valuation of the selective process is a just one and failure to recognise its cogency vitiates such criticism of Natural Selection as that of Hogben (1931, p. 180), who, in contrasting the Darwinian conception of selection with that of the modern experimentalist, suggests that a given mutant may spread and attain a representation in a population, without discussing how it survives the incidence of the normal death-rate.

In addition to the important developments just mentioned, a number of inquiries all relevant to the theory have been developed since Darwin's time, the results of which have enlarged the field of inquiry. It is needless to mention them in detail, but it will be apparent that the advances in the experimental study of heredity, in animal ecology and in the intensive study of variation in natural populations—to mention the more outstanding developments—have profoundly altered our views on the efficacy of selection. It is perhaps pertinent to add that study of the living organism as a whole, its development, reactions and organisation, has also modified our estimate of selection as an important agency in evolution.

It would take us very far from our course of inquiry to describe the changes in the attitude of students of biology and

evolution towards the theory of selection.   At the present time
some students have a firm conviction as to its validity and are
prepared to offer in its support, not the naïve and anecdotal
evidence offered by a past generation, but the results of critical
and intensive investigation, while to others the theory is a
' dead letter ' and an historical curiosity.   It is, for example,
instructive to compare (*e.g.*) the attitude of Fisher in this
country, who regards the efficacy of selection as an established
fact scarcely worth verification, with that of Radl (1930), who
dismisses it contemptuously as fundamentally unsound and
unworthy of serious consideration.   To cite two isolated cases
like these does not give an entirely disproportionate picture
of the divergence in the minds of biological students as a whole,
and the more this divergence is studied the more apparent
does it become to our minds that it arises just as much from
the lack of any systematic arrangement of the unwieldy mass
of data as from prejudice and bias.   Candid and scholarly
examinations of the evidence have been by no means lacking.
The analyses of Kellogg (1907) and Plate (1913) are of this
type.   But of recent years their critical and unprejudiced
treatment has not been followed up and the mass of observations, inference and assumptions has grown unchecked and
little attention has been paid to the logical procedure and the
types of evidence required for the purpose of either confirming
or destroying the theory.

Woodger (1929) has indicated the stages by which a
scientific doctrine advances from the status of a hypothesis to
that of a law.   If we ask if Natural Selection has attained the
status of a law, the obvious answer is that many students *believe*
it has and others do not.   This may mean one of two things—
either that judgment of the doctrine is still clouded by prejudice
or that the data so far obtained are in fact insufficient to
command universal conviction.   It would take us too far out
of our way to consider the steps by which a scientific theory
obtains universal acceptance, the reactions of our minds to
evidence and the part played by prejudice in scientific inquiry.
It is enough to express the belief that on the evidence available
at present Natural Selection has been accepted and its prestige
created very largely on the desire for some such hypothesis.
No other explanation of the wide acceptance of the theory is
forthcoming in face of the guarded and qualified opinions of

Darwin himself and the imperfect nature of the evidence. Nevertheless, the doctrine has not attained the status of a universally accepted law, and this, we believe, is because as strong a prejudice is brought to bear against it as for it, and (for the relatively small body of highly critical students) because of the intrinsic difficulty of obtaining the right kind of evidence for either its rejection or its confirmation.

It is a very unsatisfactory state of affairs for biological science that a first-class theory should still dominate the field of inquiry though largely held on faith or rejected on account of prejudice. To be just, the biologist is not wholly to blame for this position. Any attempt to bring the method of evolutionary inquiry into line with that in use in more exact branches of science and to formulate for it a logical system of proof must recognise that the circumstances of animal and plant life and its transformation are peculiarly complex. The number of variables is so large that it is doubtful whether they admit of treatment and presentation on the same terms as the data of other sciences. If biology is not an exact science (an accusation often made against it), this is largely due to the nature of its data. At the very offset the units with which zoology and botany deal are not exactly definable as regards their morphological, physiological and bionomic properties, as the limits of species and varieties in terms of structure, habits, reactions, etc., are very variable. Furthermore, the background of natural forces, which, either directly or indirectly, is held to modify animals and plants, is homogeneous neither in time nor in space. Finally, the phenomena of growth and numerical multiplication introduce other variables. It is thus hardly to be expected that a ' cut and dried ' formularisation of so many variables would be feasible.

The fact that biological science and the study of evolution in particular are embarrassed by the complexity of their subject-matter affords one explanation of their defects. For the rest it seems that the lack of the exact discipline imposed, *e.g.* by mathematical procedure, has given rise to the looseness of statement that is unfortunately characteristic of much biological thought. There is something also to be seen in the pathetic trust in observation *per se*. Nothing else can explain the fact that wholly inadequate data have sometimes been brought forward in support of the adaptive origin of certain examples of mimicry, protective coloration, etc. The extent to which evolutionary inquiry has become a prey to historical influences is seen remarkably clearly in the frequency with which long-discredited evidence is quoted in support of Natural Selection (*e.g.*) without any reference to information or reasoning subsequently brought to bear upon it.

Procedure.—It seems to us that the unwieldy mass of facts and arguments that has been brought forward both for and against this theory may, for the purposes of this analysis, be dealt with in the following order :

I. Artificial selection. (*a*) Under domestication. (*b*) Under experimental conditions.

II. Direct evidence for Natural Selection—studies of the incidence of death-rates in nature.

III. The nature of variation. Do living organisms vary in such a way that a selective death-rate would be expected to be operative ?

IV. Indirect evidence for and against the Natural Selection theory. Do the structure and constitution of living organisms suggest that Natural Selection has been an important agent in their evolution ?

It should be noted that the following discussion is concerned with two main controversial points :

(1) Evidence for and against the existence of a selective process in nature.

(2) Evidence for and against the theory that such a process has been responsible for the evolution of the lower taxonomic categories.

(1) is mainly dealt with in the second section ; until the point at issue here is settled, any discussion of IV is irrelevant. But as the chance of any such settlement appears to be very remote, we have in the meanwhile to consider (2) independently.

I. **Artificial Selection.**—(*a*) *The origin of domesticated races.*—It is a curious fact that the value of the major proof brought forward by Darwin in favour of Natural Selection— viz. that selection (either conscious or unconscious) by man has produced forms as divergent as natural races and species— has not been finally settled. By some it is considered worthless as evidence and is simply neglected. Others (*e.g.* Goodrich,

1924, p. 117) hold ' that Darwin's views [on this subject] have been brilliantly confirmed by the modern work on Mendelian lines.'

There are really two questions involved here—(i) have domesticated races and forms been produced by the means which Darwin considered to be influential? and (ii) is there any analogy between Artificial and Natural Selection?

Darwin's opinions on this subject in the sixth edition of ' The Origin of Species ' and in ' Variation of Animals and Plants under Domestication ' are in agreement—(a) domesticated forms vary more than the wild parent forms ; (b) such variation is largely due to ' changed condition of life ' and ' perhaps a great effect may be attributed to the increased use or disuse of parts ' (id. 1905, vol. ii, pp. 349–50) ; (c) in some cases the origin of domesticated breeds seems to have been due to ' the intercrossing of aboriginally distinct species ' (l.c.), though he is definitely in doubt as to how far it is really efficacious in producing new forms, and elsewhere (l.c. p. 94) holds that the effect of crossing has been ' greatly exaggerated.' It is quite apparent that he held that there was a rich source of variation for selection to draw on.   There is no evidence of his having attempted to discover how much of the variation referred to ' changed conditions ' is inherited and therefore the basis of new fixed races and strains, though he admits (l.c. p. 49) that ' the greater or less force of inheritance and reversion determines whether variations shall endure.'   He did not, of course, distinguish between mutations and variation due to factorial recombination.   It is clear, however, that in spite of this somewhat ill-defined knowledge of the material available, he held that human selection, applied to the ever-present store of variation, had been effective.   Goodrich (l.c.), in stating the case in modern terms, holds that ' one mutation after another is isolated and bred from, and so almost any desired form is obtained.'

This belief in the frequency of mutation is in radical contrast to the view that the efficacy of selection depends on the progressive isolation of pre-existent hereditary material and the continuous and carefully planned crossing of stocks of known hereditary constitution, by which appropriate combinations can be formed.   The husbandman has been successful, according to this view, because in stock-rearing like can be mated with like, which accelerates race-formation, while the selection of parents on 'performance' (*i.e.* by the quality of their offspring) also increases the effectiveness of selection.

We thus have two distinct and opposed views as to the origin of domesticated races. According to the first they have been produced mainly by the action of selection applied to a plentiful stock of variations. According to the second they are the result of appropriate crosses combined with pedigree breeding and other devices. If the second view is correct, the success of the breeder has been due to a procedure not fully represented in nature and the analogy between Artificial and Natural Selection breaks down. If we disregard the question of mutation-rate, as mutations are perhaps liable to turn up with equal frequency in nature and under domestication, the issue can be narrowed down to the question—is there as much opportunity for crossing in nature as there is in the practice of stock-raising ? If the numerous crosses made by man are the source of the fresh steps in the development of domesticated breeds, and if there is nothing comparable in nature, we think the analogy must break down. The very great diversity of the means by which isolation is established in nature between subspecies and species inevitably suggests that the chances of factorial recombination must be limited. It would seem *a priori* that there could be no comparison between the amount of crossing practised by man and that which occurs between natural groups. Nevertheless some of the data in Chapter IV show clearly that a large number of wild forms are highly polymorphic, and that the polymorphism is due to genetical causes. We very frequently find subspecies and species that exhibit various combinations of a common stock of characters, and even among animals with a limited range, sedentary habits and poor means of dispersal (such as land snails), there are numerous instances of acute polymorphism. Nevertheless we do not suggest that this polymorphism in any way approaches the mixture of genotypes produced in domesticated forms. We feel that some concrete measure of the difference is desirable before this question is finally disposed of. However, the critical point in this train of reasoning is that those who seek to destroy the force of Darwin's analogy do not say that selection is powerless. What they assert is that there is more variation for it to work on among domesticated forms, and that there are more opportunities for the rapid achievement of results (*e.g.* by pedigree breeding). If this is true, the processes of Artificial and Natural Selection differ rather in the relative abundance of their material and the means for rapidly producing and stabilising new combinations than in any more fundamental difference. Though we may admit that much polymorphism occurs in nature, there is nothing equivalent to the judicious utilisation of suitable crosses coupled with the isolation of desirable combinations, when once established. It seems then that the analogy does on examination become divested of much of its original force. If it is argued that selection is nevertheless the transforming agency, it is only reasonable to admit this, but it is a selection applied in circumstances that can scarcely be ever realised in nature.

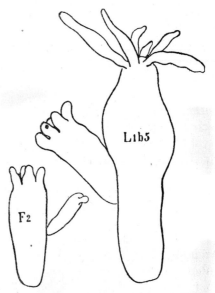

FIG. 21.—INDIVIDUALS OF TWO DIFFERENT CLONES OF *Hydra*, KEPT UNDER SIMILAR CONDITIONS.

(From Lashley, 1916.)

(*b*) *Experimental selection.*—Since Johannsen's classical 'pure-line' experiments several attempts have been made to modify inbred stock by selection. Results similar to those obtained by Johannsen have been obtained by Ewing (1916), Jennings (1910), Ackert (1916), Lashley (1916), and Zeleny and Mattoon (1915). In these experiments selection shifted the mean of a given character to some extent and was subsequently ineffective. More definite progressive modification was obtained by Banta (1921), Jennings (1916), and Castle (1919). It is as well, however, to remember that the ' residual heredity ' (*i.e.* the amount of variation that a strain heterozygous for several characters is capable of manifesting) of one stock may be more extensive than that of another, and that more time may be required to exhaust it. Selection may be carried on successfully over a certain number of generations and then stopped before improvement has ended. All that we are entitled to infer from this is that selection has been successful up to a point. We are not entitled to assume that it will continue to be so. Castle (*l.c.*) considered that the extensive changes in pattern which he produced in rats were due to the effects of selection on the ' residual heredity ' and ' not to any change in the gene for the hooded character.' That this interpretation is correct is shown by the result of back-crossing both the selected types to unselected ' selfs.' But even so, the modification produced was very extensive, whatever the underlying cause of variation may have been. Even if selection had ceased eventually to be effective (' the variability of the stock had not been diminished during twenty (selected) generations'), the amount of change wrought by it was very large, and it seems quite irrelevant whether it was due to a change in the hooded gene or to residual heredity. It should also be noticed that in this case selection brought about substantial results without any fresh stock being introduced.

The negative results cited certainly show that the initial variability of a stock may be easily exhausted and its capacity for improvement by selection may be very limited, unless reinforced by new gene mutations. But it is equally clear that in other heterozygous stocks there is a large opportunity for selective modification. This conclusion shows that the effect of selection is entirely a question of the initial variability of a stock and its subsequent mutations, and that Darwin's general assumption of unlimited variability is scarcely justified. It also points our way to the really crucial question—viz. how frequent in nature are species which are heterozygous for many characters ? As we saw in Chapter II (p. 26), we are still far from being able to give an answer.

II. **Direct Evidence for Natural Selection.**[1]—*The incidence of death-rates in nature.*—The facts and arguments dealt with in the preceding section do not, of course, cast any light on what is, after all, the most important question—viz. Is there a selective process in nature ? As we have already pointed out, for Darwin

---

[1] In the present chapter we use the term ' adaptation ' in a comprehensive sense. In Chapter IX it is subjected to more detailed analysis.

himself, Natural Selection appeared as an inevitable consequence of certain satisfactorily established phenomena, viz. numerical multiplication, competition, etc. He did not produce evidence for the actual occurrence of a differential death-rate.

Pearl (1930) has set out concisely the requirements of a proof that Natural Selection has altered a race. These are :

(a) Proof of somatic difference between survivors and eliminated.

(b) Proof of genetic differences between survivors and eliminated.

(c) Proof of effective time of elimination.

(d) Proof of the somatic alteration of the race.

(e) Proof of the genetic alteration of the race.

(c) implies that selection must occur before reproduction is complete.

As will be seen from the examination of the direct evidence (pp. 196–212), most of the investigators have concerned themselves with (a) only.

Before considering the evidence that a selective process is or is not actually at work, certain general considerations as to the death-rates of animals in nature may be brought forward. Thompson and Parker (1928) in their study of *Pyrausta nubilalis*, the European Cornborer, find that at least 90 per cent. of the young larvæ are killed off before any predators or parasites have begun their attack. According to these authors, ' more individuals disappear because of their highly restricted adaptive powers than through all the other controlling factors taken together.' The young larvæ are extremely delicate. If they fall to the ground or into a drop of water, or if they emerge when the food-plant is too hard, they are likely to die. A slight injury or deprivation of food for a short period causes a high mortality. In a rapidly fluctuating environment many larvæ, even though on the whole better adapted than their neighbours, must succumb without a chance of justifying themselves.

Salt recently (1931), in a very careful study of the Wheatstem Sawfly (*Cephus pallipes*), found that a part only of the larval mortality accounted for 89 per cent. of the pre-adult individuals. Thorpe (1930a) found in the Pine-shoot Moth (*Rhyacionia buoliana*) that the insect parasites account for about 60 per cent. of the larvæ. In all insects death from unfavourable climatic conditions is also very frequent in the early stages, so far as the facts have been recorded (Uvarov, 1931). Kirkpatrick (1923) has provided an elaborate account of the Egyptian cotton-seed bug (*Oxycarenus hyalinipennis*). At the end of the breeding season this insect may be present at the rate of 7–12 millions per acre, while at the end of the winter not more than 100,000 per acre are left. During the whole of his work no parasitic or predacious enemies were discovered, and all effective control appears to result from the operation of normal weather conditions. Sunlight kills some of the eggs, and some of the young nymphs die, possibly through lack of moisture or failure to penetrate the boll quickly enough. Heavy rainfalls and the harvesting of the bolls account for many more. During the winter the death-rate from drought must be enormous, especially as many of the bugs leave their hibernacula on warm days and probably fail to regain suitable quarters when the weather alters. Yet, in spite of its rather imperfect adaptation, this species can maintain itself in great abundance.

Russell (1932) has summarised some of the data as to the fluctuations of certain marine organisms. The populations of bottom-living Mollusca seem to undergo extreme variation, and in certain cases it is thought that this is due to variations in the course of currents by which the larvæ are carried passively. When the larvæ settle down, only those survive which happen to have drifted over areas of suitable bottom. The very large mortality amongst those which have been carried to unsuitable areas must be largely random. It would, in fact, appear to be a general rule that the more directly dependent an organism is on its environment, the larger will be the element of chance in the death-rate.

In many mammals, as Elton's well-known studies have shown, the decimation of the population is a periodic phenomenon. A period during which the death-rate is relatively low culminates in an enormous increase in numbers, leading in turn to a catastrophic reduction, often as a result of an epidemic. Many examples are given by Elton in his book, ' Animal Ecology and Evolution ' (1930, pp. 19–23).

It has been argued (*e.g.* Muir, 1931) that because 90 per cent. of the individuals perish before reaching maturity, a selective process acting purely on the adult can have little effect. It is true that selection amongst larvæ (so far as this heavy death-rate is not purely random) will tend to produce unexpected results in the adult stage, the most numerous types of the latter being chosen for the characters they bore as larvæ and not for their actual facies. But this will not avert the effect of selection amongst the adults (see Fisher, 1930, p. 134). If there is a differential death-rate amongst the adults, a certain genotype will be favoured, and this form will occur in an increased proportion amongst the larvæ. As long as the incidence of larval mortality does not actually tell against the adult character, then, on the theory of chances, the survivors of the larval holocaust will still show on the average the same increased proportion of the adult genotype.

The real conclusions that should be drawn from such studies as those we have mentioned appear to be the following :

α. Most animals—all those with a high rate of reproduction—have a very high mortality, especially in the early stages.

β. This mortality often appears to be random : but the appearance may be deceptive, and certainly a random death-rate cannot as yet be directly verified.

γ. However large the random death-rate may be, it cannot nullify the effect of any selective death-rate, even if very much smaller. This is at least true when two populations in competition are both of considerable size, and is necessarily a result of the *random* nature of the main death-rate—*i.e.* the proportions of each form can be influenced only by death-rates which are not random. Actually, if one population were very small, as when a rare mutant competes with the dominant type of a species, a large number of trials might be necessary before the inherent impartiality of the random process was actually observed—*i.e.* the mutation might have to occur often enough for the mutant individuals in the aggregate to form a fairly large population.

δ. The only satisfactory way to investigate whether death-rates are selective or not is to study in nature the actual death-rates of competing forms, whether species, varieties or mutants.

The view has been expressed that ' it is impossible to conceive that the detailed action of Natural Selection could ever be completely within human knowledge ' (Fisher, 1930, p. 47). The process might nevertheless be brought sufficiently within human observation to provide direct visual proof. Obviously the conditions for observing an act of adaptive transformation are very rarely available for a human observer. The coincidence of several propitious circumstances, that is rarely realised, is required : but it will be seen that the opportunity is not so rare as Fisher suggests, and that more efforts should be made by field workers to locate likely situations and bring them to the notice of those able to carry out the necessary observations.

Many observations and experiments have been made on animals living freely or in captivity which are claimed to prove either the elimination of certain types of variant and the survival of others, or the absence of selective elimination. These studies are not of the same kind.[1] The problems they set out to solve and the procedure adopted are not of the same order, and it is necessary to show at the offset exactly what they aim at demonstrating, before proceeding to detail the results obtained and the criticisms that may be made as to their interpretation.

(1) In a certain number of cases the observations (with or without control experiments) relate to animals living freely and exposed to a known or reasonably assumed cause of death (Weldon, 1899 ; Harrison, 1920 ; Trueman, 1916 ; Haviland and Pitt, 1919 ; Jameson, 1898 ; Kane, 1896).

(2) In six cases the observations relate to animals either subjected to laboratory or other experimental conditions or experimentally exposed to natural enemies, the cause of death being known or assumed (di Cesnola, 1904, and Beljajeff, 1927 ; Poulton and Saunders, 1899, and Moss, 1933 ; Boettger, 1931 ; Lutz, 1915 ; Davenport, 1908 ; Pearl, 1911).

(3) In two cases the animals observed were living under natural conditions, but the cause of death was unknown (Crampton, 1904 ; Thompson, Bell and Pearson, 1911).

---

[1] Studies comparable with some included in 1–19 below are also to be found in our section dealing with Protective Resemblance and Mimicry (pp. 232–265).

(4) In one case the observations involve merely a comparison between the variation of the natural population (a) over a single season, and (b) over a period of years (Kellogg and Bell, 1904).

(5) One case related to the survival or death of animals brought into laboratory conditions after a preliminary exposure to a generalised eliminating factor, though the actual causes of death were not controlled (Bumpus, 1899).

(6) In three cases a special procedure was adopted, viz. that of comparing the variation of juvenile stages with adult (Weldon, 1901, 1904 ; di Cesnola, 1907).

(1) *Weldon (1899)*.

These experiments and observations are so well known that they do not need to be explained in detail. Series of measurements made by Weldon and his collaborator Thompson over the years 1893–1898 on the crab *Carcinus maenas* in Plymouth Sound showed that the mean frontal width of the carapace (M.F.W.) (expressed as a proportion of the length of the carapace taken as = 1000) decreased in crabs of a similar carapace length. Weldon attributed this to the elimination of crabs of high M.F.W. through the action of silt in the gill-chamber clogging the gills. He stated that the amount of silt in the Sound had increased owing to the building of a breakwater which prevented the escape of the detritus from china-clay workings which was being washed into the Sound. Experimental controls showed the following confirmatory results : (i) Crabs were placed in vessels containing clay silt in suspension. Those that died had M.F.W. larger than that of the survivors. (ii) Small crabs were collected on the shore and kept in clean water. Some died—(?) from the effect of putrid food. After the first moult the survivors were killed and measured, and it was found that they were broader than wild crabs of a similar size—which, on Weldon's hypothesis, is what one would expect in the silt-free conditions.

This work has been criticised by Cunningham (1928, summary), Vernon (1903), Pearl (1917), and Robson (1928). The criticism falls into three categories : (a) as to the external conditions ; (b) as to Weldon's assumption concerning the relation between M.F.W. and filtration of the gill-chamber ;

and (c) as to the interpretation of the measurements. It is necessary to make it clear that there is a definite differential (heterogonic) growth-effect involved in the relation of M.F.W. to carapace length. M.F.W. decreases in proportion to the total length of the carapace.

(a) (i) Weldon did not show that the amount of silt had *increased* in the period under consideration ; he merely assumed that it had.

(ii) He did not take into consideration the exceptional climatic conditions of 1893, which may have had a marked effect on growth and in consequence on measurements correlated with absolute size.

(b) Weldon assumed that M.F.W. would affect the filtration of water in the gill-chamber, the narrower frontal breadth forming a better filter. It seems very strange that the actual entrance of the gill-chamber itself was not measured. Weldon makes no attempt to show that there is any relation between the two dimensions. As Cunningham (*l.c.* p. 193) points out, ' the exclusion of particles of silt must depend on the absolute size of the entrance to the gill-chamber, not on the proportion which that size bears to the body-length.'

(c) (i) Vernon (*l.c.* p. 340) objects that to take length for age is a dangerous procedure. Silt may retard growth. 12-mm. crabs of 1898 may have a narrower M.F.W. because they are older than those of 1893. This objection assumes, of course, that M.F.W. may be determined by age and not by size.

(ii) A more serious objection is that of Cunningham (*l.c.* p. 192). He points out that ' it would follow from Weldon's argument that the proportional frontal breadths which were fatal to small crabs of a given carapace length, permitted the survival of others which were only $\frac{1}{5}$ mm. shorter.' Thus, if in 1895 the M.F.W. of size-class 14·5 mm. has been reduced by selection from 762·00 to 754·45 in 1895, how is it that we find all those less than 13·7 mm. size surviving in which the M.F.W. is *over 762·00*?

(iii) There are no control measurements given of the wild population in silt-free conditions from which one could see if the changes do or do not occur there.

(iv) The control experiments are criticised by Cunningham (*l.c.* p. 196). As regards the first, he points out that it is not stated that the survivors were, on the average, of the same carapace length as the dead. As regards the second series, in which the M.F.W. under silt-free conditions was larger than in the wild population, it is rather difficult to give the facts in a condensed form, because there was a preliminary mortality due (?) to the presence of putrescence in the water, and the shells of the survivors at the first moult were less than those of wild forms, which Weldon put down to the fact that those of greater M.F.W. were selectively eliminated. Cunningham makes it amply clear: (*a*) that necessary comparisons were not made, and (*b*) that Weldon omitted to consider the effect of food-supply and temperature on the size of the experimental animals.

On the whole the objections raised as to Weldon's results are so serious that the latter cannot be accepted as good evidence for the efficacy of selection.

(2) *Harrison (1920).*

In the Cleveland district of Yorkshire a colony of the moth *Oporabia autumnata* was originally broken into two parts, one ultimately inhabiting a coniferous wood, the other a birch wood. The colour of the two colonies was found to differ, those moths living in the birch wood being paler (no statistics given). Harrison attributes the difference to the elimination by nocturnal birds and bats of the pale forms in the coniferous wood, on the assumption that these moths are more conspicuous. His proof is that of 15 pairs of wings (remains of moths attacked by enemies [?]) found on the ground in that wood the majority (numbers not given) are pale, though in the total population the dark forms outnumber the pale in the ratio of 25 : 1. He states that owls, nightjars and bats are numerous in the pine wood, while in the birch wood few, if any, birds occur, as the wood is not well grown enough to afford cover.

This case is very summarily expressed. The number of likely enemies in the two woods is not discussed in detail. It is quite uncertain how the individuals whose remains were found actually met their fate—*i.e.* whether they were killed by birds or bats. There is no statement as to how many of the 15 pairs of wings were pale (? 14 : 1 or 8 : 7). Nevertheless if, as he says, the population of the pine wood is preponderatingly dark, a 'majority' of light eliminated forms is significant.

On its surface value this case might pass as definite evidence for selective elimination. It seems to us to be open to two main criticisms : (1) the lack of definitely expressed evidence as to the frequency of enemies in the two woods, and (2) the small number of observations and the failure to state what is meant by a 'majority,' particularly in regard to the frequency of each variety.

(3) *Trueman (1916)*: *alleged selection of 'banded shells of* Cepea.'

It has long been known that birds feed on the common snails *C. hortensis* and *C. nemoralis*, taking them to stones on which the shells are broken in order that the bodies may be extracted. Masses of shells are often found around these 'anvils,' and Woodruffe-Peacock (1909) suggested that it might be possible to detect from the broken shells any selection of a particular type, *e.g.* as between the banded and unbanded types. Peacock's observations did not include a survey of the percentage occurrence of the various types in the local population from which the victims were taken, and are therefore useless.

Trueman compared his shells from 'anvils' with a *standard* collection, not a local one, and his conclusions are also valueless, inasmuch as the local percentage of banded and unbanded forms varies very much from district to district. He also fails to give the actual numbers of shells obtained, expressing his results as percentages, of which the following is the essential result :

	'Standard' collection	*Found on 'anvils'*
Unbanded	25 per cent.	38 per cent.
5-banded	42 ,, ,,	23 ,, ,,

He claims that this shows preferential selection of the unbanded.

Expressed in this form the figures are worthless from the statistical point of view.   His results have been criticised (on the lines already suggested) by the under-mentioned authors (4).

(4) *Haviland and Pitt* (*1919*).

These writers, in addition to a criticism of Trueman's work, supply the results of their own experiments, etc.

(i)   Banded and unbanded snails were tethered to pegs, and the selection by birds was observed.   It was found that both types were taken.   More of the banded were killed, but the numbers were small.

(ii) Collections from 'anvils' were compared with the local population, and it was found that there was no preference as between the banded and unbanded.

(iii) A captive Thrush was kept under observation and, when offered the two types, exercised no discrimination.

(i) and (iii) are of little value as evidence.   The comparison of a large series of shells from 'anvils' with the local population is clearly indicative of no selection.

(5) *Jameson* (*1898*) : *colour of* Mus musculus *on sandhills.*

Jameson observed the coat-colour of mice on sandhills on an island in Dublin Bay.   There was evidence that the island was about a hundred years old.   The mean colour of the mice was lighter than that of the typical form.   Thirty-six specimens were examined : of these 5 were as dark as the typical form ; 5 were intermediate ; the remaining 26 were distinctly more pallid than the typical form.   Jameson states that the island is infested by short-eared owls and hawks, and that these 'most readily capture those mice which contrast most strongly with the sand and arid vegetation.'   He does not say that this was actually observed, and there is no statement as to what types were actually seen captured.   As there is no direct evidence that one type is captured in preference to another, this case cannot rank as one of direct evidence.

(6) *Kane (1896) : melanic forms of* Camptogramma bilineata.

Kane found that by 1892 the melanic form, var. *isolata*, of this species had entirely superseded the lighter-coloured typical form on Dursey Island, Ballinskelligs Bay, co. Kerry. He points out that in this area the cliffs and islands are of a dark slate formation. They are ' haunted by Rock Pipits, Wheatears, Bats and small Gulls (all insectivores).' In 1893–1894 there was a great destruction of the *Silene* on which the moth lived, and a potential increase in the intensity of destruction—so much indeed that in this period the species virtually became extinct. He thinks that the dark form under intense competition was favoured by its colour (as against the dark background). Some additional evidence is supplied from a study of the distribution of dark forms on heather and peat, and more especially of the prevalence of light forms on the pale grey limestones of co. Clare. Other species tend to show a parallel variation in relation to habitat. Some of the Dursey Island melanics were shown to be of a fixed heredity (Kane, *l.c.* 1897, p. 44).

There is no actual evidence as to the discrimination by the alleged enemies. The author attempts to get round the traditional explanation that the occurrence of melanism is correlated with rainfall. We require far more evidence as to the selective value of the dark colour and of the discrimination by the alleged enemies.

(7) *di Cesnola (1904) and Beljajeff (1927) : experiments with* Mantis religiosa.

di Cesnola conducted his experiment as follows :

20 green *Mantis* were tethered to green plants.
25　,,　　,,　　,,　　,,　　,, brown ,,
20 brown ,,　　,,　　,,　　,,　　,, ,,
45　,,　　,,　　,,　　,,　　,, green ,,

The insects were left exposed for 17 days. At the end of that period the 40 ' harmonising ' insects had all survived. Of the 25 ' green on brown ' all had been killed (20 certainly by birds) ; of the 45 ' brown on green ' 10 only were left. All the rest were killed by birds.

He concludes that the ' concealing ' background does discriminate one type from the other.

The results, if we allow for the rather low numbers, demonstrate the value of the harmonising colours. As Robson (*l.c.* p. 213) suggested, the selective value of the colour would only be established for animals living freely if it could be shown that it was accompanied by the habit of choosing an appropriate background. Further, the contrast provided in the experiment would be sharper than that usually found in nature. Beljajeff (1927) repeated these experiments, using brown, yellow and green forms of *Mantis*. On a brown background, out of 20 of each form, 11 green, 12 yellow and 4 brown were eaten in a fortnight. In a second experiment some crows in 24 hours ate 11 green, 12 yellow and 12 brown from the same background.

(8) *Poulton and Saunders (1899) : differential elimination of the pupæ of* Vanessa urticae *in different situations.*

The authors exposed the pupæ on backgrounds of various kinds (tree-trunks, fences, etc.) at four stations : two in Switzerland, one at Oxford and one in the Isle of Wight. The mortality was very low in the Swiss loci, which the authors attribute to the lack of insectivorous birds. At the other loci, where the pupæ were suspended to a background which concealed them (from the human observer's eye), there was a lower mortality and more of the pupæ emerged. Thus at St. Helens 90 were taken by birds (?) and only 8 emerged among those suspended on fences, whereas on backgrounds which served to conceal better, destruction and emergence were more balanced. The numbers in the Oxford experiment were low and of little value.

The experiments tend to show elimination of pupæ if they are placed in conspicuous situations. Experiments involving the concealing value of colour led to very ambiguous results and the authors ' cannot make any statement ' as to their value. Moss (1933) came to a similar conclusion after experiments with pupæ of *Pieris brassicae.*

(9) *Boettger (1931) : observations on the selection of* Cepea *by captive birds.*

The author made experiments on the selection and rejection of various colour- and band-types of *C. nemoralis* and *Arianta arbustorum* by captive pheasants in the Berlin Zoological

Gardens. The snails were put into the enclosures in which the pheasants were kept in such a way that all four types were accessible to the birds.

There were six experiments with six different species of birds (including one hybrid).

In experiments I–III and VI (*Phasianus colchicus colchicus*, *P. c. torquatus*, *Crossoptilon mantchuricum* and *Lophophorus impejanus*) no selection of any type was observed. In experiment IV (hybrid of *Chrysolophus pictus* and *amherstiae*) the dark shells were taken and the light and banded left. The author does not state what background these forms were on, except to say that the dark forms were difficult for the human observer to see, and that he thought the birds revolted from the light-coloured snails. In experiment V (*Gennaeus nyctimerus*) the dark forms and red and yellow unbanded forms were taken and the banded left alone. He says that on the pale greenish-yellow grass in the enclosure the banded snails were inconspicuous to the human eye.

The value of these experiments is very problematical. The author admits that the captive birds are accustomed to being fed by the public. He does not mention how many experimental snails were used. In the two cases in which he claims that selection of certain types was observed, he says (experiment IV) one kind was taken 'zuerst ausnahmlos'; in his second, that the selected types were 'grössenteils gefressen.'

(10) *Lutz (1915)* : *experimental observations on* Drosophila.

This author studied the effect of starvation on *D. ampelophila* in relation to the duration of the embryonic period and on two structural characters (length of first posterior cell in wing and breadth of wing).

Two methods were adopted : (i) the comparison of the mean of the characters of the survivors and eliminated ; and (ii) the correlation of a given character and the ability to survive.

(a) There was a negative correlation between the length of adult life and the duration of the embryonic period. Those with shortest embryonic period lived the longest.

(b) There was no significant correlation between the ability to withstand starvation and the length of the embryonic period.

(c) There was a selective death-rate in respect of the length of the embryonic period in the fed animals, but none in the starved ones.

(d) As regards the structural characters, there was a positive correlation between the length of the first posterior cell and the breadth of the wing and ability to survive. In two cases (breadth of wing in ♂ ; length of cell in ♀) the correlation is statistically significant ; in the other two cases it is barely significant.

(e) As far as the difference of the means (in size) was concerned (comparison of survivors and eliminated), it is clear that larger flies were better able to survive starvation.

Lutz notes ' discordant results as regards [reduction of] variability.' The results are, on the whole, unsatisfactory— e.g. in the difference between male and female. Also the males which withstood starvation were distinctly more variable as regards egg-larval period, but less so in the structural characters. In the female the differences were insignificant.

(11) *Pearl (1911) : observations on conspicuousness in fowls.*

Observations were made on a number of ' self-coloured ' and ' barred ' fowls on a poultry farm in which they were exposed to the attacks of various carnivorous enemies. Out of 3,007 ' barred ' fowls 290 were killed, and out of 336 ' self-coloured ' birds 35 were killed (9·6 per cent. and 10·7 per cent.). Only one year's results were obtained. Pearl seems to have made careful observations as to how the eliminated were killed. Photographs show that, as far as the human observer is concerned, the ' barred ' birds are more inconspicuous than the ' self-coloured.' He concludes that ' the relative conspicuousness of the barred colour-pattern afforded its possessors no great or striking protection against elimination by natural enemies during a period of seven months, during which they were exposed to the attacks of predators.'

(12) *Davenport (1908)* : *attacks on poultry by crows.*

The author observed the attacks by crows on 300 chicks in a poultry run. Of 300 chicks 24 were killed. The constitution of the original 300 was as follows :

40 per cent. white.
40 „ „ black.
20 „ „ more or less like the Jungle Fowl ('pencilled').

If there had been no selection, the expectation would be that of the 24 killed, 9·6 would be white, 9·6 black and 4·8 'pencilled.'

Actually of the killed, 10 were white, 13 black, and 1 was 'grey and buff.' No pencilled birds were killed.

Davenport assumes that the inconspicuous 'pencilled' type is preserved by its colour.

We think that the extremely low total of 24 birds is quite inadequate as a basis of estimating the effects of selection. It seems to us extremely problematical whether the 'pencilled' birds are in fact less conspicuous than the white and black.

(13) *Crampton (1904)* : *death-rate of the pupæ of a Saturniid Moth.*

Crampton, observing that numerous cocoons of *Philosamia cynthia* contained dead individuals, attempted to discover the causes of pupal and imaginal elimination. He obtained from trees 1,090 cocoons, of which 55 had not pupated and 93 had left the pupal case. Of the remaining 942 pupæ, 623 had pupated, but were dead. Only 319 'selected' individuals were alive.

Equal numbers of dead and survivors were measured for length of antenna and various proportions of the 'bust.' The survivors were kept till the metamorphosis was over.

(i) *Pupal stage.*—Estimates were made for 'type' (*i.e.* the average sizes and proportions) and 'variability' in 8 characters. When the measurements of dead and survivors (δ) were statistically compared, it was found that the differences suggested that selection must have occurred in 5/8 characters, that it was probable in 2/8 and possible in 1/8. Where the variability was compared, the survivors were less variable in 1/8 cases, possibly so in another, and not less variable in 6/8.   The reduction of variability is, of course, assumed to show that 'selection' has been operative.   Thus there is definite selection for ' type,' but very little for 'variability.'   In the females there is selection shown both for ' type ' and ' variability.'

(ii) *Imaginal stage.*—Ten characters were examined.   (*a*) ♂ : Selection for ' type ' occurs probably in only 3 characters, possibly in 2, and is not shown in the remaining 5.   Selection for ' variability ' is certain in 1 character, probable in 2, possible in 4, and absent in 3.   (*b*) ♀ : In the females selection for ' type ' was certain in 4, probable in 2, possible in 1, and absent in 3.   Selection for ' variability ' is reversed (survivors are more variable) in 7, possible in 1, and absent in 2.

Crampton points out that the actual characters cannot possibly be of service.   He thinks that the basis of selection is ' the proper co-ordination of functional and structural elements.'   If we understand him correctly, he means that the deviations eliminated are indices of a structural nonconformity and lack of developmental harmony.   This is somewhat vague : but the fact remains that survivors and eliminated are statistically different (significantly).   There are certain ambiguities which require explanation—*e.g.* why there is selection for variability in the females and not in the males at the pupal stage, and why there is less selection in males at the imaginal stage than at the pupal stage.

As this work was conducted on rigorous statistical principles and the numbers were fairly high, it is to be accepted as proving that the survivors at each stage differed structurally from the eliminated.   The failure to find a basis for selection in the characters studied is not necessarily a limitation.

(14) *Thompson, Bell and Pearson (1911) : variation and correlation in* Vespa vulgaris.

These authors undertook a study of the means, variation and correlation of certain wing-characters (dimensions of wings and of individual cells) in the general populations of autumn and spring queens of the Common Wasp.   Their object was to study the influence of hibernation on these characters.

They found (p. 6) that certain linear measurements of the autumn queens are on the average 10–12 per cent. and certain indices 18–22 per cent. more variable than in the spring queens. They also found that there is a slightly higher correlation between the parts of the wing in the spring, as opposed to the autumn queens. According to the principle that selection increases correlation, they argue that ' the only reasonable assumption to make is that there has been a direct selection of correlation as well as selection round a type' (p. 4).

We assume that the authors infer that these differences in variability and correlation were due to some selective agency at work during the winter. What that agency was they do not discuss. They say (p. 6) that the ' fitness for survival of the queen during the period in which she is seeking winter quarters, hibernating and starting to form a new colony, seems to depend more considerably on the ratio of the parts of the wing than on their absolute size.' The only further light cast on this matter is the authors' analogy (*l.c.*) between the wing of an insect and the parts of an aeroplane, reliability in the latter being due to minute details comparable to those of the insect wing !

This case is similar to that of *Philosamia* (p. 206), and we should rather expect that the cell-characters of the wing were correlated with some physiological character determining survival rather than that it was of actual utility. We are somewhat doubtful as to the value of inferences based merely on the reduction of variability. To assign the latter to selection on purely theoretical grounds seems to us dangerous, and we think other causes reducing variability might be operative. There is no proof that the characters ' selected ' are heritable.

(15) *Kellogg and Bell (1904) : observations on the variation of various species of insects.*

The authors point out that the variation in various insects, in spite of exposure for a season to all kinds of rigorous external factors, is just as great as at the beginning of the season, and none of the types of variation is eliminated. This is very well seen in the ladybird (*Hippodamia convergens*) and in the Honey Bee (*Apis mellifera*).

' Determinate variation ' (*i.e.* statistical change in the constitution of the population) is seen in the pattern of the elytra of the beetle *Diabrotica soror* over the period 1895–1902. The difference consisted in the dominance in 1901–1902 of a modal condition which was not dominant in 1895.

Beyond stating that it is not likely that the change in position of the spots or the elytra would serve as a basis for selection, the authors produce no evidence that the change is not due to selection.

(16) *Bumpus (1899)* : *alleged selective elimination in* Passer domesticus.

' After a severe storm of snow, rain and sleet a number of English Sparrows were brought to the Anatomical Laboratory of Brown University. Seventy-two of these birds revived : sixty-four perished.' It was the purpose of Bumpus's study to show that the birds which perished did not die from accident but because they were physically disqualified, and that the survivors lived because they possessed ' certain physical characters' which enabled them to withstand a particular phase of selective elimination. He measured 9 characters (*e.g.* length, weight, alar extent, etc.) of the dead and survivors. He divided his specimens according as they were adult or young and male or female. He found that there were differences in some characters as between survivors and eliminated and not in others, and he assumed (p. 213) that there were funda- mental differences between the dead and the survivors. As the numbers in each group thus discriminated are low (the total which died was only 64, of which 24 were adult ♂ and 12 were young ♂), and as he compared the averages of the various groups, it will strike the modern statistical biologist that his conclusion is premature. These observations, sug- gesting a selective elimination, have been widely cited as proving the general occurrence of such elimination.

Harris (1911), however, on the very full data published by Bumpus, produced the necessary statistical constants (standard deviation, etc.) and applied the usual tests for significance. His treatment of the subject is rather peculiar. He admitted that, by applying the usual statistical tests, differences of a statistical value varying from ' significant' to ' possibly significant' were actually to be obtained from Bumpus's figures for some (but by no means all) of the charac- ters. Yet he concludes that, ' though the cautious biometrician

P

would hesitate to allow that Bumpus's case was proved, the action of selection is likely.' He stresses the fact that the number of individual variates is low, and is clearly divided between an adherence to a rigid statistical principle (which, when applied to the data, gives 'significant' differences in some characters) and an apprehension that, on account of the paucity of data, the statistical principle may be fallacious. Incidentally we may note that we have applied the current tests to Bumpus's figures as a check on Harris's procedure and find that his conclusions as to 'significance' are valid.

The matter might be left to remain in this rather unsatisfactory condition, with the admission that, statistically at least, Bumpus's conclusions are sound. But there is, however, a further question to be decided, which we think invalidates these observations at their source. As one of us has pointed out (Robson, *l.c.* p. 214), the cause of the death of the eliminated is uncertain. What Bumpus did was to compare the birds which recovered with those which died after being blown down. All the birds were, it is admitted, blown down by the gale ; but those which did not recover might have died from various causes (*e.g.* from dashing in their fall against a stone or a tree, from exposure and starvation, from the immediate effects of strain and exhaustion). In short, the birds might, we agree, be all blown down on account of some structural deficiency, but their survival or death after failure to sustain themselves in the gale might very easily be determined by quite a distinct set of causes. In short, we are plainly dealing with two distinct phenomena—the fact of being blown down on the one hand, and the multiple causes of death connected with the subsequent experience of those who were blown down. It might be urged that the acid test is really between death and survival—that at all events we know there were some significant differences between those which died and those which survived. But in reply we must, obviously, ask how any structural character (such as weight, wing spread, etc.) which might determine whether a bird was blown down or not, could determine whether a bird survived or died after it was blown down—a result which might be determined by such purely accidental causes as whether it hit a branch or stone in its fall, or whether it was able to withstand exposure and shock.

Finally, if all the birds had been left out of doors, probably all would have died, and the real selective agency was human interference (*i.e.* the bringing of the birds into the laboratory). It is most unfortunate that Bumpus did not investigate the actual cause of death in each case, and for this reason (coupled, of course, with the actual paucity of individual variates) we hold that the quite clearly established ' significant ' differences are suspect.

(17) *Weldon (1901) : comparison of earlier and later whorls of the shell of* Clausilia laminata.

A series of measurements of the earlier and later whorls of the shell (made on sections) shows that ' the mean spiral of the young generation is sensibly identical with that of the parental generation [earlier as opposed to later whorls] and is not altered by any process of selective destruction.'

As, however, the variability of younger shells is greater than that of adults, it is inferred that there is ' periodic selection ' (reduction of variation at each generation). The fact that the mean remains the same is held to be an indication of the effect of selection.

We are not convinced that if a difference between the early whorls and the later had been shown, it would necessarily imply that the difference was due to selection as Weldon suggests. It seems that any changes that might have been found could have been due to environmental causes. As for the reduction of variability in the adult stage, we think that this might possibly have been due to greater plasticity of the young, as well as to selection.

(18) *Weldon (1904) : shells of* Clausilia itala.

The same type of measurement was undertaken on the shells of 100 young and 100 adult *C. itala.* No difference between the young and adult shells was found. Weldon suggests that this might be explained in two main ways : either that (1) no selection was operating, or (2) the lack of selection was due to the specimens having been collected in the spring. If measured in the autumn differences might have been shown (?).

(19) *di Cesnola (1907)*: *comparison of earlier and later whorls of the shell of* Helix (= *Arianta*) arbustorum.

The procedure was identical with that of the preceding studies (17), (18). The characters of the young shells were similar to those of the adult. 'The mean character does not sensibly alter during growth, but is the same in young and adult.' The same difference in the variability of young and older shells was found as in *Clausilia*, and was held to prove the occurrence of periodic selection.

The same criticism may be applied to this study as to (17).

We give in tabular form what we hope is a fair assessment of the value of these studies.

(1) Selection probable	(2) Analogy with natural process doubtful	(3) Other explanations possible
Lutz (1915) ?	di Cesnola (1904)	Weldon (1899)
Crampton (1904)	Poulton and	Kane (1896)
Thompson, Bell and	Saunders (1899)	Lutz (1915)
Pearson (1911)	Boettger (1932)	Weldon (1901)
	Bumpus (1899)	di Cesnola (1907)
	Beljajeff (1927)	

(4) Procedure defective : or numbers too low	(5) No selection found	(6) Selective agency unknown or doubtful
Harrison (1920)	Haviland and Pitt	Harrison (1920)
Trueman (1916)	(1919)	Jameson (1898)
Jameson (1898)	Pearl (1911) ?	Kane (1896)
Kane (1896)	Weldon (1904)	Crampton (1904)
Boettger (1931)		Thompson, Bell and
Davenport (1908)		Pearson (1911)
Kellogg and Bell		Bumpus (1899)
(1904)		
Bumpus (1899)		

It will be seen that on this analysis (which should be checked by reference to the actual accounts) there is a little evidence suggesting a significant difference between survivors and eliminated. It must be admitted that any amount of *positive* evidence, however slight, is of value. On the other hand, it is of the greatest importance that, in all the cases in which selective elimination appears to be established, the distinguishing features of the survivors are not known to be heritable.

Lastly, we think it desirable to give in a condensed form some direct observations on the alteration of the composition of natural populations. Sometimes, as in (4), a 'new' character appears to have spread ; but we do not really know that the character is a novelty in the history of the species.

(1) Adlerz (1902*a*). The butterfly *Polyommatus vigaureae* was very abundant in Sweden in 1896. A peculiar form of the female (with blue spots on the light band of upper side of hind wings) was common. In 1897 the species was not common. The variety was relatively and absolutely rarer. In 1901 the species was again very abundant and the variety made up about half the individuals. Ford and Ford (1930) have found that in *Melitaea aurinia* there is an increase of variation during local numerical increase.

(2) Scudder (1889, p. 1213). *Pieris rapae*, first introduced at Quebec in 1860, appeared in New York in 1868. A variety with yellow wings (var. *novangliae*) first appeared in Canada in 1864. Later it was found also in the United States, where it occurred about once in 500 specimens. It died out again by 1878. In Europe the variety is excessively rare, only one or two doubtful specimens being on record.

(3) Probably the best instance of the appearance and multiplication of a new variant is that of the melanic form (*doubledayaria*) of *Amphidasys betularia*, the Peppered Moth. The actual facts are too well known to require repetition here. It is enough to remind the reader that (*a*) the melanic variety first appeared near Manchester in 1850 and has in many places in England now completely superseded the type form ; (*b*) a similar course of events occurred on the Continent, though beginning at a later date ; and (*c*) in the twenty-seven years that have elapsed since the original study (summarised by Doncaster, 1906) was made, the melanic forms (originally largely restricted to the North and Midlands of England) are now far more frequent in the South. An analogous north to south invasion is found in France (Demaison, 1927, p. 295). (*d*) Similar melanic forms occur in other genera in the same areas. (*e*) We can find no evidence in contradiction of

Bateson's contention (1913, p. 138) that between *doubledayaria* and the typical form there are few if any intermediates.

Three explanations of this history are available.

(a) Protective value of the dark colour in industrial districts.

It has been suggested that the dark colour affords a protective resemblance (against birds) to smoke-darkened foliage, etc., in the industrial districts in which it undoubtedly arose. This has been answered by Bateson, who, reasonably enough, points out (i) that *doubledayaria* is conspicuous anywhere except on actually black materials, and (ii) that it occurs in country districts between the towns. Bateson's criticisms overlook the possibility that, if even 1 per cent. of the *doubledayaria* were protected when on very sooty or dirty backgrounds, it would give them an advantage. Furthermore, Mr. A. W. McKenny Hughes informs us that Bateson very much minimises the concealing effect of the dusky colour, which Mr. Hughes asserts is marked. It should be noted that Kane (*supra*, p. 202) claims that dark forms of moths are protectively coloured on certain rocks on the coast of W. Ireland, and have multiplied accordingly.

(b) Greater viability, etc., of the melanics.

Bowater (1914, pp. 300, 303, 308) states that in the course of breeding experiments on *Spilosoma lubricipeda* and other forms the melanics are larger and stronger than the type and are double-brooded. This was not actually observed by him in *betularia*, and, in view of the capricious incidence of physiological variation, we would hesitate to assert that it is likely to be also found in that species.[1] It nevertheless remains a possible explanation.

(c) Harrison's theory.

As far as the actual origin of the melanic character is concerned, Harrison and Garrett (1926) and Harrison (1928) endeavoured to show that it was due to the salts contained in the soot-covered food in industrial areas. They did not commit themselves to theorising how the mutants spread beyond the industrialised area.

---

[1] Harrison (1928) stated that the artificially produced melanics of other moths are more delicate than the typical form.

It is a great pity that this problem has not been attacked more resolutely. There has been a tendency to accept someone's provisional hypothesis and let the matter drop. The fact remains that we have a very clear-cut case of evolutionary change transforming a population rapidly and under our eyes, and the cause has not yet been ascertained. We believe that Bowater's discovery should be followed up.

(4) Ford (1924, p. 733) states that the varietal constitution of *Heodes phlaeas* is noticeably different in Madeira from that observed by Wollaston seventy years previously.

(5) Crampton (1925, p. 17) found that the distribution of the variants of *Partula suturalis* is very different from what obtained in Garrett's collecting period (1875). The number and range of the sinistral form have increased. So too in *P. mooreana* (*l.c.* p. 24) : in 1904 the banded type was 44 per cent. of the population ; in 1919 it was 8 per cent., and in 1923 it was 2 per cent. In *mooreana* also a ' new ' colour-variety has arisen since 1875.

(6) Woltereck (1928) summarises the data concerning the appearance and spread of certain new (?) forms of *Daphnia longirostris*. He (p. 39, *supra*) attributes their origin to environmental causes—a view which is attacked by Wesenberg-Lund (1926), who advances an adaptive explanation. This subject is in its present stage too controversial to discuss in detail.

(7) Stresemann (1925, p. 163) states that the melanic variant of *Rhipidura flabellifera* sixty years ago was known only in S. Island, New Zealand. In 1864 it was taken in N. Island, and has now spread all over N. Island.

(8) Bateson (1913, p. 143) describes the spread of the melanic form of *Coereba saccharina*, which was originally found on St. Vincent (W.I.) and now is the dominant form, the typical *saccharina* being ' perhaps actually extinct.'

Summary.—The value of these observations, in so far as presumptive new characters are concerned, is not very great, because in no instance do we really know that the new characters are, in fact, genetic novelties and had not been previously present in a few individuals which had escaped attention. There is in no instance any evidence as to why the observed increase took place, but there is very definite proof of periodic change in the percentage representation of the classes of variants in natural populations. Aubertin, Ellis and Robson (1931) have studied separate colonies of a land snail over three years in a fairly circumscribed area, and have found a rather limited degree of change in the individual colonies in the period of observation.

III. **The Nature of Variation.**—The causes, kinds and incidence of variation are discussed elsewhere in this work (Chapter II). What we have to ask here is whether our present knowledge of these is consistent with a belief in the efficacy of Natural Selection as the chief agency in evolution.

As already pointed out (p. 183), Darwin took all the facts of variation at their face value. In the most active period of his work at least, he believed that a substantial part of variation was due to environmental effects, and he was at no pains to distinguish between the somatic and germinal origin of variation. Still less did he explicitly distinguish between what are now known as gene-mutations and the variation which is due to factorial combination (p. 189), though he was, in fact, familiar with the variation due to crossing. There was, in short, available for the action of Natural Selection a large store of variation, the hereditary fate of which he did not seriously consider and the potentialities of which for permanent improvement he did not explore. This vagueness was in some measure clarified by de Vries on the one hand and Weismann on the other, and the evolutionary speculations of the period about 1880–1920 were based on the recognition of germinal as opposed to ' fluctuating ' variation, of which the former alone was held to be of evolutionary significance. Furthermore, genetical investigations revealed the distinction between mutation (change in the constitution of a gene or of a chromosome) and the variation due to heterozygosis in the parents.

In Chapter II we have examined the evidence as to the inheritance of induced modifications. We concluded that some of the data suggest that this, at least, is possible in certain circumstances. Although the conditions under which such a process can operate appear, at present, to be rather restricted, its mere possibility cannot but make the premises of all evolutionary speculation somewhat uncertain. As we have pointed out, the problem of the evolution of habit and instinct still requires a solution, without which any theory deduced merely from the study of structure will be unconvincing (*cf.* also p. 300). For this reason evolutionary speculation may be said to be halting on the very threshold of its field of inquiry. Nevertheless, the following statements seem justified : (1) that much variation in animals is seen definitely to be of the fluctuational order, and to be of no evolutionary importance ; (2) that some mutations arise with no apparent cause in the environment ; (3) that a limited number are known to be related to extrinsic factors ; and (4) that factorial combination is responsible for a good deal of variation.

It is necessary to return for a moment to the question we have posed on pp. 28-9. We drew attention there to the highly suggestive nature of some of the recent work on induced heritable variation, and we restated the doubt originally expressed by Robson (1928, p. 254), whether ' germinal ' change is likely to be a purely spontaneous phenomenon and entirely independent of external stimulus. We freely admit that certain gene-mutations appear to arise without any specific external stimulus and in the present state of our knowledge must be treated as ' spontaneous.' The recent work on the induction of mutation by raising the temperature of cultures or exposing them to radiation cannot be said as yet to explain the bulk of ordinary mutation, and we regard the ultimate causes of gene-mutations as highly problematical. With this uncertainty in the background, it cannot be said that evolutionary inquiry is ready to answer in a very authoritative fashion the questions which it raises.

Of course it may be argued that, even if gene-mutations are ultimately due to external stimuli, we have still to account for their spread and multiplication. It is, indeed, theoretically possible that a local population may be transformed *en masse* by the action of the environment. There is some slight evidence in favour of this, but it is not enough to convince us that this is a very important factor in evolution. Moreover, the appeal to a general environmental modification of a population involves us in a number of difficult questions (Robson, *l.c.* p. 174).

Even if we begin by admitting the possibility of some induced variation being hereditary, and thereby acknowledge that the general situation is obscured by doubt on a very crucial issue, it is still possible to discuss a part of this question to some purpose. In the first place, we have to-day enough evidence from experiment to convince us that much variation is purely somatic and non-heritable. Darwin's unlimited variation no longer appears as an inexhaustible fund for selection to draw upon, and the question begins to shape itself in our minds—with this reduction made, are heritable variations frequent enough to provide a reasonable chance that they will coincide with the crises that supposedly lead to selection?

The initiation of a mathematical treatment of Natural Selection was due to Pearson and his collaborators. Pearson himself (1903) contributed an attempt to give a mathematical expression to the action of selection, and studied the special effects of selection in reducing variability and causing correlation. As regards his main theory, 'the calculations,' as Haldane (1932, p. 171) has pointed out, 'rest on the particular theory of genetics held by Pearson, and the results are not in harmony with experimental results obtained in other organisms.' Of recent years several attempts have been made to develop a mathematical theory of selection which is based on our experimental knowledge of the laws of heredity. These studies (Hardy, 1908 ; Fisher, 1930 ; Haldane, 1932 ; Wright, 1931) do not in fact provide any proof of the efficacy of selection, though Fisher and Haldane imply that selection is the only means of accounting for the spread of variants that occur as single or few individuals. Selection is always taken as a *vera causa*, and the various mathematical expressions of its activity are based on this assumption. Moreover, although most authors are aware of the fact that ' all-round adaptiveness ' cannot be neglected, the action of selection is sometimes considered rather *in vacuo* as a unitary process affecting single genes, whereas in nature survival and extinction are probably issues in which the organism as a whole is involved.

As we have already indicated, we do not think any deductive argument can really replace the crucial direct evidence that a selective process actually occurs in nature. But if for the moment we neglect this point, we believe that it is easy to be misled by concentrating too much on the genetical evidence, which is necessarily drawn from a few intensively studied species (for many purposes a single species of *Drosophila*). After all, what we have to explain is the normal cause of evolution rather than the origin of the peculiarities of a few species.

We believe that the study of the *Drosophila* mutations has led to a wrong conception of adaptation, which reacts in turn on the present form of the Natural Selection theory. The Fisher-Haldane modification of the Natural Selection theory requires that animals should be extraordinarily closely adapted to their environment. Direct evidence of this is hard to obtain. Much use has been made of the well-known fact that most of the mutations in *Drosophila* are less viable than the wild type. From this it is argued that even the relatively slight changes involved in most of these mutations are more than the delicate adjustments of the animal can tolerate. Thus it is assumed that the material with which Natural Selection works consists of much smaller mutations, not large enough to upset the general adaptation of the animal, but still big enough to affect the chance of survival of the mutants. Small beneficial mutants of this type have not (or scarcely ever) been observed, but Fisher (1930, p. 19) says : ' In addition to the defective mutations, which by their conspicuousness attract attention, we may reasonably suppose that other less obvious mutations are occurring which, at least in certain surroundings or in certain genetic combinations, might prove to be beneficial.'

It seems to us a somewhat questionable procedure to postulate the occurrence of beneficial mutations when in fact we are so much more familiar with harmful ones. But the argument appears to be open to a much more serious criticism. Both the wild type and the mutants of *Drosophila* are kept in exceedingly artificial conditions. The greater viability of the wild type in these conditions provides no evidence as to closeness of its adaptation to natural conditions—in fact the insect can evidently survive in a wide range. All we can safely say is that the internal adjustments of the mutants are in some way less perfect, and we may deduce, only, that the internal adaptations of *Drosophila* are very complex and delicate (which we might have suspected previously), not that *Drosophila* is highly adapted to its external environment. We do not, of course, maintain that animals are never selected for life in a particular environment, but we think that in many cases it is more important for an animal to be able to survive in all or **many** environments. To accomplish this, an evolution of internal rather than external relations is required. There may be competition between different degrees of organisation rather than passive selection by the external environment. But we shall return to this question in our last two chapters.

Again, it may be questioned whether the pathological character of many of the mutants is not a more important feature than the small structural details by which they have actually been identified. If this is so, the statement that even the minute structural changes seen in *Drosophila* mutants involve loss of viability, is a truism obscured by the way it is expressed. It is possible that we ought rather to say that even the pathological mutations of *Drosophila* produce visible struc-tural variations. In its natural environment it is possible that an animal can throw considerably larger mutations which have no ill effect at all.

The mathematical analysis of Natural Selection and of the multiplication of variants is necessary and desirable, and has, we believe, already led to important results. The most important, as must be expected from the novelty of the methods, are a reorientation of old evidence and the indication of new problems, rather than any far-reaching 'explanation' of evolution.

We are not competent to criticise from the mathematical side the methods of the various writers, but, on general grounds, it appears that three main assumptions have to be made before mathematical analysis can begin. These are :

(*a*) A definite mutation-rate.
(*b*) A definite, even if only average, survival value for a given mutant.
(*c*) A system of random mating.

We shall consider these assumptions in the above order.

(*a*) *The mutation-rate.*—It is much to be regretted that our present knowledge of the frequency of gene-mutations is very limited. Almost all our information (gleaned in somewhat exceptional circumstances) is derived from observations on mutation in *Drosophila* and *Gammarus*,[1] and we have no means

---

[1] It is not quite certain how long Nabours's protracted observations on the genetical behaviour of the colour-pattern in the grouse-locusts have been carried on, but it seems that they have been at least twenty years in hand (Nabours, 1929, p. 55). During that time only one mutation has been detected (Nabours, 1930, p. 351).

of ascertaining how far these are to be considered representative. Now that temperature is known to affect the mutation-rate, the actual numerical value of the observed rate must be received with added caution. But there are more serious difficulties. It is admitted that mutations may be easily passed over, so that the observed rates can be only minimum values. On the other hand, at any given moment there can be only a limited number of directions in which profitable mutations can occur, and it is the frequency of these rare mutations that most interest us. Now statistical methods are not well fitted for dealing with *very* rare occurrences. On this point an interesting article by Bridgman (1932) on the application of statistics to thermodynamics may be consulted. He comes to a conclusion that appears relevant to the present discussion. ' In order to establish with sufficient probability that the actual physical system has those properties which are assumed in estimating the frequency of rare occurrences, it is necessary to make a number of observations so great that the probability is good that the rare occurrence has already been observed.' It would seem likely that the occurrence of mutations in desired directions would be rare enough to make it impossible to estimate their frequency apart from direct observation.

Probably the most important contribution from the mathematical evolutionists is the basic contention that the known mutation-rates are insufficient to account for evolutionary change, if they are unaccompanied by a selective process. It had been for a long time felt by some authors, who were inclined to discount the value of Natural Selection, that a mutation which conferred no advantage on its possessor (or was not correlated with an advantageous mutation) would have little chance of surviving the normal incidence of elimination. Fisher (*l.c.* p. 20) has stated this difficulty clearly. He points out that, as the mutation-rate in *Drosophila* is of the order of 1 : 100,000, ' a lapse of time of the order of 100,000 generations would be required to produce an important change in *Drosophila* ' at the known rate. Thus, ' for mutations (alone) to dominate the trend of evolution, it is necessary to postulate mutation-rates immensely greater than those which are known to occur and of an order of magnitude incompatible with particulate inheritance.' There is thus held to be a strong theoretical case against the survival of non-advantageous gene-mutations. But at the same time, by stressing the rarity of mutation of any sort, Fisher introduces a serious doubt as to the fate of mutations, even if Natural Selection is operative. For if gene-mutations are infrequent and often injurious, as Wright (1931, p. 143) points out, what are the chances that a viable and useful mutation of this order of rarity will always occur in those individuals which are allowed to survive by a death-rate which is probably always at least 50 per cent. random in its incidence ?

It is most unfortunate that all our exact knowledge of the rate, nature and hereditary behaviour of gene-mutations is founded on studies in which the mutations are mainly disadvantageous and even lethal (eye- and wing-mutations of *Drosophila*, eye-mutations of *Gammarus*). Exactly how many of the mutations in *Drosophila* are of this nature it is not easy to say. We have taken the list of 389 mutations given by Morgan, Bridges and Sturtevant (1925, p. 218 and foll.) and analysed them as far as possible, with the following result :

Lethal . . .	90	
Defective . . .	120 } 210 } 226
Viability poor . .	16	
? Defective . . .	9	
Uncertain or normal .	114	
Eye colour only . .	40	
	389	

These figures are only approximate, as it is not possible to be certain which should be regarded as defective ; also we are uncertain whether the reduction of pigment in the eyes (*e.g.* ' pink ') is to be treated as defects : we have accordingly grouped them in a separate category. In ' Uncertain or normal ' are included a fairly large number of types (*e.g.* ' ebony 3,' ' dusky ') which are plainly normal from the point of view of their viability. Speaking generally, it may be said that nearly 60 per cent. of the mutants are certainly defective, and a certain small percentage is normal. Sexton, Clark and Spooner (1930, p. 189) say of the *Gammarus* mutants that they ' would have but little chance, in normal conditions of nature, of survival through the early critical period. Each new mutation has shown greatly lowered vitality during its earlier generations, accompanied by marked abnormalities in breeding.' Once established, however, the mutant strains ' tend to become healthier with each generation.'

The value of calculations and theories based on the mutation rates and types in *Drosophila* and *Gammarus* seems to us to be very questionable. In these forms we are dealing with a type of variation which is in all probability of an exceptional order. Wright (*l.c.* p. 143) speaks of gene-mutations as ' generally injurious,' and suggests that they must necessarily be of this nature. Fisher (*l.c.* p. 19) assumes ' that we may *reasonably infer* that other less obvious mutations occur which are not necessarily harmful or lethal.' The position, then, is that many gene-mutations which have been exactly observed are disadvantageous, but there may be others which are not. Surely it is a reasonable inference that, whatever may have been their frequency of original occurrence, very many viable mutations of the same magnitude as those in *Drosophila* and *Gammarus* must have occurred. Sturtevant (1921*a*, p. 120) even records the natural occurrence of eye colours resembling those of the mutants observed in cultures. From the only exact sources of information on the subject it seems that we can draw very few useful conclusions as to either the frequency or the nature of gene-mutations. If our theories as to the process by which evolutionary change has been effected are to be rigorously held to exact evidence, then we have no option but to admit candidly that, as far as the frequency[1] and nature of observed changes in the gene are concerned, we know nothing that entitles us to erect a general hypothesis.

(*b*) *The survival value of mutants.*—We have already discussed the small (or negative) survival value of most of the best-known mutants. We wish here, however, to deal more generally with the whole conception of an average survival value as applied to the minor variants which may arise in any species.

Apart from the uncertainty as to mutation-rates, the mathematical treatment of the early stages of the spread of mutants does not seem to be very satisfactory. The particulate

---

[1] The observations of Goldschmidt (1929), Jollos (1930) and others on the induction of mutation by high temperatures suggest that in exceptional environmental circumstances high mutation-rates might actually be observed.

theory of inheritance has been supposed to have an enormous advantage over the blending theory held by Darwin. For with blending, a new variant, unless isolated, is always liable to be swamped by the excess of normal individuals in the population. Hagedoorn and Hagedoorn (1921) have emphasised that, even with particulate inheritance, the establishment of a variant from a few individuals almost equally demands the aid of isolation. In almost all animals the number of individuals which breed in any one year is only a small fraction of those which existed at the end of the previous breeding season. This seasonal fluctuation in numbers means that on the average only very common types can survive and the chance of any *particular* rare variant surviving is very small. The total variance of the population is being repeatedly reduced, and the additional chance of survival conferred on a variant slightly better adapted to some one feature in the environment is very small—much smaller than would be the case in more stable conditions. With isolation, though the same factors would be at work, a new variant might form a far more significant proportion of the population.

It may be argued that though the chance of survival is small, yet, if the mutation occurs often enough, it may still become established ; and that though the mutation-rate be low, yet, in a species including thousands of millions of individuals, each type will occur relatively frequently in each generation. It may be held that, even when the population is reduced to a minimum, the numbers may still be very large compared with those in which a mutant might be expected to occur. In other words, as long as a mutant has a positive survival value and the species is not a rare one, the actual value of the mutation-rate is relatively unimportant, at least within wide limits.

In a species with a wide range, extending over a considerable variety of environments, in each of which conditions are subject to fluctuations of daily, yearly or of longer periods, it is somewhat difficult to assign a definite survival value to a particular mutant. The genetic make-up of the species is itself unlikely to be homogeneous over large areas. The idea of an average survival value is necessarily an unreal and artificial simplification. What is useful in one place or in one year will be harmful or neutral in another. Survival value may have a more definite meaning when applied to the population inhabiting a small part of the range, but when the problem is numerically reduced to this extent the actual values of mutation-rate (as distinct from survival value) and population density become highly relevant.

The small positive or negative survival values which have to be arbitrarily assigned to mutants for the purpose of mathematical calculation can have little relation to the facts of nature, and we may doubt whether the predictions based on them are very likely to be fulfilled. The actual course of evolution appears too much determined by special circumstances to be very amenable to generalised mathematical treatment.

(c) *Random mating.*—Practically all speculation as to the spread of mutants has been based on the assumption of random mating. It is evident that nothing approaching real random mating actually occurs—*i.e.* it is not true that within a species any male is equally likely to mate with any female. On the other hand, if we attempted to allow for selective mating, our ignorance of the facts would force us to make very large assumptions which would detract from the otherwise convincing argument. It might be possible, for instance, to introduce a factor relating the likelihood of mating to the distance apart at which the individuals live, but of course it cannot really be held that the degree of isolation would be a linear function of the distance.

In Chapter V we considered this subject and were forced to conclude that permanent isolation of species depended on a variety of factors working in conjunction, and in any one section of the population one of the factors may have a potency which it lacks elsewhere. The species itself must be expected to be broken up into minor populations, and much of the evidence presented in Chapter IV supports this.

If mating is not strictly at random, this will reduce the effective size of the population in which any one evolutionary step is proceeding. It may not diminish the power of selection to spread beneficial variants, but it will make the process of spread irregular and very difficult to predict, and once more it is suggested that the numerical values of the mutation-rate may not be so unimportant as has been supposed.

We have hitherto considered variation in terms of single mutants. We will now turn to the question of recombinations of the existing hereditary material. We believe that this must be quite a secondary problem, since the very possibility of recombination depends, in our opinion, mainly on the prior spread of single mutants through large sections of the population. But, though in this sense the problem is secondary, it demands a brief consideration.

The complex genetic basis of a combination puts it at a disadvantage with changes in a single gene as regards rate of establishment. This disadvantage might be compensated for by a substantial measure of isolation. In some crosses between plants where the parents are rather unlike, the hybrid may be itself a new type which breeds true and cannot effectively cross with the parents (polyploids) : but in animals such a process is almost unknown.

Fisher (1930, p. 96) points out that, while it is clear that without mutation evolutionary change must come to a standstill, ' it has not often been realised how very far existing species are from such a state of stagnation or how easily, with no more than 100 factors, a species may be modified to a condition considerably outside the range of its previous variation.' We have already alluded to this subject (p. 192) in discussing the experimental production of new races by selection, and we saw that in practice, though entirely novel forms may be produced, selection may come to an end very soon. We hardly think Fisher is right in speaking of residual heredity with such confidence as a source of evolutionary change. Moreover, it seems hardly correct to picture a typical character as determined by as many as a hundred factors, each subject to selection. Such a rich source of variation as Fisher indicates no doubt exists if all the segregating characters of a species are reckoned together : but, if the character subject to selection is mainly dependent (as is more likely) on a few factors, the amount of residual variability will be low and Natural Selection would not be capable of carrying out protracted improvement. Fisher is right in saying that there are millions of different ways in which a species may be modified : but this does not mean that all these are available for a single selective step or for continued development in any one direction.

We do not deny that in the last resort gene-mutations

constitute the basis of all new evolutionary steps. We are inclined to counter the argument that, because they are found in *certain forms* to be very rare, they must depend on Natural Selection for their survival and spread, by suggesting that we do not as yet know enough about the mutation-rate at large, especially under natural conditions. But, however that may be, we have still to discover what is the part played by factorial recombination. We have mentioned above (p. 25) that this is capable of producing novel forms (*e.g.* the numerous cases of ' novelties produced [immediately] by recombination ' ; Castle's production of the hooded pattern in rats). Furthermore, the species within a genus tend to comprise very many that represent permutation and combination of a common stock of characters, and may very well (though we do not know of any specific instances) exhibit distinctive and peculiar characters which arise from factorial recombination. There are, we admit, limitations to the possibilities involved in ' evolution by hybridisation,' but, given a reasonable amount of isolation, it seems to us likely that a considerable part of the early stages of evolutionary divergence may be of this nature.

The Evolution of Dominance.—Before closing this section we propose to discuss very briefly Fisher's theory of the evolution of dominance. His case is put forward in his book (1930, chapter iii) and in a review (1931). Ford (1930, 1931) has also summarised the evidence. Wright (1929) and Haldane (1932) have not accepted Fisher's hypothesis.

Fisher realises that the genetic conception of ' wild type ' is in need of some explanation. The wild type exists because the majority of genes in animals in nature are dominant to their allelomorphs which have been detected in the laboratory. Fisher endeavours to explain the dominance characteristic of the wild form as the result of selection of the gene-complex in such a direction that any given mutant will produce the minimum possible visible effect in the heterozygote. It is assumed from the data on *Drosophila* that most mutants, especially the easily visible ones, will be harmful, and therefore it will be to the advantage of the species to suppress their effects as far as possible, *i.e.* in the heterozygote. The arguments in favour of the theory may be considered under three headings.

(a) Observations indicating that dominance is not a fixed property of the gene, but depends on the genetic environment in which it is placed. We shall not deal with this, since we consider that, as far as it goes, the evidence is satisfactory.

(b) Observations indicating that *Drosophila* mutants are recessive in their external effects but neutral in certain slight internal ones.

(c) Observations on certain cases of polymorphism, in which the phenomenon of dominance presents unusual features.

(b) Ford (1931, p. 37) and Fisher (1931, p. 353) have pointed out that certain *Drosophila* mutants produce a visible effect (*e.g.* white eye) and an internal effect (*e.g.* change in proportions of the spermatheca). In all the examples investigated the external effect is recessive and the internal one is neutral, *i.e.* the heterozygotes are intermediate. It is argued from this that selection has acted only on those effects of the gene which are harmful, visible changes such as those in eye colour being more likely to affect the life of an animal than minute changes in internal structures. This argument appears to us to fail in two directions. First, the small internal effects are just the sorts of variants which, in the case of specific differences, are assumed to be selected. Secondly, many specific characters are admitted to be probably of no survival value to their possessors, but are supposed to be correlated with more important, possibly physiological, adaptations. If the dominance of the wild type has been evolved by selection, we can see why the adaptive characters would have been made dominant, but the useless specific characters should have remained neutral. So far as the conception of the wild type has any meaning at all, this is not the case. As a rule we do not know why the mutant forms of *Drosophila* are less viable than the wild type. Sometimes, as in serious malformations, the character by which the mutant is recognised might be expected to have a direct effect, but in most mutants this is not the case. We might therefore have expected the unknown harmful effects to have become recessive, while the small visible effect would have remained neutral. Possibly it is wrong to assume that selection can alter one part of the effects of a gene and not the remainder, but in that case also this part of Fisher's argument is invalidated.

(c) We cannot consider Fisher's evidence as to polymorphic species (grouse-locusts, land snails, butterflies) in detail. All the examples are highly complicated and admittedly in need of further investigation. In order to support the theory of the evolution of dominance it is necessary to assume that a selective process has been favouring the heterozygotes at the expense of the dominants. There is no direct evidence that such selection occurs, and in the case of land snails (*Cepea*) there is some evidence that the attacks of birds on the different colour-forms are indiscriminate. The number of such polymorphic species is much larger than is perhaps realised (*cf.* Chapter IV, p. 94), and the development of an *ad hoc* explanation for each of them would be a thankless task.

Ford has also pointed out (1931, p. 55) that selection in the direction of suitable gene environment will be going on in many different directions at once, some of which may be antagonistic. He argues that the number of relevant environments for any one gene may be relatively small, so that a number of selective processes could proceed simultaneously without interference. We find this argument unsatisfactory, and must regard the theory of evolution of dominance as still in need of verification. There is no direct evidence that most mutants are not recessive *ab initio*.

Summary of Section

The preceding paragraphs may be summarised as follows. If we examine the little we know as to the causes and frequency of *new* variations, we find the data are far too scanty to warrant any generalisation. We are not able to say whether mutation-rates in nature are as low as suggested. This, of course, has no direct bearing on the value of the Natural Selection theory, but it does mean that extensions of the original theory should not be made to depend on the mutation-rate of *Drosophila* as observed in laboratory conditions. The data for a convincing mathematical treatment of Natural Selection are not yet available. The formulæ at present proposed rely to a large extent on assumptions which have to take the place of the missing evidence. None of the formulæ seems likely to approximate to the actualities of fluctuating environments and populations. This appears to hold whether they define the conditions governing the spread of new mutations or of new combinations. The theory of the evolution of dominance has also been considered. It seems at present to lack sufficient direct verification, while some of the indirect evidence is of doubtful value.

IV. **Indirect Evidence for and against the Natural Selection Theory.**—We have seen that the direct evidence for a selective process is inadequate both in quality and quantity. This inadequacy is largely due to the difficulties involved in the necessary investigations. Recent work on insect parasites and some of the fishery investigations suggest that the direct method of attack is not so hopeless as has been thought. Under the stimulus of economic gain—*e.g.* in the Cornborer investigations—it has been possible to breed millions of insect larvæ and to determine accurately the incidence of some of the important causes of mortality, and it is not unlikely that further developments of similar methods may eventually give us a reasonably complete picture of the death-rate in a few species.

We prefer to take this optimistic view because there are grave difficulties in the employment of indirect evidence. The bulk of the latter aims at showing that certain structures or habits are 'useful.' This does not prove that they are actually, on the balance, of survival value to their possessors. To do this we should have to compare the death-rates of forms with and without the structure or habit in question. But this comparison involves the study of the *direct* evidence for the selection theory.

Again, it is usually stated that the relations of any animal to its environment are so complicated that we can never hope fully to demonstrate the action of Natural Selection, and in particular can never show it is not operative in a given case. This argument is commonly brought forward to explain the apparently non-adaptive specific characters. But the appeal to ignorance is two-edged and cuts both ways, and cannot be used to turn apparently unfavourable instances to advantage. That is too much like a marksman who, seeing his birds flying away, says that for all he knows they may belong to a variety resistant to shot.

When Darwin wrote, it was very important to convince

everyone that evolution had actually taken place. To that end he endeavoured to collect a large body of evidence that apparently could be explained only on the Natural Selection hypothesis. To-day the much greater body of morphological, taxonomical and embryological evidence is alone almost enough to prove that evolution must have occurred ; and if we admit that living organisms are always derived from previous living organisms, the picture of extinction and gradual change presented by the palæontological record completes the argument without forcing us to say exactly *how* evolution happened. In Darwin's day it was legitimate to ask, ' If these structures are not the result of Natural Selection, how do you explain them ? ' To-day we are able to answer, ' We cannot explain them,' and yet not feel that we are betraying science. This digression disposes of the argument that Natural Selection must be all-important because nothing else would explain the facts. There are many things about living organisms that are much more difficult to explain than some of their supposed ' adaptations.'

It is possible to cite a large mass of indirect evidence that has been held to prove that the structural differences that distinguish species and lower categories are related to the lives or behaviour of the animals in question in such a way that they must have arisen on account of their survival value through Natural Selection. We propose to consider part of this matter in detail and part more summarily. A word is, however, necessary beforehand as to our selection and arrangement of the matter.

Some of the phenomena and observations put forward as evidence for Natural Selection are by now biological classics. The group of observations, etc., on mimicry in divers groups is a standard example of a subject which has been intensively studied over a long period of years. Other cases have had a good measure of attention and experiment given to them, but not on the same large scale as mimicry. Lastly there are a number of isolated instances in which the field of observation is restricted to the differences between a single pair of species. We have arranged our subject-matter under these categories.

We have not included in this survey a number of miscellaneous cases of adaptation which are usually explained as due to Natural Selection. There are, for example, the flattening of the body in insects living at high altitudes, silt- and mud-adaptations of estuarine invertebrata, and the like. The evidence as to the origin of these modifications is so meagre that it is useless to discuss them. We have, however, included a short discussion on two problems which do not seem to us capable of solution but are too important to dismiss summarily.

It must be understood in the following discussion that the difficult question as to the origin of habits and the relation of the latter to differences of structure between species is momentarily left out of account. We are now concerned with discussing to what extent there is a correlation between specific differences and habitudinal ones. The question as to which arose first is discussed on p. 301.

We propose to deal with this evidence under the following heads :

A. Indirect evidence for the occurrence of Natural Selection.

> (*a*) Standard cases.
>> (1) Protective resemblance and warning coloration.
>> (2) Mimicry.
> (*b*) Less intensively studied cases.
>> (1) Adaptation of torrent-living animals.
>> (2) The colour of cuckoo's eggs.
>> (3) The deep-sea fauna.
>> (4) Cave animals.

B. Difficulties raised by the Natural Selection theory.

>> (1) Specific differences in colour and structure.
>> (2) The problem of secondary sexual characters.
>> (3) The origin of habits.
>> (4) Complex organs and ' co-adaptations.'

A. Indirect evidence for the occurrence of Natural Selection.

(*a*) **Standard Cases.** (1) *Protective resemblance and warning coloration.*

These phenomena are particular aspects of the general question of protection against predators, which includes such devices as autotomy, menacing postures, ' shamming dead,' and the development of spines and armour. We select them for consideration because they are the best documented and most amenable to exact study. We wish, however, to make one general comment which is applicable to the whole subject of protection. Cuénot (1925, p. 335 and foll.) has very clearly pointed out the difficulties involved in our assessment of what may be regarded as 'protective.' (a) The existence and efficacy of protection depend on observation on predator and victims in the field, and exact observation of this kind is very defective ; (b) the human evaluation of any protective device may be fallacious, and can be shown to be so in specific cases ; (c) owing to the enthusiasm of selectionists there is at present a reaction against the cruder adaptive interpretations. There is, however, enough evidence that particular devices are directed against specific enemies. We cannot get rid of the problem by a prejudiced disregard of these.

Protective Resemblance.—Protective resemblance includes all the methods by which animals secure their safety by their similarity to other objects, whether the latter be living organisms, particular inanimate objects or their natural background. In this sense it includes mimicry ; but the latter is dealt with in another section.

There are, as is well known, three main kinds of protective resemblance—simple homochromy or the resemblance of an animal's colour to its background; blending or deceptive coloration ('camouflage'), which includes 'countershading'; and what is sometimes termed *assimilation*, in which not only the colour but also the surface modelling and the shape combine to produce either a similarity to some inanimate object or a blending of the animal with its background.

Homochromy is in general a feature of whole genera and families, indeed of whole faunas (*e.g.* desert and arctic animals). In fact, Willey (1911, chapter iii) regards cryptic colours as a special case of a generalised primitive tendency and an adaptation to a fundamental cryptozoic or hidden mode of life. From this point of view we might admit the action of selection in maintaining, in the majority of animals, a high level of generalised protective colouring, while having little influence on the specific manifestations of the general tendency. The relatively few cases in which specific or racial colour differences appear to be adaptive are considered later (p. 279).

Many cases of homochromy are due either to individual

accommodation (produced by reflex action on the pigment cells of the skin by various sense organs) or to the deposition in the skin of pigments extracted from food-material. With these we have no concern, except to point out that in all probability we have not sufficiently realised that more cases of homochromy are due to the former cause than we are at present prepared to believe.

As is well known, there are some remarkable cases of assimilative resemblance to inanimate objects (stick insects ; *Kallima*), and we should do well to bear in mind Cuénot's warning that these are not to be lightly dismissed out of a reaction against the enthusiasm of ardent selectionists.

In commencing a critical study of this subject there are two general points to note :

1. One of the first things that attract our attention is the capricious incidence of protective resemblance. One cannot help speculating why it is brought to such a high state of perfection (*e.g.*) in Phasmids and yet is nearly entirely absent (*e.g.*) in land molluscs. The ready answer that we must seek the explanation in differences of habit not only begs the question as to the origin of habits (p. 300), but ignores the very real difficulty that a whole group of animals, like the Gastropoda, of high adaptability, exposed to numerous enemies, living in habitats in which protective resemblance might be advantageously developed, and possessing in the shell a notoriously plastic external covering, have exhibited very few convincing cases of this phenomenon.

2. Though there are abundant cases of protective resemblance of one kind or another, there are numerous instances of animals which are not thus protected, are either fairly or markedly conspicuous and are not known to be noxious or protected by some special habit. It seems that there is a general tendency to a cryptic coloration, and that in special cases this is brought to a high state of perfection. We are a little inclined to suspect that the latter is related to special kinds of habitats (*e.g.* deserts) which have a homogeneous facies, and that where the background is

more broken it is rarer. That we should find close resemblance mainly when the background is very homogeneous is somewhat important.

To what extent animals fail to develop this resemblance is very hard to estimate. Roosevelt (1911, p. 171) states that half the mammals in the United States either are not protectively coloured or owe their safety to particular habits. This estimate must be largely guess-work. The question is complicated by our lack of knowledge as to whether the habits and postures of animals are appropriate to the situations in which their colours might be advantageous (*cf.* Roosevelt and Heller, 1915). Moreover, an animal may seem to be ' protectively' coloured or modelled *vis-à-vis* a particular landscape and yet range over a variety of backgrounds. Thus di Cesnola and Poulton and Saunders (p. 202) claim to have shown that certain insects are protected by their colour when on a given type of background. As we have pointed out, the colours, etc., could be regarded as adaptive only if it could be shown that they are correlated with the habit of keeping to a particular background.

We have introduced this subject here because it is one of the standard cases adduced in favour of Natural Selection. We are not unmindful that in many cases an alternative explanation is possible. A great deal of the homochromatic resemblances might be due to individual accommodation, or even to the inherited effects of such accommodation. We know, however, of no evidence that such accommodation ever occurs in the higher vertebrates, and this explanation ought to be sought only in particular cases (insects) in which there is definite experimental evidence. Finally, we cannot believe that such causes play any part in producing assimilative resemblances.

Nevertheless, while we incline *a priori* to a selective explanation, we cannot but admit that the difficulty of establishing a solid proof of this is very considerable. The mere citation of innumerable cases of resemblance is plainly not enough. What we need is direct evidence as to how the resemblances have arisen, and that is very inadequate. It is for this reason indeed that we are obliged to neglect the bulk of the remarkable cases of assimilation and some classical cases of homochromy such as that of the flatfishes, and fall back on certain closely studied instances of simple homochromy.

It seems to us that the first thing to discover is how far, in specific instances, particular homochromatic species do match their background. Naturally we cannot discuss more than a few instances, and it may be felt that we have exercised an arbitrary selection. The cases chosen are ones which have been claimed as demonstrating a correlation between colour and habitat on the ground of accurate field work. For this to be convincing in proving the selective value of the colour it is not enough, of course, to find (*e.g.*) a few pale-coloured rodents on a sand-spit. We ought to be able to show that the resemblance occurs over at least half the range of the race or species. We have introduced one 'difficult' or negative case (*Peromyscus*) which clearly demonstrates how difficult it is to get agreement and exact evidence on a subject like this.

Dark coat-colour of Rodents on lava fields.

Dice (1929) and Benson (1932) have described dark forms of rodents from the dark lava fields of Central America and Mexico. Benson (*l.c.* p. 336) is very guarded as to the exact correlation of soil and coat-colour, because 'there are other dark races of rock-squirrels in the south-west concerning which there is little information available as to whether any relation exists between their dark colour and their environments, and, furthermore, one of these races (*Citellus grammurus couchii*) . . . exhibits dichromatism. It may be of significance, however, that the range of each of these dark races includes areas of dark-coloured rock.' The Guadalupe Mountains, which are of a paler sedimentary rock, are inhabited by the (paler) typical *C. grammurus grammurus*.

Sumner (1921, p. 75), who made an intensive study of *Peromyscus* on lava fields, could find no evidence of any higher incidence of dark types on the lava than on the adjacent brown loamy soil. Sumner's tables of the incidence of the various colours on divers backgrounds are very conclusive.

Pale race of Peromyscus on white sand-spit.

Sumner (1928) found that *P. polionotus leucocephalus* living on a white coral-sand island (Santa Rosa) were lighter than the race (*albifrons*) inhabiting the darker soil of the adjacent mainland. This interesting case was re-examined by him

(1929), and he expressed doubt as to the survival value of the pallor of the insular race, as the latter is nocturnal. Moreover, (*a*) the lack of enemies, (*b*) the fact that the white race lives not on the light sand but in the scrub of the island, and (*c*) the discovery that the light race lives on dark soil on an adjacent spit, all tend to weaken the case as Sumner originally presented it.

Sumner (1932, p. 69 and foll.) discussed this case in the light of further knowledge, and seems to waver as to the protective coloration explanation. He admits (*l.c.*) that one is almost driven to accept the latter explanation through lack of any other adequate explanation ; but he is evidently keenly alive to the difficulties inherent in the proposition. Thus he

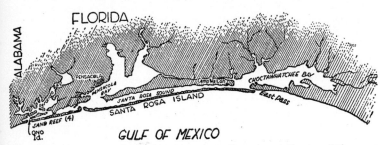

FIG. 22.—MAP SHOWING LOCALITIES IN WHICH *Peromyscus polionotus albifrons* AND
P. p. leucocephalus WERE TRAPPED BY SUMNER.
(From Sumner, 1928.)

cites his own observations on a colony of *albifrons* which lives on a similar isolated white beach but which does not show the same colour condition as *leucocephalus* ; and he is at pains to point out that depigmentation in the case of the Santa Rosa *leucocephalus* affects parts of the body which can play no part in concealment (p. 72), though he is inclined to think that ' pigmentation throughout the body depends, in part, on a common genetic basis. Thus selection with reference to coat-colour could bring about changes in the pigmentation of invisible parts.'

Eggs of Yellow Wattled Lapwing.

A very interesting case of protective coloration of the eggs of a plover has recently been described by Stuart Baker (1931, p. 249). The Indian Yellow Wattled Lapwing (*Lobipluvia malabarica*) nests on bare soil, usually in quite exposed situations.

Normally the eggs are earth-coloured with dark markings, and are very difficult to see on ordinary earth. But on a comparatively narrow strip along the Malabar coast, stretching into Travancore, the soil is composed of a brick-red laterite with dark ironstone nodules. In this region the eggs are red (pale to deep buff) with dark markings, and are again almost invisible. It is stated that rarely eggs of a colour unsuitable to their background are laid, and these are found to be very conspicuous. Stuart Baker suggests that pressure of population forced the bird to nest on the red soil, and that selection by egg-eating enemies has brought about the protective resemblance.

This example is particularly interesting because any direct effect of the environment appears highly improbable. It is unfortunate that the nests on the boundary line between the red and dark soils have not been investigated : here one would expect to find more frequent cases of misfits and selection might actually be seen at work. The actual destruction of eggs does not yet appear to have been witnessed. There are, of course, very many other birds with more or less 'protectively coloured' eggs, but there are few examples in which selective elimination is so clearly suggested.

Passerella (*Fox Sparrows*) (*Linsdale*).

Linsdale (1928, p. 361) shows fairly clearly that the Yolly Bolly Mountains race of *P. iliaca* tends to be brownish in accordance with the soil in that area, which is much darker than that within the range of the other races. This case is not statistically treated ; but Linsdale is a careful and critical observer.

Dark races of Ammomanes (*Desert Lark*).

Meinertzhagen (in Cheesman, 1926, p. 318) has described a race of the Desert Lark (*A. deserti annae*) which is almost completely black and lives on a narrow belt of black 'iron-pan' rock. On the sandy plain beyond the lava strip a pale *Ammomanes* (*A. deserti coxi*) exactly imitating the colour-tones of the desert replaces the dark bird. So, too, a pale form occurs on the white chalky limestone hills at Hufuf. These birds are apparently very restricted in their habitat (*id. l.c.* p. 319).

Galerida (*Desert Larks*).

Bannerman (1927, p. 95) has carefully studied the Desert Larks in relation to varying tracts of the soil on which they live. The general result is rather obscure. He says (p. 97) : 'For the most part the larks harmonise fairly closely with the ground upon which they were shot, but the same subspecies may be found on two or more soils widely differing in colour and composition but still matching closely the plumage of the Crested Lark'—e.g. *G. cristata carthaginis* was shot on pinkish buff soils and drab grey soils '. . . on each surface the . . . Lark was practically invisible to the eye.' He notes that another form, *G. theklae harterti,* was not nearly so difficult to see, contrasting with the dark soil on which it was shot. He goes on to make the important observation (p. 98) that in winter these birds move about and are often found on soils which they do not resemble so closely, the same subspecies being found on several differently coloured soils ; and the same statement is made by Rothschild and Hartert (1915).

Much of Bannerman's evidence does show that some of these races (see especially p. 98, on *G. theklae hilgerti*) resemble very closely the soils on which they were shot. It is similarly clear that the coloration tends to be of a generalised tint, so that the owner is invisible on more than one soil (p. 97). It seems, however, that the birds are sometimes found on soils on which they are conspicuous, and that there is no very definite preference for soils with which they harmonise. We do not think it is possible to say more than this—that, as far as the human observer is concerned, there is probably a definite concealing value in the colours of these birds, but we do not know how far the natural enemies are deceived.

The colours of desert animals considered generally.

This problem has been studied with great fullness by Buxton (1923, chapter vii). He first of all insists on the general resemblance of the desert fauna to its background and (quoting Meinertzhagen and others) of particular desert races and species to particular shades of sand, and he admits that their colour does in fact tend to make such animals difficult to see as long as they remain motionless. He next alludes to certain exceptions (*e.g.* black forms—*Tenebrionidae*, chafers, ravens, wheatears, chats). He then proceeds to pose a set of difficult questions. (1) A predacious bird like the desert Merlin, which, as it hunts on the wing, should be ' effacingly ' coloured on the under-side, is coloured paler on the upper surface than on the under. (2) It is difficult to explain why the predators which are characteristically nocturnal should be effacingly coloured, and why the subterranean form (like pocket gophers) should be 'desert-coloured.' (3) The habits of certain desert birds seem to frustrate the advantage of their coloration, as they come out to feed at sundown when their shadows render them quite conspicuous. (4) The theory of protective coloration cannot apply to animals (p. 168) which appear to be without enemies. Buxton (pp. 168–70) concludes by avowing the belief that the origin of desert coloration 'will be eventually found by studying the effects of physical conditions upon the animal life,' though he admits that no factors hitherto studied (heat, etc.) can be responsible.

Buxton has put in a very forcible manner difficulties voiced by other naturalists (*e.g.* Grinnell, Sumner). It is true that other observers have emphasised special features in desert coloration that seem to lend support to the 'protective' theory. Thus Cheesman (*l.c.* p. 316) points out that 'protectively coloured' forms are found among the ground-breeding birds and not among those which nest in holes (bee-eaters, rollers, etc.).

Colour of the lizard Anolis.

Doflein (1908, p. 245) describes three species of *Anolis* that are of very different colour living on the island of Martinique. They live together, but if disturbed they dash off each to different-coloured vegetation against which they are invisible. He observed similar behaviour in two species of grasshoppers (*l.c.* p. 246), and claims that there is a definitely established type of flight instinct which leads such animals to seek appropriately coloured backgrounds. These cases are not worked out in any detail, and there is no statistical treatment nor any intensive study of the behaviour. It is not stated how far the natural enemies are deceived.

Coral fishes.

Reighard (1908) made an extended series of observations and experiments designed to elucidate the significance of the bright colour and striking patterns of twenty-two species of coral-reef fishes in relation to the attacks of one of their habitual enemies, the Grey Snapper (*Lutianus griseus*). It was found that the pattern was not protective as the fishes were very conspicuous, and they were more obviously protected by their agility and their habit of keeping close to the coral-rock labyrinths. Reighard held that the patterns had no evident value as of warning or aggressive significance, nor as having been due to sexual selection. It must, however, be remembered that the Grey Snapper is probably only one of many enemies of the coral fishes.

Colours of arctic and subarctic mammals, etc.

The change to a white winter pelage has always been regarded as an adaptation to the snowy landscape, less generally as a means of conserving heat. That the coat-colour of some forms bears a steady relation to the type of background is, we think, quite clearly seen in such forms as the Stoat, which does not have a pale moult in the south of the British Isles but shows it in the north. In the Stoat the pale moult is not directly influenced by climate, as it is found to take place sometimes in early autumn and is occasionally found in southern forms.

A still more interesting case is that of the subspecies *Putorius nivalis monticola*, which has a pale moult in winter, even when living at low altitudes along with the typical dark form (Cuénot, 1921, p. 311).

The incidence of the pale moult in subarctic regions is very instructive, and at the same time appears somewhat paradoxical. The Lemming has no moult (Hinton, 1926), nor have the Rabbit, the Pine Marten nor the Common Fox, at least in the north of the British Isles. On the other hand, the Weasel, Stoat and Varying Hare show the change. Possibly the habits of these animals may serve to explain the difference. Thus the Pine Marten is a forest animal, and the Rabbit tends to feed near its warren, to which it has a rapid escape. But the Fox ranges into the same terrain as the protected (?) Varying Hare. The Lemming is a burrowing animal, and in winter may live under the snow.

Instances might be accumulated of mammals with an extensive range from warm into cold climates which exhibit a change towards paler colour in the northern part of their range (tigers (Pocock, 1929)). Whether this tendency is adaptive in origin or due to climate it is impossible to say, but

R

the lack of a pale moult in some northern mammals is as much an argument against the general effect of environment as a cause as it is against the adaptive origin.

No one would attempt to deny that the white pelage is far more frequent among arctic animals than those of warmer climates. But even in the arctic region proper there are forms which retain a dark coloration (Musk Ox, Reindeer, *Mustela zibellina*), and it is not easy to explain this by reference to special habits, etc.

As for the presumed advantage of the white colour, we find that there is little evidence to show that such animals are protected by the colour or that their habits render this feasible. The question whether white forms on a white background are not rendered conspicuous by the dark eyes, shadow and surface modelling is usually disregarded. As for the heat-conserving properties of the colour, this seems to be a negligible factor in winter, and in high latitudes where the heat-losing properties of dark and light colours are more or less the same (Cuénot, 1921).

It will be seen that the evidence on this subject is very inconclusive, and in particular that the incidence of the white moult in temperate regions and low altitudes (cf. *Putorius nivalis monticola*, supra) is of such a nature as to suggest that its origin at least is non-adaptive. It may be noted that Hadwen (1929) presents some evidence suggesting that white Reindeer and cattle are more attacked by ectoparasites than are normally coloured individuals.

The problem of 'countershading.'—The occurrence of 'countershading' was originally hailed as a remarkable demonstration of the value of a particular type of coloration. The whole subject has been very carefully reviewed by Roosevelt (1911). He points out that 'countershading' can be of no value to animals that are habitually attacked from above (*e.g.* by hawks, etc.), nor to animals that are stalked along the ground, for in most cases the carnivore which stalks in a crouching position can see only the line of the prey's back and not the line of the belly. 'Countershading' can be effective only when the prey is on a level stretch of ground, when the belly-line is revealed and not concealed by irregularities of the ground or by vegetation.

The question is complicated, as Buxton (*l.c.*) has pointed out, by the fact that in most cases not only is the under-side of the belly ' countershadowed,' but also that of the tail and feet, parts which cast so slight a shadow that the effect of counter-shading must be minimal in its efficacy.

We strongly suspect that ' countershading ' is not efficacious in the sense originally propounded by Thayer and demonstrated by his celebrated (if too plausible) models ; but we think the subject requires further investigation. No satisfactory alternative explanation of the pallor of the under-parts of ' countershaded ' animals has so far been put forward. It is just possible that it may be the expression of a ' physiological ' gradient.

Warning coloration.—Many of the exceptions to the rule of protective coloration have been considered as examples of warning colours. Familiar examples are seen in the black-and-yellow livery of wasps or the brilliant colours of some venomous snakes. There is little doubt that in the past this principle has been pushed too far. It is a familiar fact that many conspicuously coloured animals actually blend with their background when seen in their natural surroundings, as insisted by Longley (1917). Apart from this reservation, however, it is by no means easy to estimate the validity of the warning colour theory. There are a good many striking cases of brilliant colour associated with nauseous odour or some special means of protection (stings, poison fangs, urticating hairs, etc.).

An objection has been made against the warning colour hypothesis to the effect that a good number of non-noxious forms are brilliantly coloured. For example, Gadow (1911, p. 2) has shown that there are in Mexico and Central and South America 'a surprising number of harmless snakes which resemble in their coloration the poisonous *Elaps* to a wonderful extent.' These apparently contradictory cases have, of course, been explained as due to mimicry. Gadow (*l.c.*) has tried to evade this explanation, but his objections have been subjected to a searching criticism by Sternfeld (1913). The general question of mimicry is discussed elsewhere, and we are here concerned with the question whether the origin of ' warning ' colours is to be explained on the traditional lines.

Gadow (*l.c.* pp. 2–3) has made the criticism in the case of the poisonous *Elaps* that they are nocturnal and in the day-time lead a hidden life, and that against their only serious enemies (iguanas, turkeys and peccaries) the warning colours can be of no avail. Cuénot (1921, p. 512) has further objected that divers noxious forms (toads, vipers, torpedo fish) have a homochromatic coloration. Conversely we find it very difficult to obtain evidence that the striking or brilliant colours of (*e.g.*) many of our British <u>slugs</u> have any ' warning ' value. Cuénot (*l.c.* p. 513) makes the suggestion that the conspicuous colours of venomous forms may simply be due to the fact that the owners are otherwise well defended, either by their powers of flight (reef fishes) or by their hidden life (*Elaps*), and their conspicuous colours are not disadvantageous.

On the whole we have to admit that the frequency of conspicuous colours among noxious animals is high enough to require explanation, and that the ' warning ' hypothesis is not to be lightly dismissed. We think, however, that a good deal more exact investigation (*e.g.* of the frequency of the correlation) is needed, and in particular far more knowledge as to whether ' warning ' colours are actually avoided by predators.

It is very probable that in some of these animals the warning colours have an important function in saving the bearer from unnecessary attack. But there is probably an equal or greater number of examples where one or other feature of the association is lacking, and there has been a tendency to assume that brightly coloured forms must be protected without any very good evidence as to whether they are actually preserved from attack. We may consider as an example the Heteropterous bugs of the family Pentatomidae. A number of species (*e.g.* European species of *Graphosoma*) are brightly coloured and sit about very conspicuously in bright sunshine, often gregariously, so that the group stands out from its surroundings. These bugs are protected by a powerful odour, very unpleasant to man and possibly to most insectivorous animals. Yet we find that the same protective odour occurs throughout the family, of which many (perhaps the majority of) species are not brightly but <u>cryptically</u> coloured, and by no means expose themselves in conspicuous positions. It is difficult to obtain satisfactory evidence as to how far the protective devices of warningly coloured animals are efficacious ; this is particularly true where protection is by means of nauseous taste, since human predilections are of little value, and experiments on animals in captivity are liable to give very uncertain results.   Heikertinger (1929, 1929a) has recently considered the case of the Hymenoptera, many of which are protected by stings, a device whose protective value can be assumed with greater safety ; yet in this group Heikertinger has endeavoured to show that the stinging forms are more, rather than less, attacked than other groups ; his evidence is considered in a later paragraph (p. 255).

Fisher (1930, pp. 158–62) appears to be one of the few authors who have considered the difficulties involved in the development of an unpalatable character, of the sort requiring for its demonstration the actual tasting of the animal.   It would be expected that though the unpleasant taste would disgust the eater, yet the victim could not survive, and no selection in the direction of increase of unpalatability could result.   It has been maintained that some of the most conspicuous and probably unpalatable butterflies have an integument so hard or so flexible and leathery (Swynnerton, 1926, p. 504 ; Eltringham, 1910, p. 109) that the insect can survive experimental tasting, so that selection in the required direction may well occur.   Some of the Cantharid (Telephorid) beetles which have conspicuous colours and appear to be distasteful to birds have also an extremely flexible integument : in trying to box these beetles in a tin they may be clipped between the lid and the bottom to a degree which would cut any other beetle in half, but which in this case only flattens the flexible abdomen.   But these are extreme cases which are not very helpful in explaining the early stages of the development of such a character.   The difficulties are typical of those encountered by any explanation of the evolution of complex structures (see p. 306).   In any palatable insect with a normal integument, changes in palatability or in hardness or flexibility occurring alone would appear to be of little survival value, and we have no reason to assume that the appropriate variations would occur simultaneously.   We are faced with the usual dilemma that if certain characteristics could develop to a certain point ' on their own ' (e.g. if a certain degree of either unpalatability or flexibility were developed), then selection could evolve the necessary complementary features ; but that ' development on their own ' requires an evolutionary process independent of selection.

Fisher (l.c.) has advanced the alternative hypothesis that

the distasteful properties of adult insects are the result of a
nauseous principle which was also serviceable to the larva.
Such direct transference of distasteful properties is quite
possible (*cf.* p. 247). Fisher suggests that the simultaneous
evolution of bright colours and distasteful properties in caterpillars could be evolved in species with the gregarious habit.

In a number of moths all the offspring of one female feed in
a company together and, if a slight increase in distastefulness
were due to a mutation, it is possible that all or a considerable
number of the brood might share this property in common.
Then the tasting of one individual of the brood might save the
lives of his brothers, who would share his genotypic unpalatability to an extent sufficient to discriminate in favour of the
gene. Even where the larvæ are not strictly gregarious, but
the members of one brood live in moderate proximity to one
another, the territorial system of birds, which ensures that
any one pair of most of the smaller insectivorous species will do
their feeding during the breeding season over a single limited
area, might ensure the same result.

It is true that certain distasteful insects (e.g. *Acraea*—Eltringham, 1912, p. 7) have gregarious larvæ which appear, at any
rate from illustrations in the literature, to be rather conspicuous. But there seem to be many exceptions to the rule
(as admitted even by Fisher), and a number of conspicuous
larvæ are not gregarious. The theory appears to be highly
speculative, and we have still to explain the origin of the gregarious habit. In connection with the latter point Fisher says
(*l.c.* p. 160) : ' The view that nauseous flavours have generally
been acquired by the effects of selection acting upon related
larvæ living in propinquity, implies that gregariousness, or
equivalent habits, were formerly used by species which are
now distasteful, though it does not imply that species with
distasteful and even conspicuous larvæ should necessarily
have retained the gregarious habit ; for the advantages of this
habit, among which we may surmise (1) the reduced exposure
of the female during ovipositions, and (2) in the case of distasteful and conspicuous larvæ the advantage of increased
protection from predators, will not always counterbalance the
disadvantage sometimes entailed by a depletion of the food-
supply.' It appears that little light can be thrown on the
origin of the gregarious habit ; its very sporadic occurrence

throughout the Lepidoptera makes the application of the selection theory difficult.

One possible method of acquiring distasteful properties does not involve their hereditary fixation or the action of selection. Eltringham (1910, pp. 112–13) has shown that the cryptic larva of a Geometrid moth may be distasteful to lizards after feeding on ivy, though palatable when fed on other plants. It is possible that unpalatability could be acquired in this way without even being hereditarily fixed ; only the instinct to lay eggs on the particular plant would be permanent.

Direct evidence.—We have assembled in another part of this chapter the evidence so far produced that there is a selective elimination of given types. Some of this evidence relates to differences of colour, surface and modelling, and may be briefly summarised here for our immediate purpose. Ten cases relate to differences of colour, and of these three (Haviland and Pitt, Pearl, Poulton and Saunders) provided no evidence for the occurrence of selection. Five cases (Boettger, Jameson, Davenport, Harrison, and Trueman) are rated as defective in respect of the procedure adopted. For one (Kane) another possible explanation, besides that of selection, is available. In the remaining case (di Cesnola) the procedure is held to be satisfactory and a selective result is discernible ; but, as the animals in question were exposed to only one particular set of external conditions, the analogy with Natural Selection is held to be highly questionable.

On the whole, then, the direct evidence that a particular type is selected on account of its ' harmonising ' colour must be held to be defective.

Experimental and other evidences.—Morton Jones (1932) has published a very important study of the relative acceptability of insects to birds—a study in which the novelty of the methods shows how little the possibilities of testing these theories experimentally have been exhausted. The start of the experiments was the establishment of ' bird-tables ' on the edge of a piece of natural woodland. These tables were provided with water and food, to which a number of birds (seven species) nesting in the neighbourhood used to resort. During each experiment an average of fifty freshly killed insects was arranged on the tray, watch was kept to record the bird visits made and at intervals the insects remaining were tabulated. A numerical rating of

acceptability was assigned to each species in the following way :
All species removed during the first interval were given a
rating of 100 ; any left at the end of the experiment (*i.e.* when
birds ceased to visit the table for food) were given a rating of 0.
By a simple arithmetical calculation (the methods will be
found in Appendix B, p. 380, of the original paper) species
eaten during the intermediate periods were given appropriate
ratings between 0 and 100. Eventually the ratings obtained for
any one species in different experiments could be averaged to
obtain a mean value for the species. The experiments were
conducted over two seasons, and involved more than 5,000
insects of 200 species, and over 2,000 bird visits.

Some of the more important conclusions are the following :

(1) The majority of insects are more or less palatable, or
are at least occasionally eaten.

(2) That, *ceteris paribus*, large insects are more favoured
than similar forms of smaller size.

(3) That a number of species with conspicuous black and
yellow markings or brilliant metallic colours [1] are
very unacceptable. Of the species having a rating
of 25 or less twenty-four have this type of coloration,
while seven are of other types.

(4) That none of the insects with a rating of 60–100 have
these conspicuous patterns ; or, at least, when the
pattern is present, it is hidden in the resting position.

(5) That a number of other types of colour-pattern, conspicuous to human eyes, do not appear to be associated with a lower (or much lower) than average
acceptability. This is of some importance, because
some of the types are the same as or similar to
species which have been hitherto regarded as specially
protected.

(6) That species which have a procryptic pattern are
usually very acceptable. Again, there are a few exceptions (*e.g.* moth with ' dead grass ' pattern, p. 354).

(7) That some of the most strikingly marked and unacceptable species are those which feed (usually as a
larva) on plants of the families Asclepiadaceae and
Apocynaceae, which have acrid or poisonous juices.

[1] Only one species involved (22 specimens).

We believe that these experiments prove that birds have a certain power of discrimination between insects of different colour-pattern and that, on the whole, insects of a black and yellow or red colour are unacceptable. This holds at least for the area (Massachusetts) in which the experiments were carried out. Whether the experiments can be used as evidence that the colours and unacceptability have evolved as a result of selection appears to us somewhat doubtful. The following difficulties seem to be important.

In Appendix C, p. 381, the author gives a tabulation of the acceptability of each insect used. Unfortunately only the mean acceptability is recorded, and there is no indication as to whether the acceptability in different experiments was usually of nearly the same value. Unless the acceptability rating is found to be very constant, large numbers of each species are required to substantiate anything like the true value. Actually the mean number of specimens of each species used was 25 (5,000 specimens of 200 species) ; in only 12 species were more than 100 specimens used, and in only 16 species more than 80. It appears, therefore, quite possible that only the more extreme differences in the assigned ratings may be of any significance. Looked at in this way, the experiments show that birds usually distinguish between very conspicuous and dull-coloured insects, or between very nauseous and harmless or ' tasty ' insects. On the other hand, the experiments scarcely indicate whether birds have a power of discriminating between minor variations in these properties. Probably most observers would agree that birds recognise and avoid some of the very conspicuous, evil-smelling insects. But if these properties have arisen as a result of the selection of small variants, birds must be supposed to have very much keener discriminating powers than can actually be deduced from the experiments. Possibly further experiments on the same lines, employing numerous specimens of a species of variable colour-pattern, might throw some light on this difficulty.

McAtee (1932) has made another voluminous contribution to the subject. He summarises the analyses of the contents of 80,000 bird stomachs collected for the U.S. Biological Survey. McAtee's main contention is that all types of animals are preyed on in proportion to their numbers. It is not yet possible to estimate the numbers of most animals accurately, but McAtee assumes that the number of individuals will be roughly proportional to the number of described species in the group (at least as far as families are concerned), and the number of records from birds' stomachs is compared with the numbers of species recorded in each family for the U.S.A.

On the whole the correspondence between these numbers is fairly close, though, as might be expected, there are also a good number of discrepancies. We doubt, however, whether McAtee is justified in drawing from his figures the conclusion that all animals are preyed on in proportion to their abundance, and that therefore conspicuously coloured and presumably protected species actually gain no advantage. To substantiate any such far-reaching contention the correspondence would have to be very much more accurate and the results would have to be given in very much more detail. If protective or warning colours have evolved under the guidance of selective predation, we can affirm that the following state of affairs must have existed in the past (and may still exist):

That the group in question was attacked by predators.
That certain variants were somewhat less attacked than others.

Obviously such conditions might be fulfilled in a group which, even after a long evolutionary progress, was still very heavily attacked, and McAtee's data throw little light on the problem.

If the colours are of a mimetic type, then all a selectionist need affirm is that at some time in the past (and possibly also at the present day) more predatory attacks were avoided than encountered by each step in the direction of the model. This again is consistent with a relatively high rate of predatory attacks at the end of the process. In fact, the kind of evidence required to prove or disprove the theory that animal coloration has evolved under the influence of selection is exceedingly difficult to obtain. Although this difficulty may reduce the value of adverse criticism, it is also a distinct drawback to the theory as a whole.

On the other hand, we believe that McAtee has made a very important contribution, for several reasons. There can be no doubt that the examination of the actual food of predators in nature is the only way of discovering what they feed on and of investigating the extent of their discrimination. Further, such examination must be made on a really large scale to have any significance, in view of the great variation in the habits of many predators. Again, the investigation of the whole predacious fauna is very desirable ; if only a small part of the fauna is studied, it may give quite a wrong idea of the degree to which any particular group is attacked.

The great extent to which certain groups usually supposed to be distasteful are preyed upon is rather surprising, and cannot but make one hesitate (without further evidence) to treat them as specially protected. This is particularly the case in the Hemiptera, where the malodorous Pentatomidae seem to be much eaten. In other cases, as in the Hymenoptera, where only one sex is protected by a sting, the data are not sufficiently detailed to allow any conclusion to be drawn. The small extent to which butterflies appear to be attacked is rather remarkable, but may partly be due to the difficulty of identifying their fragments. Even though a selective attack constituting a very small part of the total of predation might lead to important evolutionary changes, we cannot but feel that the degree of attack recorded (if it is not really deceptively low) is minimal compared with the enormous changes that such attacks are sometimes supposed to have brought about.

(2) *Mimicry.*—The theory of mimicry is of high importance in the selectionist argument, for two reasons : the large amount and varied nature of the available data, and the fact emphasised by Fisher (1930, p. 146) that if the theory of mimicry is mainly true, then we appear to have a long series of cases in which characters either actually specific or subspecific, or of the same status as characters specific in other groups, are of adaptive value.

Mimicry in its technical sense implies convergent resemblance in colour (and often in shape, habits and habitat) between two animals, one of which (' Batesian mimicry ') or both (' Müllerian mimicry ') are in some way protected or advantaged by the resemblance. The number of established cases of such convergence is now very large, and most of the chief insect and arachnid groups contain typical examples of the phenomenon. It is probably most plentifully seen in the Lepidoptera, Hymenoptera and Diptera. The degree of convergence and the number of species involved in the case of

Müllerian groups are very varied. We find every stage, from cases where a single abundant species is resembled by a single rarer species occurring in the same neighbourhood (*Alcidis agathyrsus*, Moth : *Papilio laglaizei*, Butterfly—New Guinea) to those in which an enormous number of species of supposedly varying degrees of distastefulness are all more or less similarly coloured, as in the great African complex of species resembling Lycid beetles (partly illustrated by Marshall, 1902, pp. 575–8, plate xviii). In some cases the colour resemblance is reinforced by convergence in behaviour, as in the bee-flies *Eristalis* and *Volucella*, which when disturbed often lift one hind-leg, just like a sleepy bee.

We can only summarise here the arguments for and against the theory that such resemblances are due to the selective action of insectivorous enemies, principally birds. The following appear to be the chief points in the arguments :

(1) The extent to which the supposed methods of protection prevent the attacks of insectivorous animals.

(2) The limits of the phenomenon of parallel evolution— *i.e.* the production, in forms not closely allied, of similar colour-patterns, probably owing to certain fundamental similarities in genetic constitution.

(3) The possibility of alternative factors (probably edaphic) determining colour convergence.

(4) If we admit that the mimicry theory provides a true explanation of some of the facts, to what extent does it fail in particular cases ?

(5) How far are the characters involved in mimetic resemblances analogous to specific characters ?

(1) As a preliminary to discussing the origin of mimetic resemblances, some evidence is required that the mimics belong to groups with numerous predacious enemies. It has been established that insectivorous insects discriminate very little in their attacks and often eat protected forms, so they are little likely to be concerned in any selection of warning colour-patterns. It is therefore amongst birds (possibly also lizards and mammals to a minor extent) that the significant enemies must be found. It has always been stated by opponents of the mimicry theory that birds very rarely eat butterflies, and Heikertinger still maintains this opinion. However, there is

abundant evidence, chiefly published by Poulton (*Proc. Ent. Soc. London*, passim), that such attacks occur, so that it is impossible thereby to dismiss the subject offhand. When we consider the nature of the evidence the problem becomes more difficult. Some of it has been derived from the experiments on birds in captivity, but it is generally admitted that the reactions of birds in this state are not very reliable guides to their normal habits (*cf.* Swynnerton, 1919 ; McAtee, 1932). We are bound to rely mainly on observations on birds enjoying their freedom.

We require evidence (*a*) not merely that predators attack models and mimics, but that they gradually learn to reject them ; (*b*) that the number of such attacks and rejections bears a significant relation to the total number of individuals ; and (*c*) that a significant number of the attacks is made before the majority of the eggs have been laid by the female. With regard to (*a*) it is obviously very difficult to obtain evidence. There are undoubtedly some good observations showing that certain supposedly protected forms, though often attacked, escape or are only overcome with great difficulty. We may instance Swynnerton's observations on the African butterflies of the genus *Charaxes* (1926). Yet even here there is little evidence that young or inexperienced birds at first attack protected forms, but later reject them at sight. Though no one would expect that anything so difficult to observe would as yet be directly established, yet the absence of the necessary evidence is a definite gap in the argument for the selective origin of mimicry.

Another question which does not appear to have received adequate consideration underlies the assumption that young birds *learn* which foods are distasteful. Thus Fisher (*l.c.* p. 149), speaking of Müller's modification of the mimicry theory, says : '. . . young birds, at least, do in fact learn much by experience, and . . . during the process of self-education in what is and what is not good to eat, the total destruction suffered by two unpalatable species will be diminished and ultimately halved, if they come gradually to resemble one another so closely that the lesson of avoidance learnt from the one will be equally applicable to the other.' This statement appears to overlook the large extent to which young birds are *taught* what to eat by their parents. Thus Perkins (1912, p. 693), speaking of insectivorous birds in Hawaii, says : ' I should say the present-day Hawaiian birds are very well educated by the parents in the matter of choice of food. It was always a marvel to me why the parents should tend them so long. I have doubtless remarked on it often, but may here quote at random, from "Fauna Haw.," vol. i, p. 404, of that common species, *Vestiaria coccinea* : "the yellow, black-spotted young follow the parents sometimes till they are far advanced in their red (*i.e.* mature) plumage, but they very early learn to obtain nectar for themselves, even at a time when the parents are still feeding them on caterpillars." Again, p. 406, of *Palmeria* : "The young follow the parents often until they have arrived at almost their full plumage, and after they have acquired their full song, but in the winter months these companies are disbanded. In February and March they are generally paired." I think similar records might be made on almost every insectivorous Hawaiian bird, certainly all the common ones. I noted even of the rare and extraordinary *Pseudonestor*, p. 432 : " they are unwearying in supplying their full-fledged young with food, and when the latter are soliciting this from their parents they form a most comical group." '

It would appear that, in proportion as young birds are taught rather than teach themselves, the stringency of selection in favour of the formation of Müllerian groups would be relaxed ; but the subject is one requiring research and is not yet capable of generalisation.

As regards (*b*) we are even more in the dark. It is only in Europe and N. America that observations on the foods of birds are so extensive that any quantitative estimate of its different constituents is possible. But it is only in the tropics that mimetic phenomena, especially in butterflies, are at all common. Outside the Holarctic region we are quite unable to answer the following fundamental questions : What proportion of the total bird fauna actually attacks butterflies (or other insects involved in mimetic associations) ? In what proportions do protected and unprotected species figure in the diet of the birds making such attacks ? Do young birds make such attacks more frequently than old birds ? At what period in their life are female butterflies most attacked ?

Until these questions can be answered from knowledge based on quantitative data, we are still very much in the dark as to the extent to which selection of the kind required is really operative.

A somewhat different argument has been applied by Heikertinger (1929a) to the supposed warning colours of many Hymenoptera. He maintains that, so far from being protected, such species are the favourite food of many birds. It is perhaps significant that Myers (1931) found that unpleasant taste appeared to disgust a Coati (S. American mammal, largely insectivorous) far more than stings. Heikertinger bases his statement on the analysis of stomach-contents made in Hungary and U.S.A. The literature on the food of birds is vast and requires an adequate quantitative investigation from this point of view. Heikertinger entirely ignores the possibility that birds may have a scale of likes and dislikes ; they may perhaps eat only Hymenoptera when very hungry or when other food is scarce. There is certainly a *prima facie* case for Heikertinger's contention, but only quantitative data can settle the question (*cf.* Protective Resemblance, p. 233).

In the early stages of genetic inquiry it was thought that every mutation must always have produced as big an effect as it is seen to produce at the present day. On this basis, Punnett (1915, p. 141) and Nicholson (1927) have suggested that, as the patterns of some of the mimetic forms of butterflies are known to be inherited as units, it may be assumed that they arose in a single step. It is now known that effects of a given gene depend on the gene-complex which forms part of its environment. If this environment is altered, so will be the effects of the gene, and we have no reason, therefore, to assume that a mimetic pattern, now inherited as a unit, tells us what effect the controlling gene had initially. In this way it can be assumed that selection has acted, not on the controlling gene, but on the genetic environment with which it reacts. It may be noted that there is no *more* evidence for this theory than there is for the simpler assumption.

(2) It is not very difficult to find a few cases of close resemblance between animals living in entirely different countries. We may instance *Bombus terrestris xanthopus* of Corsica and *B. eximius* of the Himalayas, which belong to different sections of the genus. Berg (1926, chapter viii) quotes several additional examples of more or less widely separated species resembling one another in colour-pattern ; and Dewar and

Finn (1909) draw attention to the same phenomenon in birds. Possibly the frequency of such convergence is much greater than is usually supposed, since it is much less likely to be noticed than when the resemblance occurs between inhabitants of the same country. Since the action of selection is out of the question in these cases, we must assume that the number of possible colour-patterns for one group of animals is not unlimited, and that occasionally parallel evolution will lead to striking resemblances.

On *a priori* grounds the chance of this is the greater the more nearly allied are the animals, and, when members of the same family or genus are under consideration, it is quite possible that parallel evolution should be fairly common.

Species of the same genus, often, however, belonging to different subgeneric groups, not rarely show resemblances which have been claimed to be the result of selection. We mention species of the genus *Charaxes* (Swynnerton, 1926), *Heliconius* (Eltringham, 1916), or of certain Pierine genera, *Mylothris* and *Phrissura* (Eltringham, 1910, p. 83). There is no reason why some of these resemblances should not be due to parallel evolution, quite unaided by selection. The chief difficulty for such a hypothesis arises when the mimetic forms have identical geographical ranges. This difficulty is more serious when both species are polymorphic and in different parts of the range the colour-patterns still go together: in fact, evidence of this sort is far the most cogent argument in favour of the view that mimetic resemblance is due to selection. This geographical coincidence, however, is by no means fully established in a large number of cases. Thus Eltringham (1916, p. 141) states: ' To understand more fully the relationships of models to mimics in *Heliconius* we require much more information concerning geographical distribution, and also as to comparative rarity of forms and other bionomic factors. S. America is a very large area, and the commonest type of data on our labels is " Upper Amazon," " Columbia," " Peru," and even sometimes " Brazil." We might as well be told that a certain insect occurs in Europe.' It is probably true in the greater number of cases of mimetic resemblance that, though the convergent forms have been shown to occur together in certain localities, we have no knowledge of the exact range of any one form.

Some of the most striking instances of resemblance between insects belonging to widely separate groups are those between Hymenoptera and Diptera. If we consider the single dipterous family, the Syrphidae, we find some species which are indistinguishable (when flying) from wasps (*Chrysotoxum cautum*, *Paramixogaster* spp., etc.) or from bees (*Volucella bombylans*, *Pocota apiformis*, etc.). Often the resemblance is due to the modification of the body in different ways, as when a long twelve-segmented antenna is imitated by one of three long segments, or the folded wings of a wasp are imitated by a longitudinal cloud along the costal margin of the wing of a fly (*cf.* also Sturtevant, 1921 ; Nicholson, 1927). At first sight it seems impossible to attribute such resemblances to parallel evolution, even in part. But to judge the question properly it is necessary to consider the whole range of colour-pattern found in the Syrphidae. We then find that there is a complete series from ' fly-like ' forms to bee- or wasp-like forms. It is difficult to imagine that the little-modified members of such a series are really mistaken for Hymenoptera by their enemies : it would appear rather that there is a definite tendency in the Syrphidae to produce bee- and wasp-like types ; possibly, when a certain degree of resemblance has been hit off, selection may contribute to completing the resemblance. In other words, such mimicry is not the product of selection alone, and it is impossible in any particular case to say what part selection has actually played. Sturtevant (*l.c.* p. 202) has criticised the view that occurrence of parallel mutations plays much part in mimicry. He objects to drawing a distinction between mimicry and the protective resemblance of insects, etc., to other objects (as stick insects, leaf insects, etc.). But, as a matter of fact, resemblances to the inanimate background are already known to be due to more than one cause—viz. either hereditary constitution or power of changing colour during the life-history (see discussion of specific differences in colour, p. 279). Again, Sturtevant points out that parallel evolution cannot make the leg of a fly resemble the antennæ of a wasp. Generally speaking this is true, but in the Syrphidae and many other dipterous families, long, three-segmented antennæ, superficially resembling those of wasps, are well known to occur in forms not resembling wasps in colour. Lastly, it is impossible to show without elaborate genetic analysis that two mutations are the same (*i.e.* really parallel), and, in *Drosophila*, mutations with similar effects may occur in quite different loci. We think, however, that parallel evolution may have played some part in producing resemblances within restricted groups, while, if it can be shown that two unrelated groups (such as the Hymenoptera and Diptera) do in fact tend to throw parallel variation, it is not necessary to know the locus in which the mutation responsible occurred.

(3) It has always been an important argument in favour of the selective explanation of mimetic resemblances that no other factor could be suggested which would account for the phenomena. A very different view has been put forward by Berg (1926, chapter vi). He advances the theory that the ' geographical landscape ' profoundly influences the animals subjected to it. By a geographical landscape he means ' a region in which the character of the relief, climate, vegetation and soils are united in one harmonious whole, which is typical of a certain zone of the earth, recurring through its entire area ' (*l.c.* p. 264). He supposes that ' the landscape does not affect the organism by any one of its component agencies, such as by its altitude above the sea-level, its temperature, or the rocks forming its soil, but by the entire combination of all the elements which constitute any given landscape ' (*l.c.* pp. 264–5). Taken as a whole Berg's thesis appears to us a very marked example of special pleading, but there may nevertheless be some truth in his idea. It is well known (*cf.* Zimmermann, 1930, 1931) that the relation between colour and climate in the Hymenoptera is likely to lead to a certain degree of convergence in the forms inhabiting one climatic region. In some of the other cases where groups of species resemble one another, it is possible that as yet undiscovered edaphic factors determine the convergence, especially when the number of species concerned is very large, as in some of the Lycid-coloured groups. Sometimes there is great diversity in pattern as a whole, whereas certain features are convergent in particular regions. This may be seen in humble-bees (*Bombus*), which, as shown by Vogt, usually have the pale hairs white in the Caucasus and yellow in the Alps ; in the Pyrenees they are also yellow, but the pale area is always more extensive ; while England appears to form a region of melanism. In some cases the colour alteration in the particular local direction

is visible only on microscopic examination of a considerable series of specimens (Richards, 1928, p. 385). Somewhat similar resemblances among Oriental Papilios are mentioned by Jordan (1896). The remarkable convergence in colour described by Buxton (1923) in many desert animals has been already discussed (p. 239). The colour convergence may, in some rodents, extend to the soles of the feet. According to Buxton there are considerable difficulties in regarding this convergence as due to protective coloration ; on the other hand, Sumner (1932) has shown that some at least of the desert forms are hereditary races, so that determination by the environment would raise certain theoretical difficulties.

(4) The same argument may be applied to the mimicry theory as will be applied later (pp. 275–6) to the Natural Selection theory in general—viz. if it can be shown that certain cases of apparent mimicry are very unlikely to be the result of selection, then mimicry must in those cases have other causes, and it is therefore impossible, without better evidence than is usually available, to say what cause has been active in a particular case. Such an admission would make it easy to maintain that colour resemblances are due to selection, where the evidence for such selection is strongest, while allowing the less well-established cases to be left *sub judice*. This argument would appear to be applicable, even if no alternative to the selective explanation can be directly demonstrated.

One of the types of mimetic association least easy to explain on the selection hypothesis is found amongst the Hymenoptera, *e.g.* in the Hawaiian wasps (chiefly Eumeninae) described by Perkins (1912), and in the Vespids of S. America. In Hawaii, Perkins shows that wasps fall into a number of very distinct colour groups which cut right across groupings based on structural characters. A few of the colour groups are more or less confined to particular islands, but others are found on several islands and most islands have representatives of more than one group. At the present day no birds are known to prey on these Hymenoptera, though admittedly man has greatly altered the fauna in recent years. It has been maintained (Poulton, 1912) that these colour groupings are Müllerian associations ; but it is very difficult on this hypothesis to see why so many different groups should be formed in islands of relatively small size. This difficulty is accentuated if, as Perkins contends, the whole Eumenine fauna evolved from two species immigrant from the Orient. From a Müllerian standpoint one would rather have expected that all the species would have been alike, that change in colour would have been more retarded compared with change in structure. Exactly the same argument may be applied to the S. American Vespids. In most districts there is more than one large association of unrelated species with similar colour-patterns. Often quite closely related species belong to very different colour-groups.

An interesting example is known amongst the butterflies of the genus *Erebia*. This genus of Satyrines is of sombre brown hue with a cryptic under-surface. There is no evidence to suggest that they are not quite palatable to birds, and they would be considered very unlikely insects to form Müllerian associations amongst themselves. Yet Chapman (1913) and Higgins (1930) have both recorded marked colour convergence between different species in various localities in the Alps. The amount of convergence, though significant, is small and would not make much difference to their appearance on the wing, but this limited geographical polymorphism, with each species having a parallel local form in each district, is what would have been called Müllerian mimicry if the insects had been brightly coloured. It is possible that in reality some edaphic factor is involved.

These examples are only supplementary to what has already been brought forward on pp. 255-259. The matter is not one capable as yet of proof either way, and we can only state our opinion that it is very doubtful if the mimicry theory can be made to cover all the facts. We may summarise the argument of the previous paragraphs as follows : The fact of mimicry, of striking resemblance between structurally un-related forms, is well established, and the phenomenon is wide-spread, especially amongst insects. In a number of selected examples there is a considerable degree of probability [1] that

---

[1] A certain number of examples must probably be accepted on the grounds of close degree of resemblance between model and mimic, coincidence of geo-graphical range (often combined with geographical variation) and general evidence as to distastefulness of the model and relative scarcity of the mimic.

Probably there is no single example in which (*a*) a model has been proved to be distasteful by its almost invariable rejection by its potential enemies, and (*b*) a mimic of it is also regularly rejected although actually palatable. The extremely scattered evidence for the mimicry theory makes it very difficult to collate the facts recorded with regard to any particular pair of species.

selection of warning patterns has brought about colour convergence. In another series of examples it is very difficult to see how selection could have led to the observed effects. In the majority of cases of mimetic resemblance, however, it is impossible at present to estimate to what extent, if at all, selection has been active. We are left, in fact, in a state of suspended judgment : it is probable that selection has played some part in the evolution of mimetic convergence, but it is usually impossible to say how large a part in any particular case.

(5) If two species of a genus enter into two different mimetic associations, then the colour differences between them will be adaptive in so far as the mimicry is due to Natural Selection. Similarly, in a polymorphic mimetic species, the differences between the various forms may be adaptive, and if these differences are analogous to those observed between species in other cases, then we can obtain some evidence as to the extent to which specific characters are adaptive. To assess what proportion of the differences observed is actually due to adaptive change is very difficult and usually impossible. We shall first have to consider the evolution of warning colours amongst models. We are on very uncertain ground in trying to decide which patterns are most conspicuous and therefore most efficient in warning enemies (especially birds) against making attacks. It is scarcely possible (except in the broadest way) to arrange insects in a scale of distastefulness to see if this corresponds in any way with the apparent scale in conspicuousness. An even greater difficulty is the lack of adequate systematic knowledge. A few genera, such as *Acraea* and *Heliconius*, have received thorough monographic treatment (Eltringham, 1912, 1916), but even here the species are so variable, have been so little reared, and many are still so imperfectly known that it is still often impossible to come to any very definite conclusions as to the limits of species. Further, it has been a common systematic procedure to unite under one species all forms connected by more or less clear intermediate colour-forms : yet genetical experiments show that a more or less continuous range of phenotypic variation may be the expression of distinct genotypic composition, and the occurrence of apparent intermediates is not necessarily significant unless the connecting forms are ranged along a definite geographical gradient.

However, it would appear that in many instances the species of models are extraordinarily variable. Thus in *Acraea*, 70 out of 133 species have at least two distinct colour-forms (a good number of the species with no known variety are still very rare in collections) ; 46 species have three or more named forms. Sometimes as many as half a dozen forms of a species occur sporadically throughout the range, while in other cases there is sexual polymorphism or marked geographical variation. Something of the same sort would appear to be usual in *Heliconius* also. In view of this variability it is difficult to maintain that the broad features of colour-pattern are essential specific differences. Of course there are a certain number of species with a distinct colour-pattern unlike any other, but the more general position would appear to be that the main lines of colour-pattern are non-specific, and that specific characters are found more in the male and female genitalia and in the finer details of the pattern, such as the exact shape of bands or the exact number and position of spots. In this connection we may note the example given by Jordan (1896, pp. 449–50). In Malaya, *Papilio caunus* is a striking mimic of *Euploea rhadamanthus*. Races of *P. caunus*, inhabiting Malacca and Sumatra, Borneo and Java, may be separated by slight differences in the size of the white markings. These subspecific characters do not affect the general resemblance to the model, which is unmodified throughout the area.

When we turn to the mimics we find the same extreme variability. The association between polymorphism and mimicry has long been emphasised, and in many cases, as in the well-known *Papilio dardanus* (Eltringham, 1910, p. 91), several forms of one species may all occur in one place. In these highly polymorphic mimetic species colour-pattern by itself is almost of no value in specific diagnosis, and we appear justified in maintaining that, in a number of cases, mimetic differences are not of the same nature as specific differences. In simple Batesian mimicry colour-pattern is much more closely associated with specific difference, but this sort of mimicry does not appear to form a very large proportion of the known examples in butterflies.

It will be objected that, even if the colour differences between these species involved in mimicry are not actually specific, they are still analogous to the differences observed

between other species not so involved.   Two suggestions may
be made.   First, it would be instructive to compare the types
of colour-pattern found in genera involved in mimicry with
those obtaining in normal genera : it seems possible that in
the former a series of striking, sharply contrasting patterns
would be found, and in the latter a far more graded series of
minutely differentiated patterns.   The subject, however, could
be dealt with only by an expert lepidopterist.   Secondly, we
are not claiming that selection could not discriminate between
colour-patterns : merely that, as a matter of fact, this has rarely
happened in the case of specific difference in pattern.   This
involves the question considered in the last chapter—viz.
how far adaptation and specific divergence have been parallel
but quite distinct processes.

Summary of the Examination of the Mimicry Theory

In the preceding pages we have dealt very briefly with
what appear to us to be the main difficulties in the employment of the mimicry theory as important evidence in favour of
Natural Selection.   In the past some of the criticism of the
selective theory of mimicry has been misinformed, but it
seemed more necessary for us to point out what considerable
gaps there are in our knowledge than to enumerate a long
series of cases favourable to the theory.   It appeared to us
essential to distinguish between what we know and what we
infer or guess.

There is no difficulty in accepting the fact that numerous
unrelated animals resemble one another closely in colour.
There is a considerable body of evidence favouring the view
that brightly coloured animals (especially insects) tend to be
distasteful, and *vice versa* ;   there are, however, probably
sufficiently numerous exceptions to make extensive generalisations dangerous until more observations have accumulated.
On this point systematic examination of a whole local fauna is
more important than casual notes.   There is a considerable
difficulty in explaining the early stages of the evolution of
distastefulness and warning colours by the aid of selection, but
our knowledge is still too scanty to allow us to do more than
note the existence of the problem.

The existence of conspicuous distasteful forms is the *a priori* requirement of the mimicry theory, but, even when the occurrence of such forms has been fully demonstrated, it requires much additional evidence. The nature of the evidence required may be broadly outlined as follows :

(1) Detailed knowledge of the food of enemies (especially birds) in the areas where mimicry occurs. Our knowledge must be quantitative to allow us to arrive at any certain conclusions.

(2) Detailed, quantitative knowledge of the rejection of models and mimics by enemies which prey extensively on allied palatable or non-mimetic forms. For the Müllerian aspect of mimicry we require more knowledge of the process by which young birds learn to recognise appropriate foods.

(3) More evidence as to the possibility of convergence due to (a) parallel evolution, (b) exposure to similar edaphic conditions. There is not much to go on at present, but these possibilities appear to be insufficiently explored, and certain examples difficult to explain by the ordinary mimicry theory may be elucidated in this way.

When we find how little our knowledge is of these important questions it may seem remarkable that the theory has been so widely accepted. We therefore wish to emphasise the following points in its support :

The existence of fairly numerous instances in which the colour convergence has been brought about by the modification of totally distinct structures.

The geographical coincidence of model and mimic where edaphic factors are very unlikely to be responsible for the resemblance. This argument is even more important where several geographical races of both species are involved.

The considerable amount of data suggesting that the supposed models are to some extent distasteful and rejected, and that the mimics are liable to be mistaken for them.

We suggest that the data are at present not sufficiently quantitative to be very conclusive. There is a tendency to obtain part of the evidence from one species and part of it from another. There are few, if any, pairs of model and mimic (*cf.* footnote, p. 260) in which all the necessary evidence is available for that particular pair. In our view, therefore, while it is probable that selection has played some part in establishing mimetic resemblances, it is impossible as yet to estimate how large a part, and certainly dangerous to use the mimicry theory as one of the main lines of support to the Natural Selection theory. When additional facts of the right kind have accumulated it may be possible to come to a more definite conclusion.

A secondary point, of some importance to the more general questions with which we are dealing, concerns the relation between colour-pattern and specific characters in mimetic forms. We have presented some evidence that the patterns of species involved in mimetic associations are often so polymorphic that it is the finer details only, and not the broad lines of the pattern, which must be regarded as specific. This question requires examination on a quantitative basis, but it is probable that, if the majority of cases of mimetic resemblance were proved to be the result of Natural Selection, we would also have to accept the view that specific differences in colour might frequently have evolved under the same influence.

(*b*) **Less intensively studied cases.**—(1) *Adaptation to life in torrents.*—The study of the adaptation of animals of various groups which live in torrents has been recently developed by numerous workers. The study of aquatic insects in particular has been pursued, particularly by Hubault, Rousseau, Dodds and Hisaw and others. Annandale and Hora started a special study of the fauna of Indian hill streams, and Hora has recently (1930) published a masterly summary of the general question. It will be easily understood that this subject is part of the larger problem of the adaptation of aquatic animals to various habitats. This particular aspect has, however, received special attention. The following conclusions seem to be established :

(i) The habits of species of the same genus claimed to show adaptations to different speeds of water, etc., are too often only summarily expressed, and there is a dearth of statistical information—*e.g.* as to how regularly the members of a given species are found in a given habitat.

(ii) There is little doubt concerning the differential adaptation of genera.

(iii) There is enough evidence that species of the same genus do sometimes differ markedly in structural features that are of obvious use in different rates of water-flow. Thus Dodds and Hisaw (1924) describe three species of *Baetis* which live in different habitats and are obviously modified to an increasing flow of current. Morgan (1913) and Lestage (1925) show that the nymphs of *Ephemerella deficiens* and *tuberculata* differ in the structure of the femur and claw, and that it is possible to correlate these differences with differences of environment. Hora (*l.c.* p. 237) finds that the modification of the adhesive apparatus of the species of the fish *Glyptosternum* can be correlated with water-flow.

(iv) One cannot fail to observe repeatedly that habitat and structural differences are manifested between groups of species rather than between individual species of a genus—*e.g.* Tonnoir (1924) in his account of the Tasmanian Blepharoceridae cites differences between groups of species. One finds that several related species often live in the same habitat.

(v) Although in some adaptations (suckers of tadpoles, shape of insects' bodies) a Lamarckian explanation may suggest itself, it will hardly afford a satisfactory explanation of the origin of special hairs or spines in the armature of claws and legs in insects.

The general impression that this work conveys is not particularly convincing as far as the selective nature of interspecific differences is concerned. There are, it is true, certain instances that are highly suggestive of a selective origin, but one would not say that they were proved up to the hilt. It is not enough, as we have already suggested, to point to examples of different species taken in different habitats and to discover that they differ in appropriate modification. It must be shown (*a*) whether they are always found in such habitats, and (*b*) whether species not modified in this fashion are ever found in the habitats in question. Probably the evidence does show a general adaptive tendency ; but it scarcely amounts to proof of the regular correlation of structural and habitudinal differences between allied species.

(2) *The colour of cuckoo's eggs.*—This subject has been

studied for over a hundred years. The more important works are given by Jourdain (1925) in his bibliography.

The most striking feature of this phenomenon is that a single species of Cuckoo (e.g. *Cuculus canorus telephonus*) may use several different species as fosterers and in certain cases the eggs of the Cuckoo resemble those of the various fosterers very closely. It is claimed that the resemblance is brought about by the rejection by the fosterer of such Cuckoo's eggs as do not resemble its own. The salient facts, in so far as the selective explanation is involved, are as follows :

(*1*) In the first place, the instances of a species of Cuckoo utilising various fosterers, to the eggs of which its own attain a close resemblance, are well attested and striking. Moreover, where the fosterer happens to show local or geographical variation, it often happens that the parasite's eggs follow the detail of this very closely, as Stuart Baker has shown in the crows (1923).

(*2*) The degree of resemblance is very diverse. At the one end of the scale we find some fosterers (*e.g.* the Hedge Sparrow) habitually accepting and brooding Cuckoo's eggs which do not resemble their own (Jourdain, *l.c.* p. 641). At the other we have the very striking and close resemblances seen, *e.g.*, between *C. cuculus canorus* and *Emberiza cioides ciopsis*.

(*3*) The crucial question, as far as the mode of origin of the 'mimicry' is concerned, is whether there is any evidence of the rejection of unsuitably coloured eggs, and of a correlation between the closeness of resemblance and the intensity of rejection. That some fosterers do reject the Cuckoo's eggs is certain. It is remarkable that so well informed a writer as Cuénot should dismiss (1925, p. 344) as a fable the evidence that such rejection takes place. Both Stuart Baker (1923) and Jourdain (*l.c.*) assemble many instances, and point out that the dissimilar Cuckoo's eggs are eliminated in three ways : (*a*) by actual ejection from the nest, (*b*) by desertion, and (*c*) by a new nest being built over the parasitised one. What is true, however, is that the incidence of rejection ' varies enormously.' In some cases it is as low as 5 per cent. ; in others it is 80 to 100 per cent. Moreover, ' these rates are not necessarily connected with the closeness of the mimicry or the reverse ' (Jourdain, *l.c.* p. 652). What is not stated (and apparently not studied) is that the rejected eggs are more dissimilar than those which are tolerated.

At first sight this seems to be a very strong presumptive case for the occurrence of Natural Selection. There is, however, a general objection of some importance. Most authors agree that the primitive non-parasitic Cuckoos laid white eggs (Stuart Baker, 1923, pp. 278–9). If this is true, as Baker points out, we would have to accept the probability that all other birds' eggs were white at the time of the origin of the parasitic habit, and that the colours of the Cuckoo's eggs developed *pari passu* with those of the fosterers. If this were not the case—*i.e.* if the Cuckoo's eggs were white or some other neutral colour and the fosterers' were multicoloured—we must assume either that quite marked variations towards the colour of the fosterers' eggs occurred or that even slight differences were enough to influence rejection and acceptance of the Cuckoo's eggs. This dilemma confronts us, of course, in all selectionist arguments. It is true that we can plausibly imagine that the primitive colour of the Cuckoo's egg was some generalised one, a grey or a drab, and that it was gradually assimilated towards various multicoloured types. But this seems to us to place a very high strain on the potentiality for variation in the Cuckoo's constitution. If the Cuckoo's eggs were white and those of the fosterers multicoloured, it seems most unlikely that they could have been assimilated by selection alone. We therefore seem driven back on Stuart Baker's hypothesis of an evolution of the Cuckoo and the fosterers *pari passu* from a stage when they all had white eggs. But Baker holds that Cuckoos are relatively recent in their origin, and the parasitic habit is still more modern. It is inconceivable, however, that all the fosterers should have conveniently remained in the condition of having white eggs until the Cuckoos evolved.

If we are to accept the colour of the non-parasitic Cuckoo's eggs, which is white, as evidence as to that of the primitive Cuckoos, it seems that we have two courses open to us: (a) to argue that the fosterers' must also have been white at the time of the origin of the habit, which is very unlikely, or (b) on the assumption that the fosterers had multicoloured eggs, to postulate either a very surprising degree of variation in the Cuckoo, or some process (? optical stimulus) by which the Cuckoo itself produced the right sort of variation, a resort which admittedly involves just as many difficulties (*e.g.* the instances of lack of resemblance to the fosterer's eggs) as the other theory.

(3), (4) *General.*—The remarkable modifications of deep-sea animals and of cave animals are usually given as standard examples of adaptation to particularly exacting habitats. Between these two categories there is common ground. In both we find a tendency for the eyes to be reduced or lost, and in both a compensatory hypertrophy of other sense-organs. It is as well to remember that similar modifications occur in other habitats where particular factors characteristic of abyssal depths and caverns prevail, *e.g.* on muddy bottoms in shallow water (Kemp, 1917), and under rocks and in crannies (Racovitza, 1907). It is a curious fact, and one which has strangely enough excited little comment, that the striking development of phosphorescent organs in the abyssal fauna has no parallel among cave animals. Racovitza (*l.c.* p. 433) comments on this, and states that the only phosphorescent organisms in caves are some mosses and fungi.

The occurrence of many forms in both these categories which are specially modified in relation to their exceptional mode of life is very well known, and there is no need to give examples. The origin of these modifications has been often attributed to selection. But it is not possible to discuss their origin with any hope of a satisfactory conclusion, for reasons which we give at length under the two separate headings.

(3) *The deep-sea fauna.*—No bionomic category of animals exhibits more striking or sensational examples of adaptation to a special habitat than those found at great depths in the sea. When, however, we start to contrast the modifications of species which live habitually in deep water with their shallow-water relatives for the purpose of discovering the mode of origin, we encounter very grave difficulties. To begin with, the technical problems are very considerable. We know very little concerning the mode of life of abyssal forms, and it is still largely a matter of surmise and inference. The subject has been critically reviewed by one of us (Robson, 1925, 1932a), and we may note the following points :

(a) Owing to the relative infrequency of the use of closing nets, there is a serious lack of knowledge as to the vertical range of abyssal animals.

(b) There is a distinct tendency to argue from structure to habitat in explaining the origin of many modifications.

(c) The paucity of actual numbers of specimens of each species obtained makes it very difficult to reason as to the distribution of these animals and the relation of their structure to their habitat.

(d) A study of one particular group, viz. the Octopoda, impresses on one the apparently capricious incidence of modification apparently related to the abyssal habitat.

(e) Certain of the deep-sea forms exhibit modifications involving the loss or reduction of given structures (e.g. in the Cephalopoda, of eyes, the ink-sac, the musculature). The difficulties involved in a selective explanation of the loss of a given structure are considered on p. 42. Whether these anomalies will be removed by a more intensive study is very uncertain. It is enough for the present to cite the capricious modification of the eyes among species of the same genus (Robson, 1925 ; Brauer, 1908, p. 256 ; Murray and Hjort, 1912, pp. 680–5). It is quite safe to state that, between littoral or shallow-water species and those of the same genus found at greater depths, structural differences may often be found (e.g. among the Octopoda the reduction of the musculature in *Benthoctopus berryi* compared with that of *B. piscatorum*). Nevertheless, as between the shallow-water and the abyssal forms it is impossible to formulate any hard and fast diagnosis, and amongst those inhabiting deep water we find some displaying particular modifications and others which do not (cf. *Grimpoteuthis glacialis* (Robson, 1932a, p. 28)).

(4) *Cave animals.*—As regards the characters of cavernicolous animals the position is quite different from that discussed in (3). Thanks to the labours of Racovitza, Jeannel and others, the distribution, modification and conditions of life of these forms have been thoroughly investigated. The study of the origin of the special modifications, however, labours under a

very serious preliminary difficulty.   In discussing this we concentrate our attention on the question of the loss or reduction
of the eyes in these animals.   That other modifications are
found is obvious ; but the study of their origin is far less fully
documented and scarcely admits of a serious discussion.

The difficulty encountered in discussing the loss or atrophy
of the eyes is that emphasised by Cuénot (1921, p. 485) and
Racovitza (1907, p. 450 and foll.).   These authors maintain
that all the evidence suggests that the blindness of cave animals
did not originate as a modification acquired (*e.g.* by selection)
by normal immigrants from the light which wandered into
caves.   They assert that the blind occupants of caves were
'lucifuges,' which were already losing
their sight and wandered 'voluntarily'
into caves and survived there, as in
the environment best suited to them.
If this were true, of course, we would
have to look on the atrophy of the eyes
not as an adaptation to the cavernicolous habit, but the latter as an adaptation to the loss of eyes !   Cuénot (*l.c.*)
also points to the existence of animals
with normal eyes in caves, and reasonably enough affirms that, to explain this
(as is usually done) by suggesting that
they are newcomers, is pure assumption.

FIG. 23.—*Leptodirus ho-
henwarti* Schmidt (Silphi-
dae).   AN EXAMPLE OF A
HIGHLY   EVOLVED   CAVE-
BEETLE WHICH IS NEVER-
THELESS FOUND IN SEVERAL
CAVERN-SYSTEMS.   Photo,
W. H. T. Tams.

It seems to us that it is fair to suspend judgment on this question.   It is
not possible to resist Racovitza's and Cuénot's argument, even
if we suspect their anti-selectionist bias.   It is to be noted that
Jeannel in his recent summary (1926) avoids discussing the
actual mode of origin of these modifications.

B. *Difficulties raised by the Natural Selection theory.*

It is necessary at the offset to remember that the large
body of specific and racial differentia that have been described
include a certain proportion that are merely the effect of
plastic responsiveness to the environment, and are not of a
fixed heredity.   The adherent of Natural Selection may be
relieved of the necessity of explaining by his theory many
distinctions that are non-heritable (Robson, 1928, p. 186).
Thus it is quite evident from a perusal of a work like Pelseneer's

on variation in the Mollusca that the form and colour of the molluscan shell are very susceptible to plastic modification by various environmental factors, the effects of which seem on good evidence to be non-heritable.

For many years naturalists have been familiar with the resemblances between various animal structures and certain inorganic phenomena—*e.g.* between ocellated spots and Liesegang's rings. A similar parallelism has been detected between the arrangement of skeletal structures and the stresses set up in an animal viewed merely as a piece of engineering. The subject as a whole has been dealt with at some length by D'Arcy Thompson (1917), while the special data relating to a limited group, the Muscoid flies, have been ably presented by W. R. Thompson (1929). The part of the first-named author's argument which concerns our present discussion is his treatment of the relation of such mechanical adjustments to the problem of adaptation. D'Arcy Thompson argues that, as many of the structures found in animals obey well-known laws of mechanics, physics and chemistry and may be closely imitated in laboratory experiments, it is unnecessary to attempt to explain the adaptation of such structures as due to Natural Selection. A striking example is seen in the ocellated pattern on the feathers of the male Argus Pheasant, which Darwin (1901) regarded as due to the selection by the female of the males which pleased her best, but which D'Arcy Thompson would regard as closely comparable to the Liesegang's rings (formed by electrolytes crystallising out from colloid solutions) and therefore as largely outside the sphere of adaptation. On the Darwinian view the ocelli would be regarded as the result of a long process of almost imperceptible change, each stage having a slight advantage over its predecessor. On the other view, while selection might have determined the persistence of the ocellus-producing mechanism in the male sex only, the ocelli themselves could scarcely be said to have undergone evolutionary development at all.

The structure of the bones of vertebrates provides a somewhat different example employed by D'Arcy Thompson (*l.c.* chapter xvi) to illustrate the close parallelism between animate and inanimate organisation. It is well known, for instance, that the trabeculæ which fill up the greater part of the end of the cavity in the long bones of the legs are arranged in a regular way along lines of stress, just as are the cross-pieces between the girders of bridges. If the disposition of the stresses is altered (by an accidental deformation) during the life of the individual, the whole arrangement of the trabeculæ will be altered to meet the new lines of stress.

In the growth of bone we have not only a striking example of the nature of what we may call 'internal adaptations,' but we are enabled further to define the limitations to all analogy between living and non-living phenomena. If we isolate a single part of an organism, such as an ocellate marking, we may show how such a structure can result from relatively simple chemical processes ; or we may show that the mechanical adjustments of skeletal parts follow the principles of elementary dynamics. But, as soon as we consider the part in relation to the whole, we find a delicate adjustment quite unknown outside living organisms. There is nothing in the analogous laboratory experiments suggesting why the various growth processes stop just at the right point, or why one type of growth occurs at one point and one at another and yet both are so related that a delicately adjusted organism results. Though we can scarcely imagine that the functions of living organisms at any point involve processes different from those known to chemists and physicists, yet the physico-chemical processes might be called the mere bricks of which such organisms are made. It is probable that we are nearer the truth in saying that living organisms have selected certain processes to do their work and elected to follow certain laws, than in adopting the more usual viewpoint that living organisms obey physico-chemical laws. The bearing of these facts and speculations on the selection theory may seem somewhat remote, but two points emerge for consideration. First, there are many details of living organisation that are so closely paralleled by processes known to occur outside the organisms that we may believe that the same forces are at work in both cases. This possibility relieves the selectionist of part of his burden, since in such cases it may be unnecessary to treat a structure as the result of the selection of numerous small favourable variations : what would have been called the result of evolution may now be called the result of growth, and it has only to be shown that the results of, and not every stage in, such growth are adaptive. Secondly, it has been

T

suggested (*e.g.* Russell Brain, 1927, pp. 18–23) that functional adaptations, such as we have described in the case of bones of the legs, may play an important part in allowing animals to survive until the necessary inheritable variations turn up. This argument has one definite limitation, in that the mutation would have no selective advantage unless it produced a greater effect than functional adaptation or unless it produced it more economically.

To whatever extent we establish parallelisms with inorganic phenomena, we are only clearing our problem of superficial, largely man-made, difficulties. We are not solving the problem of adaptation so much as rationalising our outlook on the facts.

(1) *Specific differences.*

The most striking impressions that a taxonomic survey of any large group conveys to one's mind are the manifold diversities of species, the distinctness of the majority of these groups, the fact that they usually differ in several associated characters and the apparent triviality of these distinctions. If the theory of Natural Selection is correct, we must assume that all these differences must have arisen either because at some time or another in their owners' lives they are of adaptive value or are correlated with adaptive characters, or because they are the result of a general adaptive reorganisation. We cannot too strongly insist on the point already made that it is no use to attempt to smuggle these facts of specific differentiation into the proof of Natural Selection by an appeal to ignorance, or by an assumption of correlation, or by pointing out a few cases that seem explicable on very slender and unverified evidence. We ought to be prepared to show that at least 50 per cent. of specific differences are definitely adaptive. How far we are justified in attributing the survival of ' useless ' characters to their correlation with less obviously ' useful ' ones is discussed elsewhere (Chapter VI).

The substantiation of the selection theory has been attempted mainly by the collection of numerous individual examples of apparently useful structures or habits. It is suggested that no other theory can account for the large body of facts amassed, but this argument would carry more weight if there did not remain an even more numerous series of comparable facts still incapable of explanation (*i.e.* structures and habits of no known function). The value of a theory as a

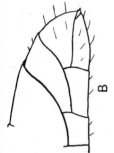

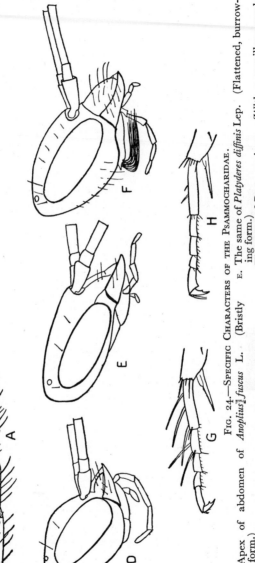

FIG. 24.—SPECIFIC CHARACTERS OF THE PSAMMOCHARIDAE.

A. Apex of abdomen of *Anoplius fuscus* L. (Bristly form.)
B. The same of *Psammochares gibbus* F. (Bare form.)
C. The same of *Ceropales maculatus* F. (Sixth sternite forming an egg-guide.)
D. Side view of head (antennæ cut short) of *Psammochares gibbus* F. (Normal form.)
E. The same of *Platyderes diffinis* Lep. (Flattened, burrowing form.)
F. The same of *Deuteragenia* sp. (With a maxillary comb for collecting spider's web.)
G. Tarsus and apex of tibia of right foreleg of female *Psammochares sahlbergi* Mor. (Long, tarsal comb.)
H. The same of *Ps. minutus* Dahlb. (Tarsal comb reduced.)

working hypothesis is reduced in proportion to the extent that it is impossible to fit in all the phenomena for whose explanation it was devised. If the selection theory was supposed to account for only a part of the facts of evolution, this criticism would have little weight, but there are some biologists who regard evolution as entirely a process of adaptation, and the diversity of the animal kingdom as due to changes which have made each *species* better fitted to its environment.

The kinds of differences which we are now to consider are those which the systematist encounters in his routine practice and experience, and the problem may, perhaps, be seen most clearly by considering a particular example. The wasps of the family Psammocharidae (Pompilidae) form an isolated group, probably best regarded as a superfamily. Almost all the species paralyse spiders to store up for their young ; a few species (*Parraferreola*) lay their eggs on living spiders (just like Ichneumonids), and one group, the Ceropalinae, is parasitic on other Psammocharids. The European members of the family have recently been monographed by Haupt (1927), who establishes approximately 127 species within his faunal limits. The following are the most important characters used in separating subfamilies, genera and species. *Head :* presence, especially in the female, of a bristle-tuft on the maxillæ ; shape and sculpture of the clypeus ; proportions of the antennal segments ; the distance separating the ocelli from the eyes, compared with that separating the ocelli from one another. *Thorax :* shape and proportions of the pronotum ; sculpture and length of the notum of the metathorax ; details of wing-venation ; number and position of bristles on the femora and tibiæ ; presence or absence of serrations on the hind tibiæ of the female ; presence or absence of a comb of bristles on the fore tarsi ; nature of the bristles at the apex of the fifth tarsal segment ; structure of the claws. *Propodeum :* shape, sculpture, arrangement of apical keels. *Abdomen :* presence or absence in female of a transverse suture on the second sternite ; arrangement of bristles on the sixth tergites and sternite of the female ; structure of the sting-sheath in the female ; structure of the apical sternites and genitalia of the male. In addition, the colour of body, legs and wings, the general surface sculpture and the extent of hairy (sometimes scaly) clothing are also utilised.

On the basis of such characters the European Psammocharidae are divided into five subfamilies, with 5 (48), 4 (11),

5 (46), 7 (15), 1 (7) genera and species respectively. From the point of view of use only the tuft of bristles of the cardo of the maxillæ, the comb of bristles on the fore tarsi, the modification of the sting-sheaths of the female, the structure of the male genitalia and colour need be considered. None of the other characters, *as far as is known*, bears any relation to the life of these insects.

Colour.—It is possible that in some species the colours give warning of the powerful sting : in a few desert species the pale yellowish colour may be protective : as a general rule, a few principal types of colour-pattern are common to the majority of species. The adaptive value of the colour-pattern of any European species is at present very doubtful.

Bristle-tuft on the maxillæ.—This is found in the females (and, in a less developed state, in the males) of the species of *Deuteragenia* and *Pseudagenia* : according to Adlerz (1903, pp. 37–8), these bristles are used to collect spiders' web, with which the entrance to the nest is in part closed.

Female sting-sheath.—This is considerably modified in the parasitic species of the Ceropalinæ. Adlerz (1902, 1903) has shown that, unlike other Psammocharids, the female, by means of it, conveys her eggs into the lung-book of a spider already a prey of another species.

Male genitalia and apical abdominal sternites.—The modifications of these probably provide the best specific characters in the family, but it is not possible at present to relate the differences in the male structure to the corresponding differences in the female. We shall return to this subject later (p. 296).

Comb on the fore tarsi, especially of the female.—This structure has a very interesting distribution amongst the species. It is absent in the Ceropalinæ (7 species) and Pepsinæ (48) ; in the Macromerinæ it is absent in three genera (10) and present in one (1) ; in the Psammocharinæ it is absent in 10 species of *Psammochares*, present in the four other genera (5) and 31 species of *Psammochares* ; in the Homonotinæ it is absent in five genera (13) and present in two genera (2). Thus the comb is present in 39 out of 127 species, and occurs in three out of five subfamilies. It is sometimes a generic character (*Ctenagenia*, Macromerinæ), sometimes only specific (*Psammochares*) ; in the latter case it is impossible to draw a sharp line between species with a very small comb and those without one at all.

In species such as *Psammochares plumbeus*, which burrows in loose sand, the well-developed comb makes the front legs a much more efficient organ for scraping away the soil. In other species with a rudimentary comb its value is doubtful, and a considerable number of species without a comb seem to be able to burrow equally well. It may be mentioned that a similar comb is developed in a number of species of sand-nesting wasps belonging to other families.

One other modification which appears to be of some value is the peculiar flattened head and thorax and thick fore femora of the species of *Aporus* which, preying on spiders living in burrows (Ferton, 1901, p. 121), are much more fossorial than the other species.

If we consider the habits of the species the problem is equally perplexing. The species of *Pseudagenia* build mud cells; those of *Deuteragenia* use ready-made crevices, old nests of other insects, or snail-shells; most Psammocharids dig burrows in sand or earth; *Parraferreola* lays its egg on a spider, which runs about with it in the open; *Ceropales* and a few species of *Psammochares* are parasitic on their allies. Apart from the exceptions already mentioned it is impossible to seize on any point in their structure which specially fits them for their mode of life. Further, these variations in habit themselves do not seem of much use to the species : all types of nest seem equally good, as far as we can see. There is a certain amount of specialisation in the nature of the prey, though further work would probably show that many species are more polyphagous than is at present known. How far such food differences can be considered adaptive is considered later (p. 301).

The following are the main conclusions to be drawn from this example, which could be reduplicated again and again from other divisions of the animal kingdom.

1. The majority of characters, separating either sub-families, genera or species, have no *known* use to the species and have no *known* relation to the special habits. In the actual example, there is no case of a useful character separating closely allied species : the characters which are useful (and possibly adaptive) are generic, or they separate distinct groups of species within the genus.

2. The differences in habits also do not appear to be definitely adaptive. We can see that, if a wasp decides to

build mud cells and stop their entrances with spider's web, it may need certain specialisations of structure, but we cannot see what advantage there was in beginning to build this type of nest.

We will now proceed to a more general consideration of the problem. One important preliminary reservation is necessary. We have spoken of structures or habits of no known use. Our knowledge of the details of the lives of most animals is still so small that it is quite legitimate to assume that a good many apparently useless characters will be found to have some function. Again, it is a well-known principle of genetics that many hereditary units have multiple effects, and it is possible that some of the useless structural differences employed in the separation of species are merely ' indicators ' of important physiological differences which may be highly adaptive (*cf.* p. 208). But there is a point beyond which it is unprofitable to go in assuming that either a use or a correlation with an adaptation will be discovered, and, when we find that probably more than half the characters defining families and probably at least 90 per cent. of the characters defining genera and species not only are not proved to be adaptive but have no known use at all, the assumption that Natural Selection has been the main agent in the evolution of natural populations is too comprehensive to help us very far. To be valuable as a working hypothesis a theory should ' work ' in not less than half the cases to which it is applied.

The next point for consideration is the number of instances known in which characters separating species are related to differences in the life-history. This raises a question not very easy to answer, chiefly because the limits of many genera are still uncertain, and what one author would call a generic, another would call a specific character. This difficulty is to some extent avoided if we consider only species which are evidently quite closely allied. Even when we have shown that a use is made of a structure, we have to prove that the use is adaptive. For convenience we shall consider the subject under two headings : (*a*) Differences in colour ; (*b*) Differences in structure.

(*a*) *Differences in colour.*—Much of the matter relevant here has already been discussed (p. 232 and foll.) in connection with the phenomena of protective coloration and mimicry. A few suggestions may be added.

It is really very difficult to estimate whether we ought to call a colour-scheme protective, warning or neutral, except in the limited number of cases in which there is striking resemblance to bark, rock, green leaves, etc., or in which the colours are very unusually conspicuous. We are probably on safer ground in affirming that a given pattern is cryptic than in saying that it is conspicuous, not only because many apparently conspicuous patterns really blend with their natural background, but because, so far as colour-pattern may have been influenced by Natural Selection, it is much more likely that cryptic rather than conspicuous patterns would have been produced.

Even so, it is difficult to believe that the colour of a large number of animals is not neutral with a slight bias in the cryptic direction. Few animals live in so well defined a habitat that resemblance to any one conspicuous feature would be serviceable, and actually cases of highly specialised protective colours are not very numerous. Where the colours are broadly cryptic, do we find that species differ in such a way as to fit them for their *particular* habitat? This question, on our present knowledge, would, with very few exceptions (see p. 236), have to be answered in the negative. But there is another possibility. If we imagine two isolated populations of a species, each under the action of selection in favour of a generalised cryptic colour-scheme, it is quite possible that a more or less successful pattern might be produced in both cases; but two patterns, not one, might result, since they would have evolved in different ways, as the result of the various mutations that happened to occur in the two populations. Later, when the populations had become fixed as species, the two might mix again, and then, though both would have a generally cryptic pattern, the differences between the two species would appear non-adaptive. Doubtless evolution has sometimes followed this programme, but it would be a big assumption to refer the greater part of specific difference in cryptic patterns to such a process. It would appear that even on this explanation, where two cryptic patterns have been built up independently under the action of selection, we have to assume that each step in the evolution of pattern was better adapted than its predecessor, and the theory demands a far more detailed correspondence between pattern and normal habitat than we can usually perceive. On our present knowledge we assume less if we suppose that the greater part of specific divergence in colour has been due to other processes, while in some cases selection has merely checked the development of bright colours and maintained a general brown, grey, or mottled ground colour.

We will now consider some of the examples in which the correspondence between colour and environment is more detailed than in many of the examples described on pp. 236–42. In nearly every instance the variations corresponding with a differently coloured background are *intraspecific* (see p. 233). We may first mention the power of colour-change in many lepidopterous larvæ and pupæ (Poulton, 1892; Bateson, 1892; *cf.* also Chapter II, p. 37), which enables them to harmonise with their general background. This harmony is acquired gradually during the life-history, and appears to be due to a direct effect on the nervous system of the insect through the eyes. A possibly similar state of affairs is seen in the beetle *Cleonus sulcirostris* (Merryfield and Poulton, 1899) and the adult moth *Gnophos obscurata* (Poulton, 1892), both of which have marked local colour-variation corresponding to changes in the nature of the soil. Such cases could be multiplied, and Poulton (1926) has recently dealt rather fully with the phenomenon in grasshoppers. All collectors of these insects are aware of the general agreement between the colour of a species and the background, so that we have green forms on grass, green and brown forms on heather, sandy forms, black forms, etc. Poulton deals with a large series of black or black and pale streaked species occurring on areas of burnt grass in Africa.

It is not unlikely that the permanent colour-harmony established in many inhabitants of deserts may be of the same nature. What was once a power of response to the various backgrounds on which the species had to live has now become fixed, giving an unvarying and close correspondence with the colour of what has become the permanent habitat.

On the selectionist hypothesis it is supposed that it is the power of responding to the colour of the background that has been built up by selection, since the actual changes in the individuals are evidently not as a rule inherited. It is impossible to show that this colour-response has not been established by selection, but there is also no direct evidence that it has. The important point is, however, that this power of response provides, at least in some cases, a method by which species can assume a generally cryptic coloration while maintaining non-adaptive specific differences in pattern.

Before leaving the question of specific differences in colour we will briefly mention the question of colour-polymorphism entirely unconnected with mimicry. Several examples (birds and mammals) have been given by Elton (1927, p. 184). Further examples may be found in the following papers : birds (Stresemann, 1925) ; Mollusca (Crampton, *passim*) ; Lepidoptera (Goldschmidt, 1923, pp. 145–6) ; dragon-flies (Walker, 1912, p. 29 ; Tillyard, 1917, p. 257). Dobrzansky (1924) in his study of the colour variation of the ladybird (*Harmonia axyridis*) shows that this beetle is extremely polymorphic, the colour ranging from yellow to black, the variants tending to fall into eight main classes. Most of the variants are found all over the range in different proportions, with the exception that in the westernmost part there is a tendency for one form to dominate all the others.

The occurrence together of two or more very distinct colour-forms of a species over a large part of its range does not suggest that colour in these cases is a matter of life and death. And, when allied forms have patterns very like one or other phase of the polymorphic species, we may further doubt the adaptive significance of colour in the non-polymorphic species. Fisher (1930, pp. 166–8) has attempted to explain the co-existence of polymorphic forms in another way, basing his argument on Gerould's (1923) work on heredity in certain Pierine butterflies of the genus *Colias*, in which both white and yellow forms of the female are known. There is some evidence that the white phase is not viable in a homozygous condition, and it is possible to argue that, if there is selection in favour of white wing-colour, a stable gene-ratio could be formed between yellow (at a slight selective disadvantage but capable of existing as a homozygote) and white (slightly favoured by selection but only occurring as a heterozygote). As, however, there is no evidence of such white-favouring selection, the 'explanation' appears a good example of the tendency to use the selection theory to explain away the facts on which it should be based.

(b) *Differences in structure.*—We have already examined a particular group (the Psammocharidae) and have shown the difficulty of finding an adaptive meaning in the specific and generic characters. We will now describe some instances in which adaptive significance has been claimed for interspecific, etc., characters.

Robson (1928, pp. 191–4) reviewed a number of these, which, with some additions, are reconsidered here.

1. *Suckers of fish living in currents of varying strength (Annandale and Hora, 1922, p. 507).*

The differences between the oral structures in the species of *Glyptosternum* are discussed under the general subject of the adaptation of torrent-dwelling forms (p. 265).

2. *Character of sculpture of sternites, etc., in the Scorpions* Opisthophthalmus (*Hewitt, 1918, p. 98*).

Hewitt states that the coarse granulation of the sternites and of the lower surfaces of the anterior caudal segments in various species of this genus ' perhaps serves the purpose of securing a better grip on the substratum, and it is interesting to note that such coarse granulation is completely absent in the species characterised by weak and elongated hands in the male, in which species apparently the characteristic burrowing habit of *Opisthophthalmus* is lacking ; still it should be added that certain species with smooth sternites are undoubtedly burrowers.' He goes on to say that the granulation is restricted to this genus, in which the burrowing habit is most developed. He points out that a somewhat analogous adaptation (?) is met with in *Parabuthus brevimanus* and *Karasbergia methueni*, which have independently acquired a peculiar modification of the crests of the anterior caudal segments, ' which would seem to indicate an adaptation to the sandy habitat in which they live.'

On re-examining this case it seems to us that there is no very exact correlation between the granulation and the sandy habitat (' certain species with smooth sternites are undoubtedly burrowers '). There does indeed seem a tendency for the sand-living forms to develop some kind of roughness on various segments, and, as Hewitt says (*l.c.* p. 99), ' it is difficult to imagine that the result is a mere coincidence of purposeless variation.' But no exact differentiation of the species on this basis is shown, and we must note, as Robson (*l.c.* p. 192) pointed out, that these observations are rather of the nature of casual field notes.

3. *Length of ovipositor in the cricket* Gryllus (*Lutz, 1908*).

Following earlier observations of Uhler, Lutz measured the length of the ovipositor in 200 female crickets from three

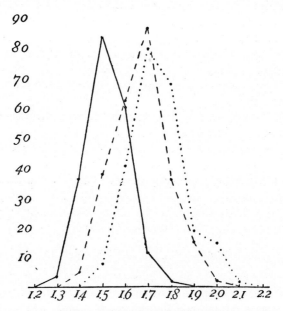

FIG. 25.—*Gryllus*. POLYGONS OF FREQUENCY FOR RATIO OF OVIPOSITOR TO TEGMINA FOR MAINLAND (———), BASE OF SPIT (-- -- --), AND APEX OF SPIT (. . . . . .), AT COLD SPRING HARBOUR, NEW YORK.

(Text-fig. 6 from Lutz, 1908.)

stations on a spit projecting into Cold Spring Harbour. One was from the sandy soil at the apex of the spit ; the second was from the base, where there was some humus mixed with the sand ; the third was from the ' mainland ' further inland, where there was a considerable amount of humus. (The estimation of the amount of sand and humus is loosely expressed.) The ovipositors of the crickets from the apex were longer than those from the base of the spit, and the latter were longer than those from the 'mainland' habitat. Lutz believes that 'where the soil is loose'—as on the sand-spit, especially at the apex—those eggs which are not deeply buried will almost certainly perish. In this way selection acts against the off-spring of females having short ovipositors in a habitat where the soil is loose.

Confirmatory evidence is found in *G. arenaceus*, which lives regularly on sand and has a long ovipositor, though it is not stated whether the correlation is found throughout the genus. Differences of unknown significance in the tegmina and wings accompany the lengthening of the ovipositor. The difference in average length between the ovipositors of the crickets at the apex and those on the mainland is only 2 mm., which is scarcely likely to provide sufficient extra depth to be of much account. The range of variation overlaps very considerably (see fig. 25).

It is not easy to arrive at a decision concerning this case. There is no evidence that eggs buried in the sand are uncovered and destroyed more frequently than those of the mainland animals. No exact expression of the density of the soil is given. The differences in tegmina and wings, which are not proposed as adaptive, might indicate a general 'colonial' divergence due to isolation between the three groups. This is not much more than a fair theoretical case.

4. *Reciprocal modification of the head of the beetle* Carabus mor-billosus *and the shell of the snail* Otala tigri (*Boettger, 1921, p. 321*).

Boettger states that in Morocco and Algeria, where the snail develops a larger oral denticle than usual, which serves to close the mouth of the shell, the Carabids, which prey on the snail, have narrower heads. He gives certain facts concerning the geographical variation which tend to confirm his hypothesis ; but many difficult questions are not met, *e.g.* whether in areas from which the Carabid is absent the snail has a less pronounced denticle. Boettger also (p. 325) weakens his case by suggesting that the denticle may be a ' Verdunstungsschutz,' and is evidently in two minds as to what its origin really may be. The subject is not treated statistically and is scarcely evidential, though it is perhaps suggestive.

5. *Snout of desert Blind Snakes (Hewitt, 1914, p. 11)*.

Hewitt states that *Typhlosaurus lineatus* and *Typhlops schiuri* ' are both separated from their allies by the possession of a sharp cutting snout enabling them to burrow in the sun-baked soil of the Kalahari.' Mr. Hewitt is an extremely competent observer, but we feel that the critical differences are too summarily expressed to be of much value. To begin with, there is no statistical statement of the frequency of occurrence. Next, Mr. H. W. Parker informs us that, at least in *Typhlops*, the sharp snout tends to occur sporadically throughout the genus, even in individuals of species normally not possessing it, and no one has suggested a general correlation between it and the desert habitat. Mr. Parker informs us that a similar snout occurs in species of the Amphisbaenid *Agamadon* in areas (W. Africa, S. America) which are not characterised by desert. Lastly, we are inclined to be rather suspicious of Mr. Hewitt's ' sun-baked soil ' of the Kalahari and to express the surmise that other soils than those of deserts become ' sun-baked.'

6. *Attachment of ticks to their hosts (Nuttall, 1911, p. 54)*.

Nuttall states that in the Argasidae *Ornithodorus megnini*, which remains for a long time attached to its host as a nymph,

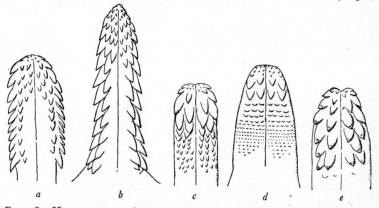

FIG. 26.—HYPOSTOMES OF LARVAL AND ADULT TICKS OF THE GENUS *Argas*, TO ILLUSTRATE DIFFERENCES IN ARMATURE.

a. *A. persicus* larva (similar in larva of *A. reflexus*).
b. *A. vespertilionis* (larva).
c. *A. persicus* (adult).
d. *A. reflexus* (adult).
e. *A. vespertilionis* (nymph).

(After Nuttall, 1911.)

the hyposternum is very powerfully armed, whereas in *O. moubata*, in which the nymphs are rapid feeders, the dentition is reduced. The exact rapidity of feeding is not given. From Nuttall's figures (*l.c.* p. 55) of the adults of *savignyi*, which he groups with *moubata* as 'rapid feeders,' it seems that there is a marked difference in degree of armature between the forms grouped as rapid feeders. The situation is complicated by the fact that *Argus persicus*, which appears to be intermediate in the length of its attachment, seems (Nuttall's fig. 13) to be about as heavily armed as *moubata*. The contrast between *megnini* and *moubata* is sufficiently striking ; but its value is somewhat minimised by the above-mentioned differences between *savignyi* and *moubata*. It is to be regretted that more exact figures as to the duration of fixation in the various forms were not available.

7. *Number of gill-rakers in* Salmo (*Regan, 1926, p. 5*).

S. obtusirostris, which lives in the rivers of Dalmatia and Albania, differs from the common Salmon parr in having more numerous gill-rakers on the lower part of the first gill-arch. According to Regan, the number of the gill-rakers in fishes generally is related to the nature of the food, being numerous in microphagous forms and few in piscivorous types. ' It has been recorded that *obtusirostris* subsists mainly on the larvæ of Ephemeridae,' and it seems that the increased number of gill-rakers, contrasted with that of the Salmon, which is a piscivorous form, is due to this difference in diet.

Like some of the preceding cases there is a good general assumption that the difference in question is related to an environmental difference, though it is open to question how far the diet of the Salmon parr and of *S. obtusirostris* is exactly known.

8. *Number of vertebræ in* Zoarces viviparus (*Schmidt, 1918 ; Regan, l.c. pp. 5–6*).

Schmidt showed that in the viviparous Blenny the number of vertebræ decreased the further they live up certain Danish fjords. Regan suggested that this is due to the diminished activity of the fish in the quieter conditions of the fjord water, as there is a general relation between the number of vertebræ and the degree of agitation of the water.

As the number of vertebræ in fish has been in general

related to environmental factors, we think it better for the present to regard it as an open question whether, as Regan suggests, it has an adaptive significance.

9. *Functional significance of ribbing of shell in* Helicigona cingulata *(Boettger, 1932, p. 209).*

Boettger observed that there is a high frequency of snails with strongly ribbed shells in the Alps. He devised an apparatus by which the shells could be subjected to crushing by a measurable force, and used it for testing the resistance to crushing shown by the smooth *Helicigona cingulata colubrina* and the ribbed *H. c. gobanzi.* Ten of each species were used, and Boettger found that *colubrina* was crushed at an average weight of 1,420 grammes, and *gobanzi* at an average of 1,506. From this he concluded that the ribs are adaptive, as they serve to strengthen the shell against crushing, and the high frequency of ribbed forms in the Alps is due to their greater power of resisting falling stones.

It will be noted that the difference between the two varieties in the matter of their resistance is not very great ; but it is perhaps enough to give the ribbed form sufficient selective advantage. Boettger's case is not very well made out. He says nothing specific about the distribution of ribbed and unribbed forms and their frequency in places where stone-falls are likely to be of regular occurrence. He simply affirms that ribbed forms are more common in the Alps. He certainly points out that ribbed forms of *Arianta arbustorum* occur in the Alps and are never found in the plains. He disposes of the suggestion which has been already made, that the ribbing is a ' Kaltanpassung,' by pointing out that ribbing does not become more frequent towards high latitudes.

As to the two varieties in question, not only does Boettger not give any figures for their frequency of occurrence in the relevant habitats, or any statement as to whether the ribbed form is more dominant in places exposed to avalanches and rock-falls, but he does not even say where his specimens came from. It seems that *gobanzi* is restricted to the upper Val Sarca, near Candino (Val Vestino), and has a very limited range there (Kobelt, 1876, p. 37 : 'auf eine Kleine Strecke beschränkt, aber dort in Menge . . .') in a kind of enclave in the *colubrina* area, where indeed (Kobelt, *l.c.*) they seem to live in contact. Kobelt points out the highly interesting fact that Gredler has noted that in this area (if not in exactly the same spot) are to be found ribbed Clausilias which are obviously derived from smooth species (*rossmässleri* and *stenzii*).

10. Linsdale (1928) has shown (with full statistical data) that there is a correlation between certain osteological characters and the length of migration route in the Fox Sparrow (*Passerella iliaca*). She treats the skeletal modifications as adaptations to longer flight. But there is nothing to show that they are not merely somatic modifications.

11. Chapin (in Linsdale, *l.c.*) records that the bills of various species of *Pyrenestes* vary in shape and size, and that the variation is correlated with diversity of food. Linsdale (*l.c.* p. 360), however, finds that the bill in *Passerella* exhibits marked racial variation, though the food of the species is uniform.

12. Annandale (1915) noticed that the oscula of the Sponge *Tetilla dactyloides* var. differ from those of the typical form in diameter, which he considers is due to their being adapted to silt-laden water. This case is only generally stated.

13. Pickford (1926) states that in moist soils it is customary to find 'superpapillate' forms of various species of earthworms. This is supposed to be an adaptation necessitated by locomotion over slippery soil. The facts are not presented very fully, and there are no figures showing the incidence of the various types on various soils.

14. *Colour-pattern in lizards of the genus* Cnemidophorus (*Gadow, 1903*).

Gadow studied the colour-pattern of these Central American lizards, which seems to display an orthogenetic development analogous to that observed in the Mediterranean Wall Lizard by Eimer (1881). He found the same tendency for a pattern theme to pass through various similar stages in allied species. He claims that in some cases it is possible to relate the various stages in the modification of the pattern, of which the essential feature is the break-up of a primitive series of stripes into spots which are ultimately assembled into transverse bands, to the habitat occupied by the various species and subspecies. Thus in sandy terrain with moderate vegetation he found *C. guttatus*

striatus, and in ' tropical forest with much undergrowth '
C. guttatus guttatus, which differs from the former in the marked
increase of spotting. This difference is connected (*l.c.* p. 121)
with ' the different features in the distribution of light in the
various terrains on which these lizards live.' His primary
contention is that there is a direct influence of the amount of
light on the distribution of pigment in the skin ; but (p. 122)
he also contends that there may be a selective advantage in
having, *e.g.*, a broken pattern in habitats where the light is
broken by the characteristic vegetation. He expresses a
doubt (p. 123) whether selection can act in this way ; but
he stresses the fact that differences between the juvenile
and adult livery seem to be related to differences in habitat
noticed between young and adult forms of the same species.
This is a highly interesting case, in so far as the author
attempts to find an environmental basis for what would otherwise pass as an ' orthogenetic ' series. It is, however, impossible
to judge the value of his suggestion, as his data are not statistically treated and the incidence of the various types in the
particular habitats is not expressed numerically.

15. *Ovipositors of Noctuid moths (Edelsten, 1907)*.

Edelsten records that in the two Noctuid moths *Nonagria
cannae* and *N. sparganii* the ovipositors differ, being adapted in
one species to pierce plant-tissues and in the other to roll up a
leaf, so that the egg can be laid on the under-side. There is no
indication as to why one form of oviposition is better than the
other. Doubtless the difference in ovipositor is necessary, but
can we say the same for the habits ? (*Cf.* also p. 300.)

16. *Teeth of* Varanus niloticus (*Lonnberg, 1903*).

Lönnberg states that most species of *Varanus* (lizards) have
sharp, pointed teeth, but *V. niloticus*, which appears to be
exceptional in feeding on Mollusca, has blunt teeth adapted to
crushing them. Similar observations have been made on the
teeth of fishes ; but it is far from clear to what extent allied
species are distinguished by such differences.

The great defect in most evidence of this kind is (*a*) the
casual and anecdotal nature of the evidence, (*b*) the failure to
show that the correlation between structural diversity and habit
is of wide occurrence within given groups, and (*c*) the general

failure to show that all the species in a genus are distinguished by adaptations. Usually a pair of species are picked out and contrasted and the other species are left out of account.

On the whole this type of evidence does not carry very much weight. At the most one would say that two cases (Lutz, 1908 ; Boettger, 1921) are suggestive that sections of a population may be adaptively differentiated. Against this very inconclusive evidence one has to set an enormous array of instances of species and subspecies which are tolerably well known and for the structural differentia of which no adaptive explanation is available. Particular attention is directed to those intensive studies of racial diversity (Crampton, Gulick, etc.) in which a high degree of local differentiation is found amid uniform environmental and bionomic conditions. This is particularly well seen in Crampton's Partulas of the Society Islands, where we have ample evidence of the origin of clearly differentiated local groups amid uniform conditions. Isolation coupled with rapid mutation seems to have played the major part in promoting divergence.

The number of such examples could probably be considerably extended, more especially by admitting less closely allied pairs of species, though in the latter case many authors would probably regard the characters as generic rather than specific. But, even if the above list were multiplied many times over, it would still be possible to compile a parallel and much longer list of specific characters of no adaptive significance. We may mention the careful study by Whedon (1918) of the morphology and functions of the abdomen in dragon-flies. In these insects some of the most remarkable structural modifications are very difficult to explain on a functional basis, and, in the genus *Lestes*, females with very different abdomen-lengths all occur together and lay their eggs in the same plants, so that the theory originally propounded that length of abdomen was correlated with egg-laying habits seems difficult to maintain.

The establishment of a use for structural specific characters advances our problem only one stage. We have still to show that the change of function has been a real advantage. This question we consider in section (3) (p. 300).

(2) *The problem of secondary sexual characters.*—Secondary sexual characters, more especially male characters, form a very

important part of those used in distinguishing species. In many groups of insects, for instance, the dichotomic identification keys have to be constructed separately for each sex, because of the great use made of secondary sexual characters.

Sex-limited specific characters may be roughly divided into four[1] groups, viz. : (a) colours or structures apparently of an ornamental nature or probably used in fighting for mates ; (b) apparatus for holding the sexes together during mating (apart from the genitalia) ; (c) small differences in colour or structure of no apparent significance ; (d) differences in the male and female genitalia. All these categories intergrade, but it is easy to find examples which appear to belong definitely to one or another.

(a) Typical examples are the bright colours and ornamental excrescences of many male birds and butterflies, sound-producing organs in many insects, horns and antlers in various mammals, and enlarged chelæ in some Crustacea. Sexual selection, in its original meaning, was a process by which certain individuals of a species were favoured at the expense of the remainder ; the selection was supposed to be purely intraspecific and not beneficial to the species as a whole, except in so far as it might lead to a reduction of the period elapsing between sexual maturity and successful mating. In recent years the tendency has been to lay stress on the latter function and less on the supposed advantage to individuals (see Sturtevant, 1915 ; Huxley, 1923 ; Richards, 1927a). As Fisher (1930, p. 138) has pointed out, even with a relatively low death-rate per week, a distinct advantage would accrue to individuals mating earliest. Some of the ornaments and weapons found in the animal kingdom are probably of use to their possessors and may have been largely evolved under the influence of some form of sexual selection, though we can hardly claim that there has been as yet sufficient experiment to put the matter on a very sound basis. The problem of the great specific diversity exhibited in ornaments is not nearly so difficult as in the case of the diversity of cryptic patterns (p. 280). Our knowledge of the emotional life of animals is extraordinarily small ; but it appears legitimate to assume that any colour or structure which ' caught the eye ' of the

---

[1] In a number of species the female is modified in connection with her maternal duties, giving a fifth type of secondary sexual difference.

female might be effective, so that a great variety in adornment might be adapted to the same end. Any bright-coloured patch in the male might serve to raise sexual excitement in the female and so hasten mating, and it would not be surprising if in one species a blue patch and in another a red one first gave the opportunity to selection.

Much the same argument can be applied to the development of scent-producing organs, which occur so widely in insects (Richards, 1927a), are not uncommon in mammals (Pocock, 1916), and also play some part in the courtship of spiders (Bristowe and Locket, 1926). They appear usually to be the main factor in bringing the sexes of insects together, and in others also seem to be employed to stimulate sexual excitement in the female. In the latter rôle they are exactly comparable to an ornament, but when used for attraction and recognition of members of the other sex the evolution of specific diversity is more difficult to explain, since changes in production would have to be very closely correlated with changes in perception. Exactly the same difficulty has to be met with in trying to explain the evolution of male genitalia (p. 299).

With weapons the case appears rather different, since we might expect a much closer degree of correspondence between the structure evolved and the needs of the animal in fighting. It is very doubtful if such correspondence could at present be established, but our information is very scanty on the observational side. Although horned mammals certainly fight to a considerable extent in the breeding season, the remarkable horn-like structures found in many male insects do not appear to have this function, and much fuller records of the behaviour in nature of animals bearing such excrescences are required before we can confidently assert how far presumptive 'weapons' are really useful either to the species or to the males. The occurrence of secondary sexual characters is very capricious —e.g. in some Pulmonate Mollusca 'darts' are present; in many they are absent (cf. also the contrast between rodents and ruminants among mammals).

(b) Special organs for grasping the female during copulation are characteristic of many invertebrates, especially arthropods. For our present purpose we are excluding the most typical grasping organs of all, those developed in connection with the genitalia. Almost any part of the body may be modified, including the mandibles, antennæ, legs or abdomen, and there is a very strong *prima facie* case for regarding the modifications as useful, the close contact of the sexes during a period long enough for successful fertilisation being an evident necessity. It is further well established that the detailed structure of grasping organs usually differs from species to species, although it is rarely possible to show any detailed correlation between the organs of different types of males and the structure of the corresponding parts in their respective females. Not only is there great specific diversity in the male without corresponding co-adaptation in the female, but the actual development of grasping organs in the males is highly sporadic. Thus, besides the marked specific differences in the nature of these structures, it is quite common to find them developed only in a few species in a genus or in a few genera in a family. Of two species, otherwise very similar in structure and habits, one will have a highly specialised grasping organ, the other none. We will give one example from the Hymenoptera. The small wasps of the family Crabronidae often have the fore tibia, the fore basitarsus, or both, enlarged in the male (fig. 27). The enlargement varies greatly in degree, from a very slight increase in width to a condition in which the whole apical part of the leg forms an elaborate shield which cannot be used for ordinary walking ; in almost every case the details of the modification are highly specific. Kohl (1915), in his monograph of the palæarctic species, divides the old genus *Crabro* into ten species-groups (by many regarded as genera or subfamilies), including in all 167 species. Only forty-two species are known from female specimens or have been insufficiently described, and of the remaining 125 species 39 have the modified foreleg ; these are distributed amongst seven of the ten species-groups. Bristowe (1929*d*, p. 348) has reviewed the structures used by male spiders for grasping the females. The differences appear to be usually familial or generic, but there is an interesting example in the genus *Pachygnatha*, in which the male cheliceræ grasp those of the female during mating. Here a marked difference in the teeth on the male cheliceræ of two species corresponds to two different *methods* of gripping the female, although her cheliceræ are not actually modified.

As far as the habits are known there is nothing to show that the species with grasping forelegs have a greater need for tightly gripping the female. There is nothing to show that the specific differences in grasping organs are adaptive, and it would even sometimes appear that the structures were

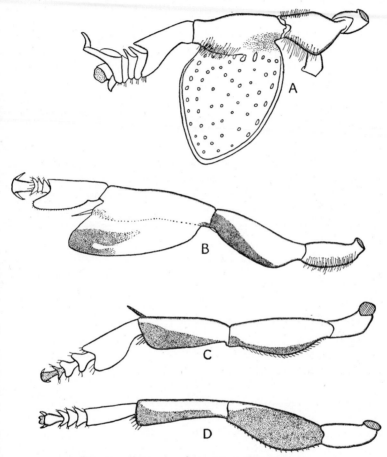

FIG. 27.—FORELEGS OF SOME MALE CRABRONIDAE.

A. *Thyreopus cribrarius* L. Left foreleg, coxa omitted. Femur abnormal; tibia strongly, tarsi moderately, broadened.
B. *Crossocerus palmarius* Schreb. Tibia and basitarsus strongly broadened.
C. *C. palmipes* van de Lind. Basitarsus broadened.
D. *C. elongatulus* van de Lind. Leg unmodified.

developed beyond the needs of the species, as far as we can gauge these by comparison with allied forms.

(*c*) The vast majority of sexually dimorphic structures, though still of great value as specific characters, appear to come under the present category (with the usual qualification that some apparently useless structures may later be found to have a function). Admittedly, experimental evidence is required to prove that a structure has no significance as an ornament, but, though this evidence is usually lacking, we can scarcely, therefore, assume that all sorts of apparently very trivial male characters are adaptive. In the wasp *Trypoxylon palliditarse*, for instance, the male differs from the female as follows (besides rather smaller size and different genitalia) : the proportions of the antennal segments, especially apically, are different ; the clypeus has an outstanding lamella with two small teeth on each side of it ; the stipes of the maxillæ bears a large angular tubercle, the mid-coxæ are set further apart and the mesosternum is more angularly emarginate between them ; the posterior margin of the metasternum is more deeply emarginate ; the antero-dorsal margin of the hind tibiæ bears a dense row of short spines ; the first abdominal sternite bears a long recurved hook ; the second and third abdominal sternites are basally impressed. None of these structures appears at all likely to be correlated with courtship or mating, except possibly the modification of the thoracic sternites, which may enable the male to fit more closely to the convex dorsum of the female.

We are aware of only one or two cases in which actual experiment has shown that secondary sexual characters are apparently without function. Lutz (1911) removed the tarsal comb in a male *Drosophila* and found that mating was in no way impeded. The tarsal comb is found in the males of certain species, for which it is an important diagnostic character. Mayer (1900) and Mayer and Soule (1906) showed that wing-colour had no influence on the mating of certain Saturniid and Lymantriid moths, in which the males and females differ markedly in colour. Painting of the wings scarlet, etc., or providing the females with male wings, has no effect on the percentage of successful matings.

It is impossible to estimate what percentage of secondary sexual characters would have to be classed as apparently useless ; it would certainly be very high and would include a large number of specific characters. The sporadic distribution of such structures is just as marked as in the case of grasping organs.

(*d*) Of recent years more and more weight has been placed

in specific diagnosis on differences in the male, and to a less extent in the female, genitalia. We may mention the studies of the os penis or baculum in mammals (Lonnberg, 1911 ; von Bittera, 1918 ; Pocock, 1923) ; the copulatory fins of fishes, *e.g.* Selachii (Leigh-Sharpe, 1920, 1921), *Gambusia* (Geiser, 1923) ; the dart and associated structures in Mollusca (Ashford, 1885) ; the genitalia in insects (see Boulangé, 1924, pp. 359–392) or the copulatory styles in the Planaria (Eggers, 1925). These differences have been recognised not only as very prevalent, but as of particular systematic importance because of the relatively high degree of discontinuity observed, so that species with sharply distinct genitalia may otherwise differ only in trivial and not easily appreciable characters.

Two main questions arise from the study of the genitalia : (1) What functions do the remarkable modifications of these organs serve ? Do they act as barriers stopping crossing between species ? (2) How have the variations in genitalia, ultimately leading to specific difference, arisen and become established in the species ?

Both these questions have been dealt with in some detail in Chapter V, and only our conclusions need be summarised. We have rejected the earlier view that the prime function of differences in the genitalia is to isolate species, chiefly because the members of different species do not in any case often try to mate, and because in some pairs of species considerable differences in the genitalia do not prohibit crossing when it is attempted. We are forced to regard specific differences in the genitalia as of essentially the same nature as other apparently useless specific characters.

As regards the second question, we have also opposed the view that differentiation of the genitalia is necessarily associated with geographical variation. We believe that even in a relatively homogeneous area divergence of species, including divergence of genitalia, is possible and probably, in many groups of insects, quite common.

Whether divergence of a type leading ultimately to cessation of interbreeding always depends on geographical isolation, or not, we have to explain how the elements in the divergence became established. It is generally agreed that a variety of habitudinal and structural differences between any pair of species contributes to the absence of interbreeding. Even those who maintain that the genitalia are the main agency of permanent isolation would probably admit that the observed differences in these organs are the result of more than one evolutionary step, except, perhaps, in some of the least modified geographical races. Further, there is no suggestion that any environmental influence has played a *direct* part in the specific modifications of the genitalia. This must be due to the spread through the population of small variations, occurring at first in a few individuals. The most obvious agency to account for such a spread would be Natural Selection. Each race of any widespread species might be so well adapted to its own area that individuals capable of crossing (with the production of intermediate forms unfitted to either one area or the other) would be at a discount. A theory very much on these lines has been propounded by Fisher (1930, pp. 125–31). He suggests, first, that any species spread over a considerable geographical area will tend to be differentiated at each end of its range into a locally adapted form which will at first be connected by a complete series of intermediates. In the course of time the end-forms would get more and more unlike and each more and more unfitted to live in the area inhabited by the other. The process of diffusion from one end to the other would gradually be retarded by the operation of selection, since the individuals with the strongest tendency to migrate to the parts of the range to which they were ill adapted would be eliminated. Further, any preference shown by individuals of one type for individuals like themselves will be advantageous, since it will lead to an intensification of local adaptation and will tend to stop locally adapted individuals from crossing with less-adapted migrants into their area. There might thus be built up a sexual preference which would hasten the process of fission and eventually make it permanent.

It should be noted that this explanation is purely formal and no example is forthcoming, as might be expected from the difficulty of obtaining the necessary evidence. In our opinion such a process is unlikely to be very prevalent, since it demands a degree of local adaptation such as we have elsewhere tried to show appears to be by no means general. Even if such a process were at work, it is doubtful if it could explain the specific differences observed in the genitalia. The latter could be adaptive in the way described above only if they were an actual impediment to racial crosses, whereas it appears much more probable in fact that differences in the genitalia are usually the *result* rather than the *cause* of the cessation of interbreeding. If this be true, then the differentiation of the genitalia cannot have taken place under the action of selection (at any rate in this particular way), since, if the forms have already ceased to interbreed, there is no advantage in developing mechanical difficulties to crossing.

Actually the specific differences in the genitalia appear to be an excellent illustration of the non-adaptive nature of specific characters. There is a general mechanical co-adaptation of the sexes, sometimes (but apparently by no means always) very close, but there is no evidence for adaptation in the extraordinary specific diversity.

There is a considerable difficulty to be met in connection with the co-adaptation of the genitalia in the sexes. This difficulty is much greater for those who believe in the ' lock-and-key ' theory, but is still of some magnitude even if the genitalia are not regarded as the most important means of isolation. Any change, in one sex, of a character (whether structural, physiological or habitudinal) directly connected with pairing appears to necessitate a correlated change in the other sex. Thus a new development in the male genitalia requires, in so far as the male and female structures are co-adapted, a corresponding development in the female. Similarly, if certain females start to produce a sex-scent of a new character, the male perceptor-organs must be able to perceive the new scent and the males must react to it in the appropriate way. It will be suggested that this parallel evolution would not be very difficult if, at all stages, the amount of change at any one step was very small ; but this gradual evolution is very difficult to explain as an adaptation. For these changes would be adaptive (in the course of the fission of a species into two or more locally adapted races) only in so far as they tended to stop interbreeding and therefore, *ipso facto*, required correlated change in the other sex ; if the changes were too small to require correlated variation, then they would appear to have no adaptive value in the promotion of fission. It is probable that the division between adaptive and non-adaptive changes in sexual characters may not be quite so sharply marked as has been suggested above ; yet there does appear to be a real difficulty. Petersen (1909, p. 308) has attempted to solve it by assuming that effects of the organs on one another during use are inherited.

(3) *The origin of habits.*—It has not rarely been assumed that if we can show that some insignificant structure is definitely related to some part of the normal habits of the animal, that structure has been proved to be adaptive. A little analysis of a few concrete cases, however, reveals that this is a rather naïve assumption unless the adaptive nature of the habit itself is proved. Before conducting these analyses a short consideration of the relation of structure to habits is desirable.

Woodger (1929, chapter vii) has endeavoured to show that the antithesis often drawn by biologists between function and structure is false—that the two are only aspects of one entity, structure alone being a mere abstraction of the anatomist, who ignores the element of time which is really inseparable from a living organism. Woodger's argument appears incontestable when applied to any of the intricate internal adaptations which are characteristic of living organisms. Even in a simple case, as when a structural change in the eye of an insect alters its phototropic response, it is illogical to speak of structure determining function or *vice versa*. But the case is different with many of the small structural or habit differences which distinguish species. Thus in the Psammocharidae (dealt with on p. 276), species either with or without a 'tarsal comb' may burrow in sand, and it is quite reasonable to inquire whether (*a*) the development of a comb enabled certain species to restrict themselves to looser soils, or whether (*b*) only certain of the species which had adopted loose soils for their habitat were able to develop a comb for digging. On our present knowledge we cannot actually decide between these alternatives.

A rather different example is given by Edwards (1929, pp. 35–6) in his account of the flies of the family Blepharoceridae. Here, in several genera, the mandibles are present in the females of some species, absent in others. The species with mandibles are blood-suckers, those without them visit flowers. The mandibles are always found fully developed or absent, never in an intermediate condition. It appears in this case that the presence or absence of the mandibles (structure) determines habit, for species without mandibles could never adopt the blood-sucking habit.

In the majority of the small characters which distinguish families or genera, it appears legitimate to distinguish quite sharply between habit and structure and to inquire which changes first in the course of evolution. If we set aside the numerous structural features which seem to be functionless and the numerous habits in correlation with which no co-adapted structures have been developed, we are left with many examples of small structural characters clearly associated with small habit differences which are not necessarily adaptive. It is with regard to this residuum that the inquiry as to the priority of structure or function has to be made. First let us suppose that the structural changes precede the co-adapted change in function. Then, at the time when they occur, all such changes will be non-adaptive and they can become adaptive only after the necessary habit changes have been made and in so far as the new habit is more advantageous than the old.

Secondly, if the habits change first, then any structural change making the new habit more easy of fulfilment will be adaptive, at any rate in so far as the new habit is adaptive. It is evidently much easier to imagine evolution happening in this way, especially if Natural Selection has played a big part in it. But if we want to decide which of the two alternatives has actually been most usual, it is very difficult to find much evidence ; most authors appear to attribute the major importance to habit. It is probable that any change in habits may provide a use for some hitherto trivial structure, while the existence of so many useless structures might be regarded as an incentive to a change in habits allowing some of them to be used. The condition is one where ' pre-adaptation ' might be expected to be rife.

We will now consider how far certain typical specific differences in habits can be considered adaptive. Perhaps one of the commonest types of habit difference is in the nature of the food. We usually know very little about the variety of foods eaten by carnivores, and especially of the relative importance of the various items, and it will be simpler to consider a vegetarian animal feeding on a few allied species of one plant genus. There are quite a number of examples, for instance, where in one insect genus some species feed on poplars, others on willows. There appear to be two ways in which such a condition could have arisen : either (*a*) the species originally fed on one kind of host plant only and some individuals suddenly turned to a new food, or (*b*) the species originally fed on both plants and has since split into two, each restricted to part of the old food range.   It is probable that either of these processes may have occurred in different species.

(*a*) We are to suppose that as a result of mutation a new variety of a species arises which attacks a new food-plant.   It is only exceptionally that a vegetarian species so overeats its food-supply that it is actually limited by a shortage of food ; thus the new mutation would only be an obvious adaptation if it happened to occur at one of the periods of famine.   We also have to consider whether competition with all the various other dependants on the new host is more or less keen than that met with on the old.   It is possible that the animal was already able (as far as digestion, etc., is concerned) to eat the new plant, but hitherto lacked the instinct to attack it ; or, again, it may require, besides the new instinct to eat, changes in its physiology to ensure successful assimilation.   In the latter case the new instinct might at first be a positive disadvantage.   The new variety, even if more or less adapted to its food, could not be established permanently without the help of some sort of isolation.   Such speculations can be elaborated indefinitely without much profit ;   all that we can be sure of is that we cannot assume, in the absence of detailed knowledge, that a change of food-plant would necessarily be beneficial : it appears that such a change might be harmful, neutral or adaptive according to circumstances.

One point which seems to be of some importance is that while an extension of the food range may at no stage be of much advantage to the individuals who are actually breaking new ground, yet there is probably a considerable gain to the species as a whole.   In the course of competition with other species and in the fluctuations of conditions during geological epochs, a species with a wide range of foods has a better chance of survival than one more specialised.   But, though the species becomes in a sense better adapted, no necessary advantage accrues to the various races of which it is composed.

(*b*) We have more direct knowledge of the way in which a polyphagous species splits into several races with a restricted food range than we have of the origin of completely new food habits. It would probably be admitted that the first stage in the former process was the formation of biological races within the species, although we can, perhaps, never prove that those races are not the result of a definite change in instinct (as described in (a)) ; yet comparison with allied forms suggests rather that a species of generalised habits has become more specialised. We have dealt above (pp. 301–2) with the question of the origin of biological races. For our present purpose only two aspects of the problem concern us. First, the instinctive basis of racial specialisation does not usually appear to be hereditary, at any rate in its early stages. The female returns to lay her eggs on the substratum on which the larvæ fed, and her response can be altered in a few generations by experimental restriction to a different food : her reactions may be due to the retention of a ' larval memory ' (Thorpe, 1930, p. 202) rather than to hereditarily fixed instincts. In these circumstances the most that can be claimed for selection is that it has favoured those species endowed with the power of ' larval memory ' ; it has not been active in the initial stages of the formation of biological races. Secondly, we must consider how far each biological race is adapted to its food. A certain confusion is liable to be introduced here by the ambiguous use of the word ' adaptation ' (cf. Chapter IX). Some authors have spoken of a race A as being ' adapted ' to a particular host B, when meaning no more in reality than that A is restricted to B. The true use of the term, however, can be illustrated by considering a species with two races A and A^i, restricted to two hosts B and B^i. These races are spoken of as adapted to their hosts, only if in each case some part of their structure or physiology makes each one better able to live on its own host than on that of the other, so that not only is each race restricted to its own host in nature, but that A, transferred to B^i, would be at a definite disadvantage compared with A^i. Unfortunately we have not nearly enough evidence on this point. What evidence we have does not suggest that there is necessarily a definite adaptation to the preferred host. When one race is transferred to the food of another, it is true that there is often (perhaps usually) a considerable mortality. But a considerable number frequently survive and appear from then onwards to be physiologically conditioned to the new food. It appears that in most of the experiments the transference has not been made at a sufficiently early stage. When a certain food has been tasted it may well be understood that a transfer will be more difficult. It may be argued that the few survivors on the new substratum form a specially adapted strain which has been selected out, but this appears improbable when we find that a race once accustomed to a new substratum may be almost as difficult to retransfer to its original food as it was, in the first experiment, to rear on the new. The whole question, however, is in need of more numerous experiments on a larger scale.

If we turn to other typical instances of habit difference, we usually find our knowledge equally small and the difficulties of a straightforward adaptational explanation just as great. A large number of the minor specific differences in habits appear, as far as we can see, to be non-adaptive. For instance, in various leaf-mining insects the mine may be made on either the under or the upper surface of the leaf, or it may begin at the base, centre or margin of the leaf ; it may be of various shapes (a loosely or tightly coiled spiral, blotch, etc.) ; and the pupa (or puparium) may remain in the mine or the larvæ may pupate in the ground ; the frass of the larva in the mine may be arranged in one or more continuous rows of pellets, in discontinuous heaps, or in a single mass, or may be ejected from the mine altogether. None of these habits has any known adaptive significance.

In another large class of examples the habits appear to be adaptive in a general way without being specially adapted to the particular case under consideration. We may instance here numerous specific differences in nesting habits. Generally speaking, each method of nesting appears to be reasonably adapted to the needs of the animal, but we can rarely, if ever, indicate how one method is more adapted to the need of the particular species which employs it. It will perhaps be retorted that it is too much to expect that we should be able to demonstrate such adaptation ; but until we can (at least in a fair proportion of cases) it is not very logical to assume that all such habit differences must have some important reference to the survival of the animal.

Another difficult problem is raised by the consideration of how far the *habitat differences* between species are likely to be adaptive. It is a familiar fact that most closely allied verte-brate species (or races) occur either in different habitats or in different geographical areas. In insects and some of the other small arthropods it appears that numerous quite closely allied species may occur in one habitat, often filling, as far as we can see, the same ecological niche ; in other cases allied species occur in different habitats, as in vertebrates, but it is not yet possible to estimate which condition is most frequent.

The factors determining the habitat of an animal appear to be exceedingly complex. In the higher vertebrates a con-siderable and, at present, incalculable psychological element is certainly important. In some of the smaller arthropods, where psychological considerations are less likely to have weight, it is highly probable that the observed habitat range is due to an interaction between not only the responses of the animal to edaphic conditions, but also to the nature of its food, of its enemies and of its parasites. We have, therefore, in-sufficient knowledge to discuss any species in much detail. Certain general principles, however, can perhaps be elucidated.

A very close parallel may be drawn between species-differences in food and in habitat. And the greater part of the argument on p. 302 could be repeated here with a few merely verbal alterations. We are, in fact, faced on the one hand with the query as to whether the enlargement of the habitat range by certain individuals of a species will not benefit the species as a whole rather than those individuals. On the other hand, if we imagine a species with a wide habitat range separating into two or more races (or incipient species), each with a restricted range, then adaptation requires that each race should be better fitted to live in its particular habitat than in those of its allies. It is seldom, if ever, possible to demonstrate such ' goodness of fit ' between race (or species) and habitat. We can often indicate one factor which is predominant in deter-mining why one species occurs in one habitat and an allied species in another—*e.g.* the distribution of certain species of tiger-beetles is partly governed by the nature of the soil available for oviposition (Shelford, 1907, 1909). But to exhibit the mechanism by which an animal appears to recognise or restrict itself to its normal habitat is not the same as showing that the animal is really better adapted to that habitat than to any other. Close adaptation to the whole complex of conditions provided by the habitat may be present, but we certainly cannot yet show that it exists. The highly successful introduction of species from one country into another, or, as in the case of many pests, from one habitat to another, does not suggest that species so introduced were originally adapted to a very close range of conditions. And where several apparently closely allied species occur in one habitat and yet differ from one another in structure in much the same way as other species which live in different habitats, we find it difficult to believe that every expansion or restriction of the habitat range of a species necessarily implies a closer adaptation to the new conditions.

(4) *Complex organs and 'co-adaptations.'*

Though most organs are complex and probably all adaptations are ' co-adaptations,' both have been supposed by many authors to present a special problem, and we think a brief consideration of them may be of some value.

The difficulty of explaining the origin of complex organs by means of the selection of small variations is well set out by Darwin in his ' Origin of Species' (1884, pp. 143–9). In one respect, however, Darwin's argument has been weakened, inasmuch as Fisher (1930, pp. 73–83) has demonstrated that, if his premises are admitted, new characters which are not directly or indirectly (*i.e.* by correlation) adaptive are very unlikely to spread through a population. Now Darwin throughout his book supposes that some part of the origin of complex characters may be due to the persistence of characters not positively harmful, and this is helpful in accounting for the early stages of various evolutionary processes. This supposition, however, cannot be made if variants are supposed to arise through rare mutations which have to spread through the population and have little chance of persistence without the aid of selection. A somewhat heavier burden is thrown, therefore, on Natural Selection, which has to play the dominating part throughout the evolution of any structure.

The essential feature of any complex organ such as the mammalian eye or kidney is the co-ordination into one working whole of a number of separate structures and tissues. The difficulty of obtaining such co-ordination by the selection of random variations in the various parts is sufficiently obvious.

On the selectionist view all the parts of an organ are supposed to vary and only very minute variations would be likely to improve one element without upsetting the general balance, and it is the selection of such minute variants that is assumed. It appears to us that there is a certain danger in assuming that important evolutionary processes are due to a type of variation which is probably never demonstrated. Fisher (1930, pp. 14–16) has attempted to show that it is fallacious to suppose that the advantage conferred by a variation only very slightly in a favourable direction can be too small to be of survival value (but *cf.* p. 223). When we are dealing with a single organ or instinct the alteration of which in a particular direction is clearly beneficial to the animal, then Fisher's argument carries more weight. But it is rather different with regard to complex organs, where it would appear that the alteration of one part would be of no value without the correlated variation in all the other parts. If, however, we postulate such correlated variation, we are abrogating from selection the most important part in the formation of complex organs. We may consider as an example the eyes found in Lamellibranch molluscs. The most specialised type is seen in the Pectinidae, but in other families all gradations of structure are found (Dakin, 1928). There appears to be very little correlation between mode of life and eye-development. Some actively swimming species have complex eyes, others have simple eyes or none at all, and the same applies to the sedentary species. Experiments on *Pecten* show that, in all probability, even its very specialised eye does no more than perceive differences in light and shade, chemical stimuli being far more potent than light in directing its movements. Thus we appear to have an extremely complex organ of little adaptive value. If such an organ can develop largely without the influence of selection, then other eyes which are more obviously useful to their possessor may also partly evolve without selection. The problem is not one open to very convincing solution either way and should be left *sub judice*.

Fisher (1930, pp. 38–41) and especially Haldane (1932, p. 174) have attempted to show that no organ can be too complex for Natural Selection to evolve. The argument is a mathematical one based on the assumption that every part of an organ will be varying independently in all directions.

On this basis it can be shown that the chance that variation will lead to an improvement depends on the magnitude of the change and will approach one-half as the latter becomes small. Thus it is always possible for random variation to increase adaptation and, provided the change is small enough, the chances of improvement or the reverse are nearly equal. In a static environment and a stable organism this reasoning would appear to be incontrovertible. But in nature the individual is the only stable unit. Species are complex aggregates of numerous strains. The environment is constant only in its tendency to fluctuations and is pulling the organism in different directions in quick succession. The small variations, such as may lead to improvement in a complex organ, must usually confer only a very small advantage on the variant individuals. It is thus highly probable that the new variant will die out before it has had time to spread. We cannot prove that complex organs have not developed by means of Natural Selection, but we can see that the process will be very slow and we may even doubt if geological time has been sufficiently long. In our chapter on Adaptation we discuss the phenomenon of organisation, the most characteristic attribute of living animals. It may be suggested that complex organs are only a special instance of that process (*cf.* Chapter IX).

It is not quite the same with the problem of what Cuénot (1925) has called co-adaptations. This has been discussed in a very judicious way by Wheeler (1928, pp. 29–33), and Corset (1931) has illustrated a long series of examples in a very thorough monograph. These co-adaptations may be described as complex organs in which the co-ordination between the parts is not physiological but merely mechanical, like the relation between the blade and sheath of a penknife or the button and the button-hole. For example (see discussion, Robson, 1932), a button-like structure is actually known in some of the Cephalopoda, in which the mantle is held closed by a knob on one side fitting tightly into a socket on the other. An interesting example dealt with at some length by Wheeler is the development of ' scrobes ' or grooves for the reception of the antennæ in various insects. In ants these grooves are on the head and may run below or above the eyes, and they may have two divisions, one for the basal, the other for the apical part of the antenna. In some species only a part of the antenna can be withdrawn into the scrobe. In many beetles similar grooves are developed : in the Elateridae, for instance, but here they are situated on the under-side of the head and thorax. In the Byrrhidae each segment of the legs is grooved to contain the following one, so that the legs are almost invisible when retracted. Another type of co-adaptation is seen in the raptorial foreleg found in many groups of insects (*Mantis*, *Mantispa*, Phymatidae, etc.). Here the curved and apically spurred fore tibia can be adpressed to the strong, multispinose fore femora.

In all these co-adaptations the final form of the structure appears, at least very plausibly, to be adaptive, but it is very difficult to imagine their origin under the influence of Natural Selection. The early stages in the development of co-adapted parts [1] appear to be unsuitable for the purpose to which the finished structure is put, while in many cases the co-adaptation could be adaptive in the early stages of its evolution only if a number of independent variations occurred simultaneously, for the essence of such a structure is the co-operation between different parts. Cuénot, Wheeler and Corset all agree that many co-adaptations cannot be explained on the selection theory, though no other explanation can as yet be put forward. We shall return to this question in our discussion of orthogenesis.

SUMMARY

A preliminary examination of the data reveals that most workers have considered the deductive consequence of the Natural Selection theory rather than provided direct evidence for it. Most of the facts recorded by Darwin in 'The Origin' are evidence for evolution as opposed to 'special creation.' Only a minor part of the work deals at all directly with evidence for the theory of Natural Selection, which appears scarcely to have been distinguished in Darwin's mind from the more general proposition that species have arisen by descent with modification. The problem has been somewhat clarified by recent advances in our knowledge, but it is still on analysis of the consequences of selection rather than on the demonstration

---

[1] The special case of the co-adaptation of the male and female genitalia of a species is considered earlier (p. 151).

of its operation that attention has been concentrated. As a result, when opinions differ, as they often do on this topic, there is no body of crucial evidence to which we can appeal.

Though we are primarily interested in establishing whether or not a selective process actually occurs in nature, we are also concerned in the secondary question, whether Natural Selection, if operative at all, has played the main part in the evolution of the lower taxonomic categories. We have treated under four headings the data which enable us to form some opinion as to the answers to these questions.

We first deal with selection under artificial conditions. The discovery of the pure line is one of the major contributions of the geneticist to evolutionary theory and has revolutionised our ideas as to the significance of the superficially bewildering array of phenotypes. As a general rule, selection in any one direction appears soon to reach a definite limit beyond which progress depends on the occurrence of further mutations. It is not possible to define how circumscribed these limits are, but we no longer feel able to assume the existence of the universal storehouse of variation on which Darwin thought he was at liberty to draw. The evolution of domestic animals, during which the original types have undergone great modification, appears to have little in common with the normal course of evolution. The stock of variants has probably been greatly increased by the crossing of more than one wild species, while the strict isolation of different forms from one another and the selection for pedigree rather than for phenotypic quality have little counterpart in nature.

Secondly, we have considered the direct evidence for a selective process in nature. We have shown that no demonstration of large, apparently random, mortality can reveal whether selection is operative or not. It is the small percentage of selective deaths which is significant, not the random death-rate, even if this is extremely high. If the death-rate is largely random, this may slow down the spread of rare, beneficial mutants, but it cannot permanently inhibit it, provided they really have a greater chance of survival and reproduction.

The direct evidence for the occurrence of Natural Selection is very meagre and carries little conviction. In a few instances there is some evidence for a selective process which in some cases tends to promote the survival of the mean of the stock.

Whether this is due to the better regulated internal relations of such individuals or to their adaptation to the mean conditions of their habitat is still quite unknown. The few instances of historical changes in natural populations which we have been able to collect throw little light on the causes of the changes. Even in the melanic Lepidoptera the elimination of lighter individuals on a darkened background has not been the subject of a detailed investigation.

The direct evidence for the Natural Selection theory would carry little conviction without the support of much indirect evidence, but we have emphasised the necessary limitations of the latter, which consists, essentially, in demonstrating that organisms are more or less adapted to their environment. Now some fundamental properties of living organisms, such as irritability or cellular respiration, are definitely adaptive and yet can hardly be regarded as the result of selection, since without them we cannot imagine a living organism existing. Adaptation is therefore to some extent synonymous with life, and an extended series of adaptive relationships does not necessarily tell us very much as to how these relationships arose. The theory that Natural Selection has produced all such relationships is attractive, because there is no other widely applicable theory in the field ; but the proof of the Natural Selection theory depends, in the last resort, on observations of death-rates, not on descriptions of the adaptations of the living.

Under our third heading we have considered some of the genetical data as to the nature of variation and have endeavoured to decide whether the material provided is at all suitable for the efficient operation of a selective process. We have also criticised the purely deductive evolutionary theories which have been founded almost entirely on the mathematical treatment of genetical data. Our knowledge of mutation under laboratory conditions might be summarised by saying that mutants are relatively rare and mostly harmful. It is possible that beneficial mutants also occur, but this is still largely an assumption, though perhaps a somewhat credible one. We have no data which allow us to assume an approximate mutation-rate for most species, and, for the few in which some evidence is available, it is scarcely certain that under natural conditions the rate would be the same. Even if it is legitimate to assume the occurrence of rare, beneficial mutants, any mathematical treatment of the conditions under which they spread demands further assumptions as to their selective advantage and as to the amount of intercrossing within the species.   We have pointed out the difficulty of attributing a constant selective advantage to a mutant which has to make its way in a fluctuating environment, in a checker-board of different habitats and in a species which is far from being genetically homogeneous.   Again, apart from the great variety of factors which may produce partial isolation, the mere fact that an animal is small, while the range of the species is often large, introduces a measure of purely spatial isolation. The result is that, in order to obtain the uniform conditions necessary for mathematical calculations, a relatively small subdivision of the species can alone be treated, and here the unknown rate of mutation begins at once to be significant. The mathematical treatment of Natural Selection cannot tell us whether or not the theory is true, but it might be used to give us some idea of the time-limits for evolutionary changes and the limits and results of various types of selection.   We feel, however, that the fundamental assumptions are still very insecure and we need scarcely be bound by any purely mathematical restrictions.

Finally, we have considered the indirect evidence for the theory.   We have intentionally thrown our net wide and included material which not all zoologists would regard as relevant to the Natural Selection problem.   At one time or another almost all biological phenomena have been supposed to provide some sort of evidence for the theory, and our choice was chiefly influenced by the thoroughness with which particular lines of inquiry had been explored.   The first half of the section deals with a variety of phenomena such as protective coloration or adaptation to life in torrents, which suggest that evolutionary divergence may have been due to a selective process, while in the second half we are concerned with the problem of species and how far their characteristics are explicable on the assumption that specific divergence is mainly dependent on Natural Selection.

In our examination of numerous examples of protective coloration we take the view that a generalised colouring of this nature is probably fundamental in all groups.   It may be obtained by accommodation within the life of the individual, perhaps more often than is commonly supposed. The more striking cases of resemblance to a specialised background are one of the chief sources of indirect evidence for the Natural Selection theory. The resemblance may be either to the general background, particularly when this is unusually uniform (*e.g.* deserts), or to particular objects in the habitat (*e.g.* eggs of Cuckoos). The incidence of such specialised protection is somewhat capricious and there are some puzzling exceptions. If, however, we confine our attention to cases of clearly cryptic coloration, the following points appear to be important :

(1) There is often insufficient quantitative evidence as to the association of animals with the appropriate background.

(2) In some examples more evidence is required that the habits of the animals do not render the particular coloration unnecessary (*e.g.* nocturnal animals).

(3) There is still a lack of evidence that selection has actually produced the observed colour-correspondence. In some cases an obscure method of accommodation may be responsible. The examples of the eggs of the Yellow Wattled Lapwing and of the eggs of Cuckoos provide at least good presumptive evidence for selection.

In the special type of protective coloration commonly known as ' warning colours ' we have to beware of attributing conspicuousness to animals which are really concealed in their natural habitats. The incidence of conspicuous colours is somewhat capricious and is not universally associated with a high degree of unpalatability. On the other hand, there is a good deal of evidence suggesting that species with conspicuous patterns, particularly those made up of bands or spots of black and yellow or red, fall well below the average of palatability. The recent work of Morton Jones (p. 247) provides some of the most striking evidence amongst the Insecta. We still hold, however, that there is a great need for large-scale investigations of the actual food of predators in nature and of the extent to which different genera and species are attacked. The evidence that predators distinguish between variants differing only slightly in colour is still very meagre. Finally, we have briefly considered the joint evolution of conspicuous colours and unpalatability, and conclude that the difficulties of such a process have not been sufficiently considered.

In less well-studied cases, which we consider next (pp. 265–271), the same sort of difficulties arise, but there is much less positive information. The features which are presumed to be adaptive are found only in some members of the community living in a given habitat ; the ' adapted ' species are often not proved to be confined to that habitat, and there is little evidence that Natural Selection is the only possible agency which could have produced the results.

With the available evidence, however, it is scarcely possible to estimate the importance of selection. The negative evidence in the second half of this section must also be given due weight.

The body of facts set out in our section dealing with the mimicry theory forms the best documented argument bearing on the selectionist view of the evolution of animal colour. When all the evidence is considered, it is difficult to resist the conclusion that selection has played some part in the evolution of mimetic resemblances. As we have pointed out, the possibility of the parallel evolution of similar colour-patterns in different species has been little investigated. The first step in a mimetic resemblance is always the most difficult one to account for, and possibly parallel variation in different genera may help to bridge this gap, for there is some evidence suggesting that if birds do discriminate between colour-patterns it is chiefly between those that are rather sharply distinct from one another. We do not believe that there is as yet sufficient evidence to affirm that selection by predators, especially birds, is very highly discriminative.

In the second half of this section we consider indirect evidence against the Natural Selection theory. A survey of the characters which differentiate species (and to a less extent genera) reveals that in the vast majority of cases the specific characters have no known adaptive significance. A few special cases where such a significance has been suggested are considered in detail (pp. 283–290). Most of these examples still require confirmation. As we have frequently insisted, without some sort of direct evidence for selection such examples prove very little. It may be conceded that in a number of instances structures apparently useless may in the future be found to play an important part in the life of the species ; further, many ' useless ' characters may be correlated with less obvious features which are of real use, but, even allowing for this, the number of apparently useless specific characters is so large that any theory which merely *assumes* that they are indirectly adaptive is bound to be more a matter of predilection than of scientific reasoning.

A survey of secondary sexual characters (in which specific differences are often displayed) shows that in any one group they tend to occur very sporadically. They are often present in one species and absent in another which is otherwise very similar both in habits and structure. The explanation of the evolution of such structure by some modified form of Darwin's sexual selection theory still requires much more direct verification. We hardly feel as yet that we have enough evidence to estimate the value of the theory. The special case of specific differences in the male or female genitalia is considered at some length, and we conclude that there is very little evidence that these structures play an important part in isolating species. The evolution of such structures, where there must be some degree of co-adaptation between the sexes, is very difficult to understand, particularly if it is assumed to have resulted from the establishment of a number of small variants, each one of which was separately adaptive.

Most of the so-called ' useful ' characters are regarded as adaptive because they fulfil some rôle in the normal life-cycle of the animal rather than because they have been proved to have survival value. This tacitly assumes that any difference in habits must be adaptive. An analysis of a number of particular examples shows that the problem of habit-differences between species is by no means so simple. Quite a number of differences in habit appear to be just as useless as the bulk of structural specific characters. Where habit-differences appear superficially to be more definitely adaptive, as in differences in food- or habitat-range, each example still needs to be studied on its merits. Increase of range may be beneficial to the whole complex which forms the species, but is not often of such obvious advantage to the individuals breaking new ground. Specialisation in a more restricted range might be at least temporarily advantageous for the pioneering individuals, but there is little evidence at present that such specialisation is initiated through gene-mutations susceptible to selection.

Finally, we have considered the special difficulty of the evolution of complex organs and of co-adaptations, of which the interrelations of the male and female genitalia are one example. The argument employed by Fisher and Haldane to show that Natural Selection might account for the evolution of such structures, depends on the assumption that very minute changes in a complex situation will, as likely as not, lead to an improvement. As we have previously stated (p. 224), we are very doubtful whether the enhanced survival value conferred by such minimal variants would give a sufficiently steady selection-rate to ensure the establishment of the variant. We prefer, rather, to regard such complex structures as a special case of the elaborate internal organisation characteristic of all living organisms.

In short, we do not believe that Natural Selection can be disregarded as a possible factor in evolution. Nevertheless, there is so little positive evidence in its favour, so much that appears to tell against it, and so much that is as yet inconclusive, that we have no right to assign to it the main causative rôle in evolution.

CHAPTER VIII

In the preceding chapter we have reviewed the evidence for Natural Selection as the best documented and most elaborated theory of the cause of evolution. We held that this theory is essentially one which seeks to explain (a) how a new variant spreads through a population, and (b) how certain types are eliminated so that group divergence results. We have questioned the assumption that the whole process of evolution is to be regarded as a summation of the changes currently assumed to have been produced by selection—whether adaptation and the major trends of evolution are the product of continuous ' speciation.' This question is discussed in Chapter X. We have now to ascertain what the other theories of evolution are competent to explain.

I. **Lamarckism and ' the Inheritance of Induced Modifications.'**—The evidence on the origin of variation is dealt with in Chapter II. It remains to discuss these theories in their wider evolutionary bearing. It has been contended that they are essentially theories which explain the origin of new characters. In so far as the changes of habit and environment which affect individuals may also affect populations, they may also be held to explain how variants multiply. However, those who believe that the effects of use and disuse and the modification of the parental soma or of the germ cells by the environment are inherited have rarely considered the question whether mass transformation of this kind actually takes place. As far as we know, Rensch (1929) is the only author who has of recent years attempted to ascertain whether there is any correlation between environmental factors and structural divergence of such a nature as to satisfy the requirements of this aspect of the problem. Furthermore, it has not been considered by what means such modification by the environment has been amplified to give rise to adaptations and long-sustained evolutionary episodes. We must suppose that the exponents of this theory would refer such cumulative modification to the continuous pressure of the environment or of progressive individual effort.

From the long discussion on the origin of variation it will be seen how questionable is even the hereditary transmission of induced modification. Still more speculative is the question how far such a process could have produced (a) the progressive modification of whole populations, and (b) adaptations and complex organs. In short, though individual change and even some degree of local diversification might arise from this cause, we do not think that it is likely to have been a major evolutionary agency.

II. '**Evolution by Hybridism.**'—Lotsy's theory is discussed in Chapter II (pp. 25–27). In addition to the criticism advanced there that it offers no account of the origin of new hereditary material, it seems to us to be open to the same objection as we have put forward in the previous section—viz. that it provides no explanation of progressive adaptation and modification. That some part of the variation seen in local populations may be due to the permutation and combinations of the stock of hereditary material canalised by isolation, is not to be doubted. But the theory needs to be supplemented by other principles in dealing with the major problems of adaptation.

III. '**Chance Survival.**'—It has been suggested or implied by various writers that variant individuals, which owe their peculiar characters to spontaneous mutations, can survive and multiply without the aid of selection. This idea is in agreement with de Vries' original ' mutation theory ' in so far as it seeks to dispense with selection (and indeed with the inherited effects of modification by the environment) ; but it differs from it in its conception of the size of the evolutionary steps and of the process of species transformation.

This idea has never been seriously formulated as a theory of evolution. It has, as it were, lurked in the back of various writers' minds and is implicit in (e.g.) the writings of Bateson. This writer, though sceptical of the ' creative ' rôle of Natural Selection, conceded that selection is operative in some measure : ' by the arbitrament of Natural Selection all [variations] must succeed or fail' (Bateson, 1909, p. 289).   Nevertheless, he (1913) frequently implied that selection could not be operative in bringing about local variation and the formation of races and species, though he was aware of the necessity of explaining how single mutations can multiply and spread through a population.

Recently, however, the means whereby variant individuals could survive and multiply without selection have been formulated more definitely, and with a realisation of the difficulties involved, by Elton (1924, 1930), Cuénot (1921), and Robson (1928).

The prime difficulty in the way of this theory is of course the theoretical one that only those mutations which are of selective advantage have a chance of survival.   But any theory of evolution which depends on the chance survival of mutations unaided by any directive agency is confronted by an additional difficulty.   The facts of evolutionary history give a very decided impression that they have been influenced by some directive tendency.   That tendency, though not always adaptive, almost invariably has some definite orientation. It may not be apparent in the world of living species, which appears to us very largely as meaningless and chaotic in its divergences.   But it is inevitably forced upon our notice in any study of geological series, any morphological history and in any systematic treatment of a large group.   The evolutionary process seen in such histories scarcely looks like one of which the main tendencies have been determined by chance and random survival.   Evidence of such variation is, it is true, seen in some of the lineages disclosed by palæontology.   But the whole process is too obviously canalised and subject to direction to be the product of chance.   An attempt was made by Morgan (1919, p. 268) to reconcile this obvious aspect of the process with the operations of chance; but we do not think that his contention—viz. that a mutation in a certain direction *increases* the likelihood of further mutations in the same direction —can be sustained (*cf.* Robson, 1928, p. 248).

In addition to the appearance of a directive influence in evolutionary series, the development of organs of high complexity and of 'co-adaptations' (p. 306) renders still more improbable the likelihood that the chance survival of mutations has been the only mechanism of evolutionary change.

Difficult as it may be to explain the origin of such structures by Natural Selection, it is far more of a strain on our credulity to believe that they could be produced by chance. It will be thus seen that the view that evolution may have been produced solely by chance, labours under a serious general disadvantage, so that any evidence that the non-advantageous mutation can survive and multiply must be exceptionally strong.

With these qualifications in mind let us examine Elton's theory of the multiplication of non-adaptive mutations. As a preliminary it should be pointed out that he makes (1930, pp. 89–90) a distinction between the origin of adaptation and the origin of species. The former he attributes to Natural Selection ; the latter to his special theory which we shall examine immediately. It is necessary, however, to comment on the antithesis just noted. Much that has appeared in the past pages must seem to justify a belief that adaptation and the origin of species are separate phenomena and due to separate causes. We shall discuss this in the last chapter. It is enough now to note that Elton does not discuss their inter-relationships, nor does he question how specific differences are raised to generic. He suggests (1924, p. 156, and 1930, p. 78) that the spread of non-advantageous mutants might be facilitated by the periodic fluctuations of the numbers of animal populations. During a period when numbers are at a minimum as the result of wholesale destruction by epidemics, bad weather, etc., there would be theoretically at least a cessation of competition and an increased likelihood of the survival of a given mutant. As an extension of this idea we have to point out that a similar reduction of competition and lowering of the death-rate are observable when a predacious or parasitic enemy is reduced numerically—e.g. by an epidemic (cf. Thompson, 1928, and this work, p. 193). The incidence of disease is known to lead to big reductions in the numbers of a natural population—e.g. in Red and Grey Squirrels (Middleton, 1931 ; and cf. Elton, 1931, for the effects of epidemics in general). We believe that the frequency of epidemics among animals in nature has been seriously underestimated.

Elton's suggestion is open, however, to several serious objections which indeed he has himself considered (1930, p. 79 ; see also Haldane, 1932, p. 204).

(*a*) During periods when numbers are at their lowest the expectation of mutations will be correspondingly low.

(*b*) Even if the chances of survival are increased during one period of minimum numbers, we have still to explain the phenomenon of progressive modification. If we assume that a mutant has survived one period, we have still to assume that a further mutation carrying the modification a step further will occur in the descendants of that mutant at the next minimum.

(*c*) Elton himself (*l.c.* p. 79) points to the objection that ' at the next reduction of numbers the mutation will apparently be reduced to about its original proportion in the population and will never be able to spread beyond a certain point.'

Elton (*l.c.* pp. 79–82) has considered two of these objections, (*a*) and (*c*), and attempted to meet them ; but we are not satisfied that the reasoning he adopts in this attempt is sound.

It is not to be expected that many exact observations on the intensity of variation during a numerical increase of population would be available. Some information on this subject will be found on p. 213. So far we do not believe a very strong case has been made out for Elton's theory. Nevertheless there is a further possibility to be considered. Robson (*l.c.* p. 221) suggested that a non-advantageous mutation might spread if its appearance happened to coincide with the occupation of a new habitat. We know, as a matter of fact (Chapter II, p. 53), that species are by no means rigidly confined to strictly defined habitats, and that individuals are often found straying into situations or adopting habits not characteristic of the bulk of the species. With this tendency we may consider the very definite evidence accumulated by Elton (*l.c.*) for the frequency of migration, though in point of fact in such a suitable case for studying this phenomenon as the Migratory Locust no special increase of variation has been noted with the swarming phase (Gause, 1927).

In a new and relatively untenanted habitat a single mutant of a given type would of course not be immune from the normal risks of death, but it would be at least freed from the chances of competition peculiar to a crowded habitat. However, there still remains the objection (similar to (*c*) in the criticism of Elton's hypothesis) that in order to explain sustained change in a given direction we would have to assume

Y

that the requisite mutations always turned up with each new change of habitat.

It may be questioned, indeed, whether in fact there are in nature 'untenanted habitats' available for the spread of a species overflowing from its natural habitat. Some information may be gained from the records of the rapid spread of introduced species.

(1) The Grey Squirrel (*Sciurus carolinensis*), first introduced into England about 1876, has now spread over a large part of the south, west, and north-east counties. Middleton (1931, pp. 79–80) has shown that this squirrel has 'stepped into a practically vacant place in the British animal community,' because the Red Squirrel, originally a pine-forest denizen, had never over-populated the deciduous trees and that 'niche' was largely a vacant one. Moreover, the Red Squirrel, owing to epidemics, was numerically at a low ebb. It is thus apparent that there was in fact an untenanted habitat waiting for the Grey Squirrel.

(2) The Slipper Limpet (*Crepidula fornicata*) was first introduced into England in 1886 (Robson, 1929) and has since then spread round the east and south coasts, reaching as far west as Swanage, in Dorset. It has principally occupied oyster-beds, but may be found sporadically in other habitats.

(3) The small Gastropod *Paludestrina jenkinsi* (Robson, 1923) has similarly spread with great rapidity through the brackish and fresh waters of Great Britain.

(4) Similar cases are seen in *Cordylophora lacustris* (Harmer, 1901) and *Planorbis indicus* (Robson, MS.). Thompson (1928, p. 107), in discussing the spread of certain agricultural pests (*e.g.* the Gypsy Moth, the European Cornborer), though he allows that 'diminution of the intensity of causes of mortality of the non-parasitic order may at times be responsible for the increase and spread of introduced pests,' holds that 'the absence of parasitic or predacious enemies is the real [more frequent] cause of the increase of the imported species.' This may be true enough ; but it must be added that, even if the absence of predacious or parasitic enemies be a determining factor, there must also be available enough food, shelter, etc., to sustain the very noticeable natural increase.

How far these examples are representative of the general state of affairs in nature and whether we are entitled to assume that there are usually large gaps into which the excess population of a species may spread are uncertain.   It is certainly known that a number of intentionally introduced insects have failed to establish themselves.   But it seems likely that opportunities for spreading in this manner may not be uncommon.

The researches of Gulick, Crampton and other workers on the local and racial divergence of land snails and the studies of various workers on the local diversification of mammals, birds, reptiles and fishes have all tended to show that a very substantial amount of subspecific and specific divergence may arise in conditions in which selection may with all likelihood be excluded.   Studies such as those of Crampton make it almost certain that local divergence is established in conditions in which neither the effect of the environment nor adaptation to local conditions is to be held responsible.   But it is one thing to show that under isolation certain recombinations of characters may be maintained as separate entities or even that entirely new mutations may be established, and another to show how such divergences may be amplified until they give rise to marked and sustained evolutionary series.   In short, while it is likely that local races have arisen without the aid of selection, we do not see how such divergences could have been continuously amplified without some directive process.

Knowing as little as we do about mutation-rates in nature it is useless to indulge in speculations in which these rates are involved.   Though there is a theoretical possibility that sometimes a given mutation might turn up very frequently, such ' mass-mutation ' is not likely to be ample enough to transform whole populations.

In conclusion, it seems to us that some measure of local diversification within a species may arise in one or another of the ways just indicated.   We do not, however, believe that this accounts for the main evolutionary tendencies.

IV. **Orthogenesis.**—Various dissimilar phenomena have been described under this name and some confusion has arisen as to the correct use of the term.   A clear account of the various uses to which the term has been put and of the various concepts involved is given by Kellogg (1907, p. 275 and foll.).   We confine our historical account to a brief recital of the essentials and some additions to Kellogg's statement.

The term was first introduced by Haacke (1897) and was

used by Eimer (1897) in practically the same sense as Haacke, to denote a particular class of evolutionary phenomenon which he had detected in his studies of Lizards and Lepidoptera. As a result of his studies of the wing-pattern in the latter he concluded that the modification of the pattern is determined not by selection, but by the action of the environment upon a determinate constitution which limits the possibility of variation to certain definite evolutionary lines. There are three distinct elements in Eimer's concept—the inherited effect of modification by the environment, the predetermined (*gegebene*) constitution of the organism, and the limitation of variation to certain evolutionary lines. The ' parallel variation ' of later authors is not a cardinal point of his theory, but (*l.c.* pp. 160–1) he pointed out its occurrence as a consequence of his main theory.

The term thus applied to a definite theory of evolution has been given erroneously to two other principles.

(1) Osborn (1912) used it for his ' rectigradations,' *i.e.* adaptive modifications ' rising continuously in straight lines,' though he seems to have considered that the early stages of such rectigradation were not necessarily adaptive. Lull (1917, p. 176) considers that the importance of orthogenesis (*sensu stricto*) lies in its ' making a start in modification ' which is subsequently continued by selection. To trends of adaptive development the term *orthoselection* was given, though, as Lull points out, selection obviously produces (at least theoretically) determinate lines of evolution, so that that term is plainly redundant.

(2) The term is sometimes given to a capacity for progressive development inherent in the organism itself which is independent of external influences. This is the *Vervollkommnungsprinzip* of von Nägeli (1883). It is obviously distinct from those just mentioned and involves a totally distinct evolutionary principle which will be discussed at a later stage in this chapter.

Mention should also be made here of Cope's principles of kinetogenesis and archæsthetism (1887), which he formulated in accordance with his belief in the creative effects of use and disuse and the determining influence of consciousness over animal form. Cope's views, which were founded on his palæontological experience and embody a remarkable anticipation of certain modern ideas, are primarily Lamarckian ;

but they are akin to von Nägeli's and those of certain later authors in their recognition of an internal growth-force.

The idea of a determinate evolutionary path traversed by a group of animals without reference to Natural Selection has been adopted by a large number of authors, some of them previously to Eimer, and by some without any acceptance of the belief that the directive force is environmental. Hyatt (1894), Gadow (1911), Dunbar (1924), and Berry (1928) are exponents of Eimer's view. A number of palæontologists insisted on the determinate nature of certain evolutionary series without committing themselves to any causative agency. 'Determinate' series have been noted in the Opalinidae and Salpidae (Metcalf, 1928), Pigeons (Whitman, 1919), Garter Snakes (Ruthven, 1908), Beetles (Kellogg, 1906), and other groups. Two particular aspects of this 'determinate' evolution have been made special subjects of study and theory: (1) The progressive attainment of monstrous size, either of the whole individual or of a part (' Momentum ' (Dendy), ' Hypertely ' (Cuénot), ' Disharmony ' (Champy)). (2) The phenomena of recapitulatory series involving changes of a degenerative or ' senescent ' type have been the source of much study and speculation by the students of many groups (Ammonites, Brachiopods, Reptiles), and a particular aspect (the development and modification of spines) has been fully studied by Beecher, who has described senescent types of spine-formation in a great variety of groups. Analogous cases are found in the histories of ornaments and septa in Ammonites.

A good review of the majority of the phenomena that have at one time or another been treated as examples of determinate evolution is given by Fenton (1931), though his survey does not include a consideration of heterogonic growth and of excessive size in general.

It has often been urged that Orthogenesis is merely a term by which we designate certain kinds of evolutionary phenomena and that it does not involve any explanation of them. Whether his theory is valid or not, Eimer did in fact apply the term to a causal principle. Other writers have used it to designate certain evolutionary events for which they fail to find a satisfactory explanation in other theories and which, by implication or otherwise, they attribute to innate tendencies. In so far as the latter are not demonstrable except by their results, this use of Orthogenesis is admittedly an appeal to ignorance. But an appeal to an unknown activity (which after all is by no means absent from other theories of evolution, nor indeed from any theorising on vital activities) is not necessarily inadmissible, especially if the other available explanations are ruled out or shown to be implausible.

The bulk of the writers who have espoused the orthogenetic standpoint have perhaps wisely but timidly confined themselves to the description of facts. Eimer's 'Laws of Organic Growth' (organophysis), for example, are actually merely generalised from observation and are not in any sense a causal theory. Besides such writers as have sought a general explanation in the pressure of the environment, Dendy (1911), Champy (1924), and Lang (1921) have faced the necessity of supplying a causal explanation of the particular orthogenetic phenomena they studied. Fenton (l.c.) has attempted to harmonise the particular phenomena of recapitulation with theories of the individual life-cycle put forward by Child and others.

The facts of parallel variation enter into this discussion rather at second hand and are not directly relevant to the question as to whether a determinate evolution, undirected by selection, occurs or not. They are relevant to this extent, however, that if they are not attributable to similar selective agencies or similar environmental stresses, their occurrence is an indication of the limitation of the evolutionary potentialities of animals. In plants parallel variation is common enough to form the basis of Vavilov's law of ' Homologous Series.' In animals instances are to be found in Eimer's own work on Lepidoptera (1897), in Gadow's observations on the pattern of Coral Snakes (1911), and in Parker's study of Brevicipitid Frogs (1932). Such series certainly necessitate a modification of the conception of an all-round variability, but the mere fact of their occurrence does not necessarily involve the conclusion that they are non-adaptive. That conclusion could be arrived at only by an examination of the value of the characters on their own merits. Annandale and Hora (1922) and Prashad (1931) have clearly shown that parallel evolution of adaptive structures occurs in exceptional habitats.

It will be seen that we have three classes of phenomena that have been treated as ' orthogenetic ' on the grounds that they indicate a determinate evolutionary tendency in which it is alleged that no adaptive influence is at work.   They are : (1) Normal evolutionary series which *appear* to have been uninfluenced by selection ; (2) Recapitulatory series in which ' senescence ' is involved ; and (3) Excessive or over-complex growth.   (2) includes also certain forms of gigantism and complexity of parts considered (*e.g.* by Beecher) to be produced as a result of senescence.

We will now review these three classes and the various theories which have been put forward to explain them.   We ought to point out first that it is impossible to make a hard and fast distinction between the three classes.   Normal evolutionary series are, no doubt, easy to distinguish from extreme cases of progressive gigantism and over-elaboration of ornamentation.   But these types grade into one another. Secondly, we should bear in mind that the various theories we are to discuss may be competent to explain one or more types of phenomena.   Thus the theory of Fisher and Haldane on the effect of selection on metrical characters determined by many genes may be used to explain both normal orthogenetic processes and also excessive size.

(1) The mere *appearance* of direction in an evolutionary series and the assumption that it is non-adaptive cannot weigh much as proof.   Some of the evidence brought forward to illustrate (1) is of this kind (*e.g.* Hogben, 1919 ; Lull, 1917), and is concerned with modifications that are suspected of being non-adaptive but not proved to be so. Instances of apparently meaningless histories of progressive modifications could be multiplied almost indefinitely, and certainly in the history of the Ammonites we find changes (*e.g.* in the suture-lines and type of coiling) of such kinds that it is very likely that they are not due to the direct effects of selection.   This conclusion is reinforced when we learn that they are unaccompanied by any change in the contemporary environment (Spath, *in litt.*).

Haldane (1932, p. 194) has attempted to supply an explanation of ' useless ' orthogenesis of this kind by reference to selection.   He takes as his starting-points the effects of selection on a metrical character determined by many genes, and Fisher's analysis of the result of selection in favour of, *e.g.*, larger size. As far as we can understand the rather condensed argument, selection on any character represented by numerous genes has the effect of increasing the number of advantageous genes in such a way that they go on increasing after selection is abandoned. 'The stature (*e.g.*) will thus, so to speak, over-shoot the mark aimed at by selection. . . . We have here for the first time an explanation on strictly Darwinian lines of useless orthogenesis.' This is an *ad hoc* hypothesis and we do not know if its premises have any foundation in fact (*cf.* Chapter VII).

As regards Eimer's own attempt to account for normal orthogenesis of the *Papilio* type, it depends, of course, on two assumptions, viz. (*a*) the limitation of the capacity for variation, and (*b*) 'environmental pressure.' There is little doubt that Eimer held that induced variation was inherited. As, how-ever, he did not actually distinguish between the action of the environment as eliciting a definite germinal change as opposed to merely directing a predetermined heritable capacity, his theory is scarcely relevant in the light of modern know-ledge.

(2) *Recapitulatory series.*—Palæontologists have long been familiar with sequences of fossil forms in which species and larger groups seem to go through the same kind of develop-mental changes as those which occur in the individual life-time. Whether ontogeny recapitulates phylogeny or whether phylogeny is an expanded version of ontogeny cannot be discussed here. What we are concerned with is the undoubted fact which is stated above, and we have to seek an explanation for it.

(*a*) A special feature of the recapitulatory process is that when the life-cycles of related forms and the racial cycles of related groups are studied, it is found that they do not always follow the same programme. Tachygenesis and cenogenesis (acceleration and retardation) intervene and modify the time at which a structure or character appears in various groups. Haldane (1932 and 1932*a*, p. 20) has claimed that 'the gradual acceleration or retardation of a number of genes will lead to orthogenetic evolution.' He shows that genes can be classified according to the time at which they act. Some act in the gamete stage (G), others in the maternal zygote (MZ), others, again, on embryonic or immature structures at various stages ($Z1$–$Z3$). Noting that there has been a common tendency in evolution for development to be accelerated (*i.e.* for certain characters to appear earlier in ontogeny), or to become retarded, he suggests that this is due to the times of action of certain genes being pushed forward or back in the course of development.   He points out (p. 21) that acceleration and retardation are probably influenced by two types of selection.   In animals which produce many young (*e.g.* rodents) there will be a certain measure of prenatal competition, and rapid growth will be of great selective value, and the slower-growing individuals will be weeded out.   ' There will be a tendency to cut short the period of intense competition and push back the first appearance of characters as early as possible.   Conversely, in forms in which ' a larva or embryo is well suited to its surroundings and can go on growing in relatively slight danger there will be a tendency to prolong the embryonic phase.'   In such forms we may expect retardation.

It should be possible to check this ingenious hypothesis. If it is correct, we ought to find accelerated development in forms with numerous embryos and retarded development in those with few embryos.   Haldane (1932, p. 124) cites the retarded development of man as an instance of the latter.

Until Haldane's hypothesis is thoroughly tested on the lines suggested above, it is impossible to do more than suspend judgment as to its value.   It is a little difficult to see how it applies to (*e.g.*) the extinct forms of Brachiopods and Ammonites, in which in all probability development took place outside the maternal body.   We suspect that many tachygenetic phenomena take place in forms in which there is no such competition as Haldane describes.

Castle (1932, p. 365) points out that, though Haldane had in mind rapidity of differentiation rather than of growth in size, the principle will apply with equal force to increase of size, both in pre-natal and post-natal competition.   He instances his own very significant observation that, when ' large race ' and ' small race ' rabbits are put to a common foster-mother, the former push the smaller young away and monopolise the milk-supply.

(*b*) Attempts have been made to explain evolutionary trends which exhibit stages resembling the youthful, mature and senescent phases of individual ontogeny, in terms of progressive physiological changes.   Racial senescence is regarded as a process of the same nature as individual senescence. This theory, which was tentatively suggested by Child, was formulated by Beecher (1901) for phyletic changes in ornamentation in a great number of groups of animals. It has recently been developed with supporting evidence by Fenton (*l.c.*) in order to explain the modification of the Devonian Brachiopod *Spirifer*. Fenton (*l.c.* p. 106 and foll.) adduces as evidence in support of racial senescence in this form the fact that, in 'advanced' members of the *S. orestes* 'phratry,' the capacity for repairing the damaged shell, which is well marked in the primitive form, is reduced. He also claims that in Mollusca and Brachiopoda individual susceptibility to environmental effects is increased with age, and that in his *Spirifer* trends the more advanced members bear the marks of such effects. These physiological trends, he claims, are an index of racial senescence. It must be admitted that some of the evidence brought forward (*e.g.* by Beecher) is suggestive of a progressive change with age characterised in many groups by similar 'degenerative' modifications.

The difficulty we experience in accepting this hypothesis is twofold. (i) As Fenton himself admits, the argument from individual to racial senescence is analogical. We have no proof that racial changes are due to senescence. (ii) There seems to be no correlation between the age of a group and the amount of racial 'senescence.' Historically later stages in a given racial trend are undoubtedly older than earlier ones ; but many forms which are known to be very old historically do not exhibit the degenerative changes that are manifested in a relatively short time in other groups. For example, certain Aspidobranchiate Gastropods are of great antiquity, but forms like *Fissurella*, *Haliotis* and *Trochus* do not exhibit the senescent characters attained in a relatively short time by some Ammonite lineages.

(3) We have now to consider some special phenomena of excessive or otherwise abnormal growth and some of the attempts to explain them. There is at the present time a large volume of evidence that certain organisms in the course of their evolution have displayed phases of extravagant growth leading to large or over-elaborated structures (' Momentum,' ' Hypertely '). Such phenomena at their most acute or exaggerated expression have been attributed (Lang, *l.c.*;

Dendy, *l.c.*) to disturbances of a physiological nature in the normal developmental processes. It is as well to bear in mind the striking analogies pointed out by Bland Sutton (1890) between such phenomena and pathological growth-phenomena in the individual. On the other hand, Huxley (1932) has sought an explanation in the principle of hetero-gonic growth aided by selection, and Haldane has formulated an explanation (1932) of this type of orthogenesis ' on strictly Darwinian lines ' (p. 328). Before examining these theories, however, it is desirable to give examples of the phenomena in question.

Broadly considered, these examples can be divided into two classes, according to whether (*A*) exaggerated size of parts or (*B*) exaggerated complexity is involved. Some structures, however, exhibit excessive size accompanied by exaggerated complexity. Again, both abnormal size and exaggerated complexity are found in sexually dimorphic characters.

(*A*)   *Mammalia :*

Horns of Titanotheria (Osborn, 1929).

Canine teeth of Machaerodonts (Loomis, 1905).

Antlers of the Irish Elk (Woodward, 1909).

Tusks of *Elephas ganesa* (Lang, 1921) and *E. primi-genius* (Loomis, *l.c.*).

Horns of Water Buffalo (*Bos bubalis macrocerus*).

Reptilia :

Bony plates of Stegosauria (Loomis, *l.c.*).

Mollusca :

Lower valve of *Hippurites* and *Rudistes* (Lang, *l.c.*).

Umbonal growth (and flexure) of *Ostraea* (Lang, *l.c.*).

Heavy and elaborately ornamented shells of various genera (Lang, *l.c.*).

Insecta :

Foliaceous enlargement of tibia in *Anisoscelis* (Cuénot, 1925).

Polyzoa :

Excessive deposition of $CaCO_3$ in skeleton of Cretaceous Polyzoa (Lang, *l.c.*).

(B) The following are examples of excessive complexity :

Reptilia :
Tooth-folds of Labyrinthodonts (Loomis, *l.c.*).

Mollusca :
Ammonite suture (auctt.).
Ennea, oral denticles (auctt.).

Sponges :
Excessive elaboration of spicules (Loomis, *l.c.*).

Protozoa :
Complexity of spines in Radiolaria (Loomis, *l.c.*).

Excessive growth and elaboration of parts are manifested in certain groups as a feature of sexual dimorphism. Various appendages of male Crustacea, feathers and other parts of male birds (or of the female in some cases), tusks and horns of mammals are regularly enlarged for special purposes such as coitus, fighting or display. It is true that in many such cases the enlargement is far in excess of any imaginable exigencies of courtship, competition, etc. (*e.g.* the remarkably heavy and coiled horns of the male *Ovis poli* (Pamir or Marco Polo's Sheep) (fig. 28)). In others the appendages, etc., are enlarged in one sex without any clearly ascertained function. The best studied example of this is provided by the Fiddler Crab, *Uca* (Morgan, Huxley), in which one of the chelæ in the male is excessively large and the other is normal. Pearse (1914) has studied the behaviour of the Fiddler Crab and fails to find any definite evidence as to its use beyond a vague suggestion that it is used in display. It has also been suggested that it is used for menacing other males or for stopping the entrance to the burrows in which the animals live. When we find secondary sexual characters of this kind ' running riot ' in size and complexity it is always possible to refer them either to some exceptional but as yet unknown circumstance of courtship, etc., or to the continuation by some equally unknown means of the growth-processes originally stimulated by the sex hormones. It is argued (*cf.* Fisher, 1930, pp. 136–137) that the original impetus imparted by selection to some physiological activity (such as the secretion and laying-down of keratin) may be carried on after the particular adaptive end is attained.

When we contrast the elaborate apparatus of display in the

male Argus Pheasant or the Peacock and the unostentatious structure and subdued colour of other equally successful vertebrates, we cannot but conclude, if the display of the former is a necessary part of the mating behaviour, either that it must be evoked by very exceptional emotional conditions, or that it has no adaptive significance as far as reproduction is concerned (see p. 292).[1]

In considering the various explanations of these growth phenomena, it will be as well to bear in mind the following points :

(1) In many groups of animals individual species, genera or families tend to outrun the normal size of the group. The

Fig. 28.—Horns of *Ovis poli* (male).
(British Museum (Natural History).)

usual adaptive explanations of such excessive bulk as is seen in the Greenland Whale, the Giant Squids, etc. (viz. that large size is advantageous), are not satisfactory. One can hardly imagine that sedentary organisms like the Giant Shipworm and Giant Clam can derive any benefit from their excessive size. As Lang (*l.c.*) points out, in *Hippurites* the protection offered by the thickness of the under-valve is far in excess of any reasonable demand for safety against predators.

(2) The assessment of any structure as ' abnormal ' or ' extravagant ' is determined by purely arbitrary standards. At the best we can take very extreme cases as ' abnormal.'

(3) Some structures seem to us at first sight to be so

---

[1] Hingston (1933) in an interesting book (the main argument of which is open to criticism) supplies much evidence tending to show that the display of various male birds is entirely disregarded by the female.

gratuitously large or complex as to embarrass and be a positive hindrance or danger to the owner ; but we cannot always affirm that there are no compensating adjustments. Thus in many species of the African Land Snail *Ennea* the aperture of the shell is filled up with such a dense palisade of denticles that it seems that the owner can hardly emerge. The difficulty of emergence past this palisade must be very great in any case and can be overcome only by movements that call for peculiar modifications.

It seems that for the cases of extravagant growth we have at least four explanations, viz. : (1) The direct adaptive value of the excessive growth, (2) Huxley's theory based on the facts of heterogony, (3) Fisher and Haldane's theory of the effect of selection on a metrical character determined by many genes, and (4) the theory of an internal impulse.

(1) Haldane's theory of accelerated development (p. 328) during inter-uterine competition was not specifically framed to include rapid growth as distinct from rapid differentiation. It has, however, been adopted in this sense by Castle (1932), who has produced some evidence in its favour. It is possible that some increase of total body-size may be due to selection favouring larger and more powerful embryos and also young in the post-natal stage. But the theory can scarcely be used *by itself* to explain (*a*) the exaggerated size of the adult seen in some species, and (*b*) the size of individual parts used in adult life (*e.g.* the canine teeth of *Machaerodus*).

We may next consider from the adaptive point of view some individual instances of the excessive growth of parts in the adult phase.

(*a*) Matthew (1901, 1910), in his study of the excessive growth of the canines in the Machaerodont Tigers, objected to the theory of an internal momentum. From a study of the associated parts he affirms that these large teeth were made for a stabbing or gashing stroke and suggests that in the absence of the lighter, thinner-skinned animals that provide the prey of the modern Felidae the mid-Tertiary Machaerodonts preyed on the heavy, thick-skinned Pachyderms of various groups which could be attacked only in this way, and that their extinction was not due to the excessive growth of the canines, as has been suggested, but to the extinction or localisation of their normal prey. But quite apart from the difficulty of ascertaining whether in fact the Machaerodonts did prey on the large Pachyderms (there were plenty of smaller, more delicate mammals to prey on), Matthew's theory does not account for the fact that the series of their evolutionary history is progressive and that *Smilodon*, the Pleistocene representative, has the largest and most ungainly canines. He may show that in mid-Tertiary times there were plenty of Pachyderms of various kinds for the Machaerodonts to prey on ; he does not show that in Pleistocene times the Pachyderms were of such a kind as to necessitate the more exaggerated canines of *Smilodon*.

Matthew (1910, p. 307) very rightly asks : ' How can a race *continue* specialising in any particular direction beyond the point when the specialisation is of use . . . the moment the harmfulness of a character outbalanced its usefulness, a process of elimination must act in weeding out the individuals in which the character was most richly developed.' But it seems to us that, even if the excessively enlarged canines may have acted disadvantageously at the end of the series, Matthew has not shown why they should have attained their excessive size. We are quite ready to grant that, as soon as the canines became inconvenient or definitely disadvantageous, the line of the Machaerodonts might have been extinguished ; but we fail to see why they should have been amplified and continued in this stage in Pleistocene times, unless the Pachyderms also had become more thick-skinned or more bulky, which is the very thing Matthew fails to establish.

(*b*) Both Loomis and Lang cite the remarkable growth of the under-valve of *Hippurites*. This is a genus of Lamellibranch molluscs which lived on coral reefs in the Cretaceous. It was a sedentary form and its under-valve was, as usual, adherent to the substratum. The valve was enormously thickened until it formed a tubular structure sometimes *a foot* in length, the thin upper valve lying on top like a lid. Lang, in discussing the origin of this enlarged valve, has in mind only the protection offered by the shell against the attacks of enemies. ' A shell of half the thickness of a Hippurite shell is over-adequate for protection.' But there is another possibility, and that is that the tabular thickening of the lower valve is an adaptive change, raising the mollusc above the encroaching coral and reef-debris in the same way that many abyssal animals and forms which live in silt are raised above it.

However, it seems clear that this was not the true explanation, for (i) *Hippurites* is never found with attached coral growth on it and does not seem to have grown in such situations as exposed it to this risk, and (ii) it seems sometimes to have been orientated *horizontally*, so that in this position it was certainly not growing upwards to escape the suggested danger. There is a last possibility, suggested by the information given to us by Mr. L. R. Cox : *Hippurites* is apparently found in clumps, like a *Vermetus* or *Rocellaria*, and it is possible that the members of such colonies grew to an excessive size to avoid overcrowding. We certainly do not find such growth in recent colonial molluscs, and the explanation just offered is not very plausible, as the growth-habit is common to all the *Hippurites*. Some other circumstance in the life of this mollusc may be ultimately discovered which may suggest an adaptive explanation of the growth of the under-valve ; but at present this seems unlikely, and the suggestion that it is due to an uncontrolled production of $CaCO_3$ is more plausible.

(*c*) In the Babirusa the tusks grow first upwards, then backwards, and finally down towards the frontals, so that in some individuals they pierce the face. That this is the effect of some abnormal growth-process is suggested by the similar phenomenon in individual specimens of rodents. In the Common Rabbit, *e.g.*, the incisors are occasionally so excessively curved that they turn over the maxilla and pierce it. Darwin (1901, p. 792) points out a similar growth phenomenon in the old males of the common *Sus scrofa*. He explained the abnormal form of the upper canines of the Babirusa as fitted for defence. ' Their convex surfaces if the head were held a little laterally would serve as an excellent guard.' As Dendy (*l.c.* p. 1) says, this is hardly a sufficient explanation of their enormous development. Nor is it apparent why they should curve back to guard the thick frontals. They certainly do not guard the eyes.

We are obviously dealing here with a series of facts concerning which much that has been said in the chapter on Natural Selection is applicable—viz. that the bionomic nexus involved is unknown or incompletely known. We are dealing with probabilities, and we have to weigh them in order to see which are the more plausible.

We agree that in the background of these phenomena there

is a suggestion that at the offset growth may be exaggerated to subserve adaptive ends.   Examination of three special cases, however, shows us that the adaptive circumstances are neither established nor even plausibly suggested. Matthew's theory of the origin of the Machaerodont canine breaks down on two cardinal points.   We are, on the other hand, impressed by the analogy between individual and phyletic hypertely—between (*e.g.*) the production of excessive osseous material as the result of internal physiological disturbance in the individual and similar excessive growth phenomena in phyletic series.

(2) Huxley (1932, full bibliography) has recently put forward an explanation of orthogenetic phenomena which depends on particular studies of 'heterogonic' growth.   These studies, and in particular Huxley's empirical formula for expressing 'constant differential growth-rate,' need not be discussed very fully for our present purpose.   When an animal increases in size its parts do not all increase at the same rate, and in particular the size of some structures increases at a very much more rapid rate than the rest of the organism.   Usually there is with increasing size an increase in the relative size of a part, so that the parts of a large animal are relatively larger than those of a small one.   Huxley has investigated these rates and found them susceptible to formularisation.   He has also shown that such differential growth-rates tend to be associated with growth gradients culminating in a growth centre.   The whole architecture of the body is permeated with such gradients, each producing special effects and combining with each other. The net result of growth-rates combined with growth gradients is not, of course, always the same, and animals of the same size do not necessarily have their various parts of the same size. The Roe-deer's antlers, *e.g.*, unlike those of the Red Deer, show a negative heterogony—*i.e.* a decrease of relative antler weight with increase of absolute body weight among adult males (Huxley, *l.c.* p. 46).   Now, as we have said, Huxley's formularisation of these facts is purely empirical.   We know very little about the origin of differential growth-rates. Naturally, when we learn that one chela of the Fiddler Crab (*Uca*) shows marked heterogony in the male and not in the female, we assume that there is some functional explanation of the difference (p. 332).   Huxley suggests that the negative

z

heterogony of the Roe-deer has arisen because ' it was *for some reason* biologically desirable for the Roe-deer to have small antlers.' According to this view the ultimate causes of quantitative differences have to be sought in various circumstances of adaptation. Huxley's formulæ give us only the expression of particular relationships. If we interpret Huxley's meaning correctly, we might say that while, *e.g.*, it might be functionally desirable to have a large appendage, the precise size is determined by the absolute size of the body. It is, indeed, by no means clear to what extent increase of total bodily size alone is held to be causal. Huxley (*l.c.* p. 227) suggests that the increase of the male chela in *Uca* is due to the increase of absolute size ' owing to the specific growth-intensity of the organ, which in its turn is presumably due to a specific growth-promoting substance.' Huxley claims (pp. 218–19) that the principle of heterogony enables us to dispense with an appeal to orthogenesis (in the sense of determinate evolution), *e.g.*, in explaining the large size of the horns of the Titanotheria. ' Granted (*a*) that there existed in the germ-plasm of the ancestor of the four lines of descent the hereditary basis of growth-mechanism for a frontal horn, and (*b*) that increase of size up to a certain limit was advantageous for Titanotheres in general, as would seem inherently probable, then the results follow without any need for invoking orthogenesis. Natural Selection would account for the increase of absolute size, and increase of absolute size would evoke the latent potentialities of the horns' growth-mechanism.' The value of this explanation is, of course, entirely dependent on the validity of Huxley's assumption that increase of body size is produced by selection.

(3) The theory by which Haldane has sought to explain certain types of orthogenetic phenomena in terms of Fisher's work on the effect of selection on metrical characters determined by many genes, has been already discussed (p. 327). It was, no doubt, intended by its author to explain excessive size of parts (of the *Machaerodus* type) as well as other examples of ' useless orthogenesis.' As we pointed out (*l.c.*), the theory is an *ad hoc* construction and its premises have to be accepted on trust.

(4) From this review of theories as to the cause of excessive growth, which are based on some form of selection and on

heterogony (and with them we may couple the original theory of Fisher and the racial senescence theory in so far as senescence is sometimes assumed to involve excessive size of parts), it will be seen that none is particularly convincing.   Haldane's theory is perhaps the most satisfactory as a formal structure, though it labours under the difficulty of (*a*) having to make certain assumptions—*e.g.* that size is a character frequently acted on by selection—and (*b*) being applicable only to characters determined by many genes.   We are therefore impelled to consider the question whether the phenomena of excessive growth are due to an 'independent' internal impulse.   This notion is usually rejected on the score either that it is a mere nominal device and explains nothing, or that a generalised 'impulse' might actually turn out to be the effect of one of the other principles just discussed.

The second of these objections can, of course, be easily met on its own ground.   Either the evolutionary principles we have just discussed satisfy us or they do not.   If they do not and if there still remains the appearance of some directive force determining the magnitude of parts or of the whole organism, we have to examine the claim that this force is inherent in the vital activity of the organism.   The charge that 'orthogenesis,' as a self-determining principle, is a name by which we merely describe but do not account for certain facts, has already been discussed (p. 325).

We have three questions to ask ourselves—(i) is there any ground for believing that such an internal impetus is actually demonstrable? (ii) if there is, can we account for the progressive amplification of its results until they become of phyletic (as opposed to individual) status? and (iii) if (i) and (ii) are answerable in the affirmative, has this phenomenon anything to do with the main problem of evolution, or is it only a peculiar and special case?

(*a*) There is one fact that must attract our attention in reviewing this subject—viz. the frequent association of excessive growth with sexual differentiation.   This fact, which is the basis of Champy's theory of 'sexuality and hormones,' at once raises the question whether, if in special cases (sexual differentiation) exaggerated size is produced by the excess of a specific hormone, the same may not be true of all cases of excessive growth.   May not all instances of excessive growth be at the offset conditioned by some physiological adaptation ? The argument would run thus : We often find the males of a species possessing some excessively developed structure. The dimorphism suggests either that the excessive growth is based on some functional peculiarity which it has outstripped or that it is a by-product of some abnormal glandular activity. When the excessive growth is not associated with sexual dimorphism, but occurs in both sexes, is it not likely to have similarly originated in some adaptive phenomenon or to be due to some by-product of physiological activity ? The reasoning is merely analogical ; but it is at least suggestive. Moreover, among the cases of sexually differentiated structures there are many (combs of fowls, horns in ruminants) the growth of which is definitely known to be influenced by specific secretions. Furthermore, it is well known that irregularities of growth are associated with abnormal conditions of the thyroid and pituitary. There is little doubt, then, that a physiological basis exists for such growth principles. Lastly, individual growth disharmonies similar to the characters which distinguish genera and species are well known, and Bland Sutton (1890) has collected a large number of examples illustrating this parallelism. The rôle of such physiological and pathological factors as causing ' momentum ' in evolution has been discussed and emphasised by Dendy (1911), Keith (1922), and Lang (1921).

We admit that the case so far is analogical. We have no evidence that in a given instance an evolutionary history is determined by such causes. But the analogy is so striking that it calls for serious notice.

Of course, even if some disturbance of the normal growth processes is at work, we have still to account for the origin of the disturbance, for the removal of the normal inhibitions. For this we can but make suggestions by analogy with the known effects of the absence of certain genes, particular environmental effects or pathological disturbances. The case has been well argued by Lang (*l.c.* p. xiv). It may be contended that the apparent physiological impetus is merely the effect of selection on the appropriate physiological basis. There is, however, no actual evidence in support of this suggestion.

(*b*) If the facts and arguments presented in (*a*) seem to

indicate the activity of some physiological momentum, we have still to find some explanation of how changes of this order become characteristic of whole populations. Granting that they may arise in individuals, how do such individuals multiply? Dendy (*l.c.* p. 2) has suggested that in the first instance a monstrous structure may have been useful, and the normal inhibitions may have been subject to the adverse effects of selection favouring individuals in which they were less well developed. The inhibiting effect may have been thus progressively minimised until it was lost altogether, and the size of the given organ ran riot until the lineage so affected was extinguished by its excess.

So far we seem to be in a logical *impasse*. It is asserted that single mutations must have a certain adaptive advantage if they are to spread and become a permanent character of whole populations. Yet we seem to be dealing in all types of Orthogenesis with populations exhibiting structures of which the adaptive value, at least in the final stages of their development, seems not only questionable but in the highest degree improbable. Are there ways more effective than those we have suggested (p. 318) in which a non-adaptive character may spread, or are we wrong in rating (*e.g.*) the growth of the canines in *Babirusa* and the Machaerodonts as non-adaptive? In questions of this kind explanations which rely on the existence of a physiological momentum meet just as many difficulties as do those which depend on Natural Selection.

Of a different order from the phenomena discussed above, but similar to them in so far as they appear to be determined by factors inherent in the organism itself, are the peculiar manifestations of growth seen in patterns of various kinds (*e.g.* in the coats of mammals, the colour and ornamentation of Mollusc shells, the venation of insect wings, the spirals and carination of shells, and so on). The evolution of such forms has been referred to internal principles of growth ultimately determined either by the material of the living substance or by the differential growth-rate of the parts of the organism itself (Bateson, D'Arcy Thompson). Although we admit that many such patterns cannot be shown positively to have no adaptive value, so many of them are like the patterns produced as the result of non-vital activities that one can but suspect that they are expressions of periodic rhythms in the organism itself (*cf.* p. 272).

We have made the criticism (p. 328) against Haldane's explanation of orthogenesis by means of a selective principle that it is an *ad hoc* construction. The appeal to an internal 'momentum' seems, as we have admitted, open to the same criticism, in so far as it postulates the existence of an activity manifesting itself in long-sustained evolutionary series, the only proof of the existence of which is the analogy with certain individual pathological phenomena and growth processes. Viewed in this light neither of these explanations has much to commend itself. The one fact that inclines us to favour the second explanation is the impression we have gained that however much the living organism is limited and confined by its environment and the necessity of conforming thereto, it still retains a measure of freedom. Monstrous structures often seem void of adaptive significance ; but similar excesses in behaviour are even more surprising. A single case may be misleading, but it appears to be characteristic of much of animal behaviour. We have in mind the facts relating to the habits of the Australian Bower birds, which have been studied by Barrett and Crandall (1932). The character of the 'bowers' made by these birds and the uses to which they are put seem to be far in excess of the normal requirements of display and courtship and have little relation to the survival requirements of the species. A somewhat similar vagary of instinct is seen in some of the American woodhewers (*Homorus gutturalis*). According to Hudson (1924, p. 9), this bird, although only the size of a Missel Thrush, makes a nest four or five feet high with only a tiny cavity inside. We suggest that, if such a capacity for gratuitous elaboration over and above the basic exigencies of mating are manifested at the instinctive plane, the same freedom may be found at the level of structure, and that many of the phenomena of excessive growth and complexity are of the same order. The value of such an analogy is admittedly conjectural. We think that it is not objectionable to argue that, if some instincts have a latitude that transcends the exigencies of mere survival value, as it is currently conceived, it is not unlikely that the same is true of structural modifications. It has to be freely granted that, even if the force of the analogy is admitted, we have still to account for how this emancipation becomes characteristic of populations.

SUMMARY OF THE VARIOUS THEORIES OF ORTHOGENESIS

As there are so many different kinds of phenomena which have been loosely included under this head, and as the various theories seek to explain different manifestations of evolution, we cannot easily deal with the subject comprehensively. In general, however, three theories cover the principal array of phenomena :

(1) It is held that some selective effect (either direct or indirect) explains a considerable part of the facts.

(2) (a) The phenomena of excessive growth are explained by some by reference to abnormal physiological processes analogous to individual defects.

(b) Internal physiological processes (racial life-cycle) are held responsible for the process of recapitulation.

(3) Environmental pressure is deemed to be effective either by acting upon a limited range of variability or by maintaining or releasing normal physiological inhibitions.

We believe that none of these theories is in any way near to being proved. In fact, as far as rigorous proof is involved none can rank as more than a plausible suggestion. (1) and (2) (a) have more in support of them than the others, though the selective theories depend entirely on the assumption that selection is a *vera causa*, and to utilise (2) (a) as a theory by which the multiplication of variants is effected involves us in some very grave difficulties. It would be possible to expand the concept of a physiological momentum to include other, perhaps all, evolutionary phenomena. Indeed a very great variety of structures and habits impress themselves on us in this way, viz. as the product of non-adaptive tendencies arising within the organism itself. Nevertheless we have as yet no positive evidence as to how such changes come to characterise whole populations. On the other hand, the selective theories supply us, theoretically at least, with an explanation of both the change and its spread.

V. **Theories of Bergson and others.**—There remain for consideration certain speculations and theories that cannot be treated with the completeness which has been accorded to others. It is, however, imperative to call attention to them and allow them due weight, because they constitute a serious contribution to the subject and a challenge to the orthodox outlook. We limit ourselves to a selection of what appear to be the most important and at the same time the most relevant to what is, after all, a strictly biological inquiry. The particular views we have selected are Bergson's theory of Creative Evolution (1911), Russell's work on ' Psycho-biology' (1924), and Smuts's concept of ' Holism ' (1926). It should be noted that, while these works are concerned with the specific problems of evolution and development, they are part of that revolt against mechanistic principles which is also seen in its strictly philosophical expression in the writings of J. S. Haldane and A. N. Whitehead.

(*a*) As is well known, Bergson holds that the phenomena of evolution are the expression of an impulsion manifested by living organisms. This impulsion is not fixed and pre-determined. It has the character of spontaneity manifested in the continuous creation of new forms, and it is, as it were, inherent in and characteristic of life. What has given evolu-tion its diversity is the fact that life has had to wrestle with and overcome the inertia of the material with which it has to act. The essence of the theory is contained in a passage of remarkable vigour and imaginative breadth (*l.c.* p. 259) : ' all our analyses show us, in life, an effort to remount the incline that matter descends. In that they reveal to us the possibility, the necessity even of a process, the inverse of materiality, creative of matter by its interruption alone. The life that evolves on the surface of our planet is indeed attached to matter . . . in fact it is riveted to an organism that subjects it to the general laws of inert matter. But everything happens as if it were doing its utmost to set itself free from these laws. . . . Incapable of stopping the course of material changes, it succeeds in retarding them.' Adaptation is, he admits, a necessary condition of evolution, but the environment is merely a thing life has to reckon with. ' Adaptation explains the sinuosities of the movements of evolution, but not its general direction, still less the movement itself ' (p. 107). Concerning the nature of this *élan vital*, it is enough to say that, like Eimer's orthogenesis, it is a force continued from generation to generation, but it is not a chemico-physical impetus, but a psychological one (p. 91). It is not, however, like the conscious effort of the individual postulated by Lamarckism. That is a force which can only act in the animal kingdom, and then only on points accessible to the will. Bergson's ' impulse ' is of far greater depth and influence than the strivings of an individual will.

This theory of life and its evolution is, of course, part of a more profound system, the substance of which we cannot discuss. The nature of the impulse is involved in his theory of being and duration, and it is a question whether it can be dissociated from it and stand alone as an explanation of evolution apart from its metaphysical implications.

Probably Bergson would not admit this. By limiting our inquiry to the data of an historical process we are adopting the procedure of the physical sciences, and in his view (p. 206) the latter are incapable of dealing with life (cf. Russell, 1924, p. 124). In any case we do not think we have the means for judging the validity of this theory as an explanation of evolution. The most we could do is to express an opinion whether life has the character of an independent force or whether it is the product of its material basis. Lastly, we must point out that, whatever the ultimate origin of the creative impulse, the individual frequency and ' spread ' of modification have to be considered.

(b) Russell's ' psycho-biological ' viewpoint is at once distinct from and similar to Bergson's theory. It envisages the activity of a fundamental striving or *hormé* as characteristic of living as opposed to inorganic matter. He tries, like Bergson, to show that this *hormé* is, as it were, entangled in the net of the inorganic, and that it is continually adjusting itself to it by means of *perception*. This term is used in a definitely psychological sense, ' but in a broad way to cover all degrees of the receptive side of vital activity.' The results of this activity are seen in both behaviour and morphoplastic response, and the line between these is hard to draw. Behaviour is held to have an influence over the executive organ.

Russell does not consider the evolutionary aspect of his problem (p. 133) ; but he admits that the individual activity must be linked up with the larger process, and one is left with the inference that evolution is a summation of individual morphoplastic responses. Russell makes use of the ' mnemic ' principle that has been employed by various authors to explain heredity, development and evolution, but he rejects Semon's theory of material records or *engrams* (p. 131).

(*c*) Smuts has put forward a theory of evolution which seems to be ultimately derived from Lloyd Morgan, and, in so far as it is the result of a revolt against nineteenth-century science with its ' hard and narrow concept of causation,' resembles that of Bergson in its philosophical background. He attempts to show that there is in nature (inorganic as well as organic) a dynamic creative energy which expresses itself in progressively complex systems or ' wholes.' The universe is a hierarchy of such systems, commencing (p. 106) with the synthesis of parts in bodies of the order of chemical compounds, and passing through plants and animals to Personality and Absolute Values the activities of which result in the creation of a spiritual world. The characteristic of the *whole* in the organic world is the association of its parts in the production of a functional unity. Evolution proceeds primarily, not by selection, but by the progressive expansion of the creative energy within the organism itself. Natural Selection has but a subordinate rôle. Variations are not selected on their individual merits. In their initial stages they are helped out by the other parts of the *whole*, and selection comes in only when the variation ' has developed enough to add a sensible measure of strength to the parent organism.' Smuts asks with commendable candour what experimental verification there is for the holistic view of evolution. The answer (p. 217) is that evolution is not a process that can be repeated or verified by experiment [and, we must assume, by observation of the individual organism living or dead]. ' A correct view of evolution must be based on an intelligent appreciation of the natural processes rather than on the very limited data yielded by our laboratory experiments.'

The outstanding merit of this theory, of which we have given a very summary account, is that it recalls our attention from the details of the process of evolution to its wider aspect. The ' more or less stationary regime of casual character-combinations ' (p. 183), which we see if we concentrate on the details of the process, obscures the main issues and outcome. The theory emphasises the unity of the organism and stresses the difficulty of explaining it by selection. The particular difficulty which it encounters is discussed in the summary of the theories below.

All these theories, which differ from one another in many essentials, agree in one important feature. They reject the mechanistic view of evolution and insist on the spontaneity and self-sufficiency of life. Adaptation may canalise the evolutionary impulse, but its potentialities and their expression are implicit in life itself and are not produced by a blind sieving of variation, by the direct effect of the environment, by the conscious will of the organism or by chance. How are we to criticise this viewpoint? In particular, how are we to relate it to the mechanism of evolution of which we have some certainty, viz. its production by increments of the order of mutations? These theories are in fact accounts of evolution as a whole, and not explanations of the destiny of variations. Of the theories under discussion only that of Smuts realises the obligation to supply an account of the steps in evolution. If indeed forces such as we have been considering are operative and evolution proceeds by them, and not by selection or the direct action of the environment, the stages by which they express themselves would have to be achieved in the same way as the spread of non-adaptive mutations (p. 318). The transformations of populations which are evolving under the influence of such forces would have to be brought about in exactly the same way as we have discussed there. The fact is that all observations on adaptation, the regulation of the life processes of the individual and the occurrence of internal impulsions seem to demand some means by which mutations may spread.

CHAPTER IX

IT is usual to proceed on the assumption that, if all evolutionary divergence were adaptive, the importance of Natural Selection would be finally demonstrated. We wish now to examine what we know of adaptation, to see if it supports the view that selection by the environment has led to adaptation to it. The term *adaptation*, itself, is applied to several phenomena which are not actually of the same nature, and we must attempt to explain this difference in the use of the term.

Useful Characters.—Many observations have been made tending to show that various structures, often apparently trivial or valueless, have really some function in an animal's life-history. Structures the functions of which are known or have been surmised are usually described as adaptive, but, as Bateson (1894, p. 12) points out, such a description is misleading, for it is scarcely ever known in any particular case whether actually the structure *on the whole* confers an advantage on the individual possessing it. One might distinguish animal structure into three categories : (*a*) apparently useless structures ; (*b*) useful structures ; and (*c*) adaptive structures, which are not merely useful at one stage in the life-history but actually confer a definite advantage not counterbalanced in other ways. The distinction between (*b*) and (*c*) may be readily seen in the following example. Many Lampyrid beetles have the power of emitting flashes of light in both sexes. Repeated observations have shown the value of the flashes as a means of bringing the sexes together. The light-organ therefore falls at least into category (*b*) of useful structures. But to show that it should be placed in (*c*) it would be necessary to prove that there are no counterbalancing disadvantages—*e.g.* that the light did not also attract enemies to a dangerous extent, or that the energy expended in producing so elaborate an organ did not entail the sacrifice of efficiency in other directions (*e.g.* in egg-production).

Specialisation.—A somewhat different use of the term adaptation involves the notion of *specialisation*. This usage may be simply illustrated from amongst the solitary bees. Many species of these visit a wide range of flowers ; whereas others obtain their pollen and nectar from one or two species only. Robertson especially, in America, has recorded the habits of many ' oligolectic ' bees. It is often claimed that the bee species whose choice is so restricted are highly adapted, and the phenological data, proving an exceedingly close correspondence between the flowering-time and the active

FIG. 29.—OLIGOLECTIC AND POLYTROPHIC BEES.

A. *Macropis labiata* F., obtains its pollen only from *Lysimachia vulgaris*.
B. *Bombus lapponicus* F., restricted to regions where *Vaccinium* spp. flourish, but visits other flowers early in the year, before *Vaccinium* is in bloom.
C. *B. pratorum* L., closely allied to *B. lapponicus* but visits numerous flowers.
Photos, W. H. T. Tams.

period of the adult bee, are cited in favour of this view. It is important to note that there is normally little evidence of much structural modification of the bees to suit their particular flower. In a general way flowers with long corollas and deeply sunk nectaries are visited by long-tongued bees, and *vice versa*, but the correlation is not very high, and many oligolectic bees which visit different flowers do not appear to be specially suited to their chosen source of food. It is usual to treat such examples of specialisation as adaptations in the restricted sense, but there is little logical justification for so doing. The bees exist, therefore we may say they are sufficiently adapted to survive, but this in itself throws no light on the survival value of particular habits or structures. It is interesting to examine Darwin's views on this point. In chapter iv of ' The Origin of Species ' he examines the problem presented by the simultaneous occurrence of specialised and unspecialised (or archaic) forms. His main points are as follows : Primitive forms may have survived unmodified, because (1) no beneficial variations occurred, (2) they are not really competing with 'higher' forms, (3) unknown factors may have been at work. Alternatively, they may actually be highly evolved compared with their past state, or they may more recently have suffered retrogression.

To us these arguments do not appear to touch the central point at issue. We can often see the value of some specialisation after the first steps in that direction have been taken, but it is the first steps that require explanation. Thus, in the solitary bees, if a species began to restrict its breeding season to a short period, it might be advantageous to visit only one species of flower which was then abundantly in bloom ; or, conversely, if a bee specialised more and more in visiting one species of flower, a close phenological correspondence would be desirable. But we cannot explain why the initial specialisation began except by an appeal to ignorance, assuming either an unknown advantage or a hypothetical environmental stress. The appeal to ignorance might legitimately be used (with caution) in an endeavour to eliminate the difficulties raised by some thoroughly tested theory, but it cannot safely be used to manufacture the evidence on which to a large extent the theory is based.

We may also examine the use of the word 'adaptable.' An adaptable species is, in normal usage, one which is able to exist in a wide range of conditions. Grinnell and Swarth (1913, p. 394) include also the power of so existing without marked changes in specific characters. Such 'adaptable' species may be contrasted with what vertebrate taxonomists usually call 'adapted' species, i.e. those limited to small, well-defined areas and often showing conformity (especially in colour) with some special feature of the habitat. Doubtless the 'adapted' species are more specialised, and they may be more closely adjusted to their limited environment, but it is probable that the 'adaptable' species will leave more descendants. Specialisation is not a passport to succeeding geological periods, though it may lead temporarily to large-scale 'speciation.' It would, indeed, be possible to construct an evolutionary theory which ascribed most of the division of the animal kingdom into species to the action of Natural

Selection, while evolutionary progress was maintained only by lines which *escaped* the action of selection with the fatal, blind-alley specialisation which it entails.   To illustrate the argument by a metaphor, we may compare the evolution of a species with the course of a boat down a stream.   The banks represent the selecting environment.   If the stream is narrow and the boat is undirected, then the banks will narrowly determine the course pursued and the boat will eventually show signs of its frequent collisions.   But if the stream be very broad it is easy to imagine that even a moderately well-steered boat may within wide limits have a safer journey. For ' adaptable ' species the stream is very broad.

We do not wish to push this speculation any further at the present stage of our discussion, but it may be noted that the relation between the rate of specialisation and the rate of change of the environment in any particular habitat would be of importance.

Statistical Adaptation.—A third conception of adaptation may be called the *statistical*.[1]   From this point of view the rather exceptional interrelationships, such as those mentioned in the previous paragraphs, are less stressed, and the greatest importance is attributed to the highly complex environment in which the species must live.   If the environment is the sum of a number of conflicting and highly variable influences, no species can be adapted in all directions to the theoretically maximum degree.   A species may be regarded as the mean of innumerable selective tendencies, each dragging it in different directions.   In the unstable and unfriendly world it must make the best of a bad job, and must submit to many compromises.   A definition of adaptation in consonance with this conception has recently been supplied by Fisher (1930, p. 38), who says : ' Any *simple* example of adaptation, such as the lengthened neck and legs of the giraffes as an adaptation to browsing on high levels of foliage, or the conformity in average tint of an animal to its natural background, loses, by the very simplicity of statement, a great part of the meaning the word really conveys.   For the more complex the adaptation, the more numerous the different features of conformity, the more essentially adaptive the situation is recognised to be.   An organism is regarded as adapted to a particular

---

[1] Cuénot (1925, p. 19) has used the term *adaptation statistique* in an entirely different and, as it seems to us, inappropriate sense.

situation, or to the totality of situations which constitute its environment, only in so far as we can imagine an assemblage of slightly different situations or environments, to which the animal would on the whole be less well adapted, and equally only in so far as we can imagine an assemblage of slightly different organic forms, which would be less well adapted to that environment. This I take to be the meaning which the word is intended to convey. . . . This definition is in agreement with the view (p. 41), . . . which was regarded as obvious by the older naturalists, and I believe by all who have studied wild animals, that organisms in general are, in fact, marvellously and intricately adapted, both in their internal mechanisms and in their relations to external nature.' There are certainly some field naturalists who find it difficult to believe in the existence of the close degree of adaptation here assumed. It is doubtful how far the problem of adaptation can be studied by means of chance observations of naturalists, however talented, since the data obtained in this way can rarely be quantitative. Further criticisms will be found on p. 355.

Organismal Adaptation.—There remains a fourth conception of adaptation, which may be called the *organismal*.[1] The property of living animals which it stresses is their individuality, the result of a complex organisation which is maintained *in spite* of the environment. The adaptations which are so often held up for admiration and so pleasantly satisfy the human craving for a good story might equally well be regarded as set-backs in evolutionary progress. They show us where the organism has been forced to submit to an environment that had become too strong for it. To return for a moment to the oligolectic bees, it can be maintained that when the bee alters its flight period to coincide with the flowering of its pollen-supplier, it is taking the line of least resistance. We may contrast its behaviour with that of some of the ants who cultivate their own crops and are, therefore, independent of the seasons. The oligolectic habit might have great temporary advantages, but it also has great dangers, because it increases the direct dependence of the organism on an environment

---

[1] References to works on this aspect of adaptation may be found in Bertalanffy's recently published ' Modern Theories of Development ' (1933. Transl. J. Woodger).

which is essentially fickle and inconstant. We believe that the degree of adaptation is best measured by the power conferred over the environment. All living organisms are, of course, intimately related to their environment, but one or the other partner in the relation may ' call the tune.'

In its relation to environmental pressure the organism may take one of three courses : (1) *Modification*, (2) *Compensation*, and (3) *Independence*.

(1) *Modification* implies that subservience to the environment which we have already considered under specialisation. In a highly specialised and relatively uniform environment great temporary success may result from it, but with changing conditions it may mean annihilation. As will be seen later, this applies more especially to animals living in habitats to which only a limited number of responses are possible.

(2) *Compensation* is a fundamental property of living matter. An organism without the power of adjusting itself to changes in the environment could not maintain itself as a living entity. The essence of modifications is that, though they allow the organism to survive, they mortgage its future and reduce its liberty of action. Compensations allow the organism to continue its old types of behaviour, although the environment has altered. The simplest type of compensation is perhaps seen in migrations from one part of a habitat to another ; the most complex in such phenomena as the control of the pH of mammalian blood.

(3) *Independence* is perhaps only an ideal, but it is one towards which an organised system of compensations is evidently leading. A completely independent organism would respond to all possible changes in the environment by self-regulation. In certain features and within certain limits most animals exhibit independence, the development of which is one of the most obvious characters of the evolutionary hierarchy.

In the following paragraphs we shall further expand this argument with a number of examples. Finally, we shall consider the very difficult question of the relation of modification to compensation in the course of evolution.

The simplest type of compensatory response is seen in many aspects of animal behaviour. The comparison between structure and behaviour, as regards their power of response, illustrates this point. In the case of structure, this power is evidently limited and adjustment is a slow process. Apart from functional adaptation within the lifetime of the individual, the change requires at least one generation to modify a whole population. Variation and the multiplication of variant individuals are therefore, in regard to structure, the main method of response, which is necessarily slow.

On the physiological, and especially on the psychological plane, functional adaptation becomes more and more important. We mean that deficiency in one respect is made up for by a compensatory change elsewhere. The co-ordination of an animal's physiological activities essentially consists in keeping a balance, within certain wide limits, between all the separate activities, so that the internal environment of the organism is stabilised. The psychological activities or behaviour (we are not at present considering consciousness) of an animal are even less fixed, because the number of ways in which the problems can be answered are so much greater. It is a commonplace that the behaviour of all the more specialised animals has an element of unpredictability. This element is perhaps fundamental and not due to a mere temporary lack of data. The frequency of any one type of behaviour may be recorded without arriving at the possibility of prediction for a particular case. Thus, in Reinhard's experiment (1929, pp. 128–130) on a wasp (*Philanthus gibbosus*) a female was confined in the centre of three concentric glass funnels standing on sand. On her first attempt she burrowed under the edge of the inner one and ran up between it and the second ; on trials 2 to 15 she burrowed under all three funnels ; on trial 16 she behaved as on the first occasion ; while on trials 17 to 22 she ran straight up the neck of the inner funnel. After each trial she was recaptured and placed in the centre again, till, on the twenty-second escape, she eluded capture.

Even the most specialised behaviour (*e.g.* oviposition) involves to a greater or less extent the whole organism. A living organism is an exceedingly flexible instrument and has many ways of attaining the same end. Very similar ideas have been expressed by Elton (1930, p. 31), who sees two processes at work in at any rate the higher animals : ' the selection of the environment by the animal,' as well as ' the natural selection of the animal by the environment.' Elton emphasises the ability of nearly all animals to wander, often to migrate over great distances, so that they can find a suitable environment and need not stay passively subjected to unfavourable conditions. The influences which might be expected to act as selective agencies may merely induce migration.

A simple metaphor may be of some assistance in contrasting this idea of adaptation with that put forward by Fisher (p. 351). If we imagine the environment into which the animal has to fit as an irregular cavity in a hard substance, then on Fisher's view living organisms would resemble a liquid of relatively low viscosity which would soon, by mere force of gravity, come to fill every crevice. On our view the organism would resemble more a tennis ball, which would fill the cavity completely only if subjected to very extreme pressure. Except after prolonged and extreme exposure, it would be sufficiently elastic to regain its shape if the pressure were released, while if the pressure was not very carefully applied the ball would shoot out and leave that particular environment altogether.

We do not believe that the view that animals are very accurately adapted to the environment is now nearly so generally held by naturalists as Fisher supposes. As he admits (*l.c.* p. 41), the more adapted an animal is, the greater is its danger from deterioration of the environment. If an animal is too well adapted to one set of conditions, it must necessarily be proportionately less well adapted if the conditions change. This principle is highly important when we remember the marked environmental fluctuations experienced by nearly all animals (*cf.* Elton, 1930, pp. 19–28). The phylogeny of such a group as the Vertebrata, as revealed in their fossil history, suggests that it is the unspecialised and, therefore, the relatively less well adapted that have survived. Forms which ' dated ' met with no approval in later periods.

But as Bateson (1894, p. 12) has said, ' We, animals, live not only by virtue of, but also in spite of what we are,' and it is not difficult to find instances of highly specialised animals which live successfully in habitats to which they are quite unadapted. Thus Hudson (1892, p. 18) describes an opossum (*Didelphys azarae*) which lives on the plains of La Plata, yet still retains the specialisations which adapted it for life in the forests further north. The grasping hand, so necessary for tree-climbing, is a positive hindrance to walking on the earth, and, in fact, it can only lumber along in an ungainly fashion, trailing its prehensile tail behind it. The faculty of tree-climbing is still retained and employed if the opossum is brought up to a tree. Yet the animal ranges with apparent success over enormous treeless areas in the Argentine. Evidently lack of specialisation in some respects has been able to atone for it in others.

In insects we may cite the familiar case of the Chermesidae, which under normal conditions have a very complicated life-cycle spent on two species of coniferous host plants. All would agree that the cycle, including numerous different types of individuals, with migration from one species of tree to another, was in a broad way highly adaptive. Yet where one host is absent, as in the case of some English Chermesidae, the life-cycle is passed on one tree only (so-called anholocyclic life-history), and certain types of individuals, including as a rule the sexual forms, are no longer produced. It is difficult to reconcile this very elastic power of response with the idea of any detailed adaptation in the original state.

These examples are really complementary to the fact that the same modifications may be found in animals leading quite different lives. This point has been well illustrated in a number of groups of vertebrates by Guyénot (1930, pp. 265–79). One of the most extraordinary instances is the parallelism in a number of characters between the Cetacea and the Edentata. Certainly not all of these characters are very obviously adaptive, but some of them have been claimed to be so in one group or another. The following peculiarities are known to occur in one or more genera of both groups : ' retia mirabilia ' in the tail and legs ; presence of two venae cavae and absence of the azygos ; pterygoids forming fused palatines meeting in the median line and extending posteriorly to the opening of the fauces ; feeble mandible without a coronoid process ; double articulation of the ribs with the sternum ; ribs unusually broad ; absence of the bile reservoir.

We can see an analogous phenomenon in the wide range of country inhabited by many species. We are all familiar with species which range over areas in Europe including climatic and edaphic conditions of very varied types. Even within a small area there may be a wide range of conditions, especially in mountainous country. Of course it could be maintained that each part of the specific range, characterised by certain limiting environmental conditions, was inhabited by a specially adapted race of the species. But, though this may be true to some extent, it is a very large assumption to suggest that such racial specialisation is so general as to lead to close adaptation in all parts of the range. In fact, where extensive division into races has occurred, as in some rodents or humble bees, it appears much more likely that geographical isolation has been the important factor, and adaptation to special local conditions, if it has occurred at all, is at any rate unrecognisable. We may consider this problem in a particular instance. Filipjev (1929) has shown in his study of the chief insect pests of the U.S.S.R. that each main Russian life zone may be distinguished not merely by certain endemic or typical species, but by the pests which do most damage in them. In fact, the latter, 'dynamical' definition of the zones is more satisfactory than the former, or 'static,' since very few species are literally confined to one zone. The Noctuid moth *Feltia segetum*, for instance, does serious damage in the West Siberian Forest zone and in the Middle subzone of the Steppe ; in the former, more northern region, it is single-brooded, in the latter double-brooded. Its complete range covers a very much larger area, including the districts lying between those where damage is done. Presumably in the intervening country it is single-brooded in bad years and double-brooded in good ones : such facultative increase in brood number is very common in Lepidoptera. Even in the areas where the damage is serious the degree of severity of outbreaks depends on climatic conditions (*e.g.* rainfall), which may be more or less propitious in different years. Evidently there is some adaptation of the moth to varying conditions, but its range is too large and the climate throughout the latter too variable for the adaptation to be very close, except in some years or in certain limited districts.

In the previous paragraph we have illustrated a well-known phenomenon of geographical distribution, viz. that species have areas of optimum conditions surrounded by zones in which the environment becomes progressively more unsuitable and the species rarer. This suggests an examination of what is implied by 'optimum conditions.' The life of an animal depends on a great variety of physiological processes, each of which, considered *in vacuo*, can be carried out most efficiently in a particular environment. The optimum environment is, therefore, a statistical conception involving a compromise between a number of conflicting ideals. Even in an unvarying environment the compromise is likely to be an unstable equilibrium, and in a state of nature, where all factors are undergoing big fluctuations with a period relatively short compared with the developmental period of the species, it is doubtful if any real equilibrium can be reached. In these circumstances there will be a wide range of conditions under which the species will be as well adapted as it ever can be. On the one hand adaptation can rarely and only for short periods be very close, while, on the other, selection will have a permanent effect only when the maladjustment to the environment has become unusually gross.

Actually, in the course of evolution, increase in organisation makes the conception of optimum conditions more and more precise, but this results from the organism making its own environment which is *ipso facto* optimum. In recent years man has made great progress in the art of maintaining the atmosphere of his houses at the proper temperature and humidity, and an essentially parallel process can be seen in evolution. The establishment of approximately similar optima for the various bodily processes is an important step which has been made by the homoiothermic animals in which the blood-stream has a relatively uniform constitution. In the insects this stage does not appear to have been reached, and only a very broad definition can be given to the optimum. Thus each stage (egg, larva, pupa and adult) may have different requirements, as found by Headlee (1917, 1921) in the bean-weevil (*Bruchus obtectus*) which lives, nevertheless, in a much more constant environment than most species. Again, the optimum will differ according to which stage of activity is regarded. Thus Weber (1931), in the whitefly (*Trialeurodes vaporariorum*), finds that the optimum temperature for the survival of the last larval stage is 22° C., while the optimum for oviposition in the adult female is 25°–30° C. Maclagan (1932a), in the spring-tail (*Smynthurus viridis*) finds that the optimum temperature for growth is 16·7° C., while for egg-production it is 7° C. A comparable temperature effect is seen in the relation of many insects to their parasites. The relative rates of reproduction at different temperatures may be quite different, as in the observations of Webster and Phillips (1912) and others on the aphis *Toxoptera graminum* and its hymenopterous parasite, *Lysiphlebus tritici*. Uvarov (1931, pp. 152–5) gives further instances.

With more lowly organised animals the optimum is probably equally or even more indefinite, and it is possible that such species owe their survival to the existence of a number of strains, at least one of which may be expected to thrive in any likely combination of conditions. In this case variability, *i.e.* lack of precise organisation, is required until, at higher levels, the internal environment is better controlled.

Besides the development of internal optima we may also consider the optimum density for individuals of a species. This is a subject on which our knowledge is still very slight. A discussion will be found in Elton (1930, pp. 25–35), and studies of particular species will be found in the papers of Pearl (1927, 1932), Pearl, Miner and Parker (1927), and Maclagan (1932*a*). From the present point of view certain broad general principles are discernible.

Until an animal has some control over its environment, particularly its internal environment, it has little control over its rate of reproduction, and this rate will vary in quite close correlation with rapid environmental changes. This is known to be true in soil protozoa and bacteria, and also of many small insects (e.g. *Smynthurus viridis* (Maclagan, 1932)). Such species undergo rapid fluctuations in numbers in the course of the year, and are able to survive only on account of their extremely rapid rate of multiplication when conditions are suitable. There is easily recognisable in the evolutionary hierarchy a tendency to lose this rapid rate of multiplication and to gain an increased control over the reproductive rate. Not only does the life of the individual become longer, but reproduction is more under the control of internal relations. Even in small mammals, where fluctuations in population-density are often extreme, there is sufficient control to ensure that there is little response to sudden environmental changes. The periods of the fluctuations are measured in years rather than months. We believe that further investigation of problems of this sort may show that in the course of evolution the external environment is to a considerable extent brought into the scope of the organised system of compensations.

As regards internal organisation, the simplest type of compensation is seen in the regulation of temperature. Temperature control in vertebrates, and to a less extent in the nests of social insects, is one of the most obvious examples. Thus the temperature of the brood-cells of a beehive is much higher than the surrounding air, and is usually maintained at 32°–35° C., according to von Buttel-Reepen (1915, p. 119). The bees can also cool the hive by fanning with their wings. In ants, Wheeler (1913, chapter xii) records that the temperature of the nest may be 10° C. higher than that of the air outside. The workers, by moving the brood to different levels in the nest, can expose them to the appropriate conditions. Such species as *Formica sanguinea*, further, have separate winter and summer nests.

The control of temperature by choice of habitat is also achieved in various desert animals. Chapman, Mickel and others (1926) have shown that the temperature of the surface of the soil on the Minnesota sand-dunes at midday is high enough to kill most insects. The species which live there escape destruction by appropriate behaviour. Some are nocturnal and bury themselves deeply during the day. The sand-wasps, however, show the most interesting modification of behaviour, since they are active during some of the hottest hours and have to make a burrow for their nest through the hot surface. They take advantage of a peculiarity of the habitat, namely, that a little below the surface and a little way above it the temperatures are much lower. Thus, while burrowing, they work very rapidly for a short period and then fly up into the air for a rest. Later the burrow itself forms a refuge from the surface conditions. By their plastic behaviour the wasps avoid the destruction which might have been their lot for seeking out so unfavourable an environment.

Again, external skeletons (Arthropoda, Mollusca), tubes and cases (Vermes, Crustacea, many larval Insecta), covered runways (Isoptera, Formicidae, small mammals), clothes and houses (man) are another method of resisting or controlling the environment. Almost every feature of man's environment, except a relatively small number of parasites, is under effective control, and the chief problem is

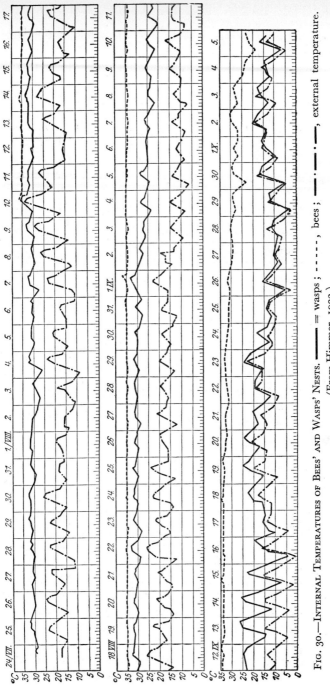

FIG. 30.—INTERNAL TEMPERATURES OF BEES' AND WASPS' NESTS. ——— = wasps; - - - - -, bees; — · — · —, external temperature.

(From Himmer, 1932.)

presented by imperfect co-ordination of the individuals within the species.

Nowhere do living animals show their characteristic organisation more conspicuously than in the course of their early development. In many species the early developmental phenomena (*e.g.* types of cell cleavage) would seem to be needlessly elaborate, but if the processes are followed through to their end, each step can be seen to lead logically to the final organisation. Experimental studies have shown, also, that in the early stages there is a considerable power of forming a perfect organism in spite of interference with the normal course of events. These facts have been so much discussed recently that we need not enlarge on them. We may, however, refer briefly to the controversy as to how far development is a purely ' physico-chemical ' process. From one point of view it is obvious that development is not merely a series of physico-chemical reactions : chemical reactions, however complicated, are not known to produce such organised systems as living animals. It is probable that each stage in development obeys a system of physico-chemical laws, but this does not imply that development is merely a chain of reactions which follow one another automatically. The regulation of the reactions so that each produces a *desired* result, no more and no less, is characteristic of organisms but not of unorganised chemical processes. Further, each organism forms part of a continuous series, and it is logically unsound to single out part of the series and regard it as a whole. Thus, even if it were maintained that the development from egg to adult is merely a chain of chemical reactions, it is still necessary to explain how the egg came to be in a situation where development was possible. We find, then, that at the start a system of organised internal relations is the fundamental, almost axiomatic, assumption in any definition of a living organism.

The automatic and self-regulating quality of animals is no less conspicuous in the life of the adult, especially in the more highly evolved forms. Thus Haldane (1929), dealing with the failure of purely mechanistic explanations in physiology, instances the phenomena of heredity and of regeneration as showing the tendency of living organisms to reach and maintain a stable form.

It is instructive to compare Haldane's statements with those of Carrell (1931) in his exposition of the principles of ' the New Cytology.' He says (p. 303) : ' The success of the new method (tissue culture) in bringing about the discovery of so many phenomena must be attributed to its power, which histology, physics and chemistry lack, to apprehend the complex system formed by the tissues and their environment. The concepts and methods of physics and chemistry are adapted to the atomic and molecular levels of the organisation of matter. When applied to the cellular and supracellular levels they detect only phenomena of the atomic and molecular orders. On the other hand, cytology and histology are concerned exclusively with the form of cellular and supracellular organisms. Therefore none of these sciences alone is capable of dealing with physiological phenomena, such as organisation and adaptation, which belong to the supracellular order and are the expression of sociological laws. The specific laws of physiology, said Claude Bernard, are the laws of organisation. Such are precisely the phenomena and the laws that the new cytology endeavours to discover by coordinating, through its own techniques, the data supplied about cells, tissues and organic fluids by physics, physical chemistry, chemistry and classical cytology and histology. Studied in this manner, cells and tissues appear as being endowed with properties which make them not only the building stones but also the builders of an organism capable of developing, maturing, growing old, repairing wounds and resisting or succumbing to diseases. It is with such an aspect of the tissues that embryology and pathology, as well as cytology, should be concerned.'

Thus the intricate adaptations within the organism are in the nature of compensatory processes which allow the characteristic form to be maintained *in spite* of pressure from one part of the organism or from the environment. In this sense adaptation is synonymous with organisation, the fundamental property of all living matter. This point of view has recently been expressed by Berg (1926, p. 7) in rather different words. He says : ' Purposive adaptation is one of the fundamental properties of the living being (not liable to further resolution into elements), such as irritability, contractility, capacity for nourishment, assimilation, reproduction. It is neither more, nor is it less, incomprehensible than any of the properties enumerated. A living being devoid of purposive structures would be inconceivable. To comprehend the origin of adaptations in the living being is to comprehend the essence of life. And the essence of life is no easier to comprehend than the essence of matter, energy, feeling, consciousness and will.' Without, perhaps, adopting so extreme an attitude, we may still believe that the tendency to maintain form and individuality is a more fundamental characteristic of living organisms than the tendency to change under external pressure, and we are led to contrast the so-called ' internal mechanisms,' which are the very life-blood of the organism, with the ' adaptations to external nature,' which indicate, at least in part, where the environment has induced modifications. We may further compare the two types of adaptation in their relation to survival : the first type is so essential to the organism that life would be impossible if even a small detail of the mechanism were out of order ; the second type, even on the most enthusiastic view, is usually only helpful in emergencies or in some small part of the life-history, and even then is not literally essential to life. A similar comparison has been made by D'Arcy Thompson (1917, p. 617), who, taking an extreme view, says (of the study of the second type of adaptations) : ' The fate of such arguments or illustrations [protective and warning coloration, etc.] is always the same. They attract and captivate for a while, they go to the building of a creed, which contemporary orthodoxy defends under its severest penalties ; but the time comes when they lose their fascination, they somehow cease to satisfy and to convince, their foundations are discovered to be insecure, and in the end no man troubles to controvert them. But of a different order from all such " adaptations " as these are those very perfect adaptations of form which, for instance, fit a fish for swimming or a bird for flight. Here we are far above the region of mere hypothesis, for we have to deal with questions of mechanical efficiency where statical and dynamical considerations can be applied and established in detail.'

The passage just quoted brings us to the crucial question in the problem of adaptation—the relation between the perfection of internal organisation and specialisation for a particular mode of life. We believe that biology is at present very far from being able to deal satisfactorily with this question, and we shall put forward only certain tentative suggestions.

The point at issue is how far structures or behaviour patterns originally elaborated in relation to a particular environment may eventually become incorporated in the general organisation of the species. We believe that some evidence may be obtained from the so-called ' Law of Irreversibility of Evolution.' In so far as this ' law ' is not merely a description of the somewhat imperfectly known geological history of animals, it suggests that animals usually fail to recover from any too detailed or too long extended specialisation. On the other hand, where life in an environment has not entailed too great specialisation, reversal is possible. We have already mentioned one example in the South American opossum, *Didelphys azarae*. Loss of flight in birds, or the reacquirement of the terrestrial habit by aquatic dipterous larvæ, will also be recalled. The process of ' fœtalisation' in the evolution of man (Bolk, 1919) also seems to show a retracement of stages in specialisation, even if not leading back to an adult ancestral type.

It appears that a distinction must be drawn between detailed specialisation for a restricted habitat and more general specialisation for a broad one. Under the former conditions it is necessarily the environment which to a large extent determines what specialisations are feasible ; under the latter there are so many different methods of successful conquest (*e.g.* conquest of the air by insects, reptiles, mammals and birds) that the method actually employed depends more on the individuality of the organism than on the peculiarities of the environment. Successful adaptation is mainly dependent on a perfect system of internal relations. In a review of the broad features of evolution, organismal adaptation would stand out as the most characteristic general tendency, but there is also much specialisation, particularly in those numerous degenerate lines which have sooner or later become extinct.

It is relatively easy to make broad generalisations, but very difficult to envisage such a twofold system of adaptation in terms of the actual origin and multiplication of new variants. The suggestion that an elaborate system of internal relations is perpetually being improved by a series of entirely random mutations is not convincing, but no other equally concrete explanation, supported by direct observation, can be brought forward. We suggest that as far as internal relations are concerned the organism itself may in some sense initiate new steps forward. If such steps took the form of mutations as we know them, the multiplication of the latter might be due to a form of Natural Selection which preserved the best organised rather than those most specialised for any particular environment.

Specialisations, in our sense, might well be due to Natural Selection of the classical type, but even here we feel that there are certain difficulties. The greatest, perhaps, is the lack of sufficient direct evidence for such a process. Even if its efficiency had been proved, it would still be uncertain whether *all* specialisations could be explained in this way.

It is known in several species that each intraspecific genotype has its own characteristic potentialities, *e.g.* viability, fecundity, etc. If such genotypes are put in competition in a standard environment, one type will finally replace all the others. It has been held (*e.g.* Haldane, 1932, chapter iv) that this proves that Natural Selection must be taking place continuously amongst such mixed assemblages in nature. No doubt, if some of the types are markedly defective, this will be true ; but usually the position is not so simple. The conditions in nature, for instance, are not standardised but highly variable, and many types may scarcely have any opportunity to exhibit their characteristic norm. Behaviour patterns and physiological attributes such as viability appear always to show a considerable range of variability, even under standard conditions, and in nature the selection of genotypes on the basis of phenotypic performance must at the best be a very slow process. As we have said in Chapter VII, selection between large populations, which already differ in many respects, is more easy to understand than selection of individual variants. We suggest that, even in specialisation, the internal relations of the organism may play a not unimportant part.

Finally, many of the small characters which differentiate species appear to be entirely useless, and here we believe random survival, combined with isolation and occasionally with hybridisation, may have played an important part.

Summary

In this chapter we contrast *specialisation* with the more fundamental property of *organisation*. Animals are not only adapted to deal with special stresses and crises of their environment, but they are also able to regulate themselves to a diversity of environmental stresses and to avoid the evolutionary ' blind alley ' of specialisation. It is important to realise that we have as yet no *a priori* method of estimating the degree of adaptation : we can only postulate that the species which actually exist must be sufficiently adapted to survive. More accurate estimates will be possible when the experimental evaluation of single factors is more advanced and adequate methods of measuring fluctuations in animal populations have been devised.

Meanwhile we can do little more than exercise great caution in attributing survival value to details of structure or habit, even when these appear to be not entirely useless. Modifications leading to more efficient organisation are more likely to be adaptive (in the strict sense), but these are usually recognisable only when we compare the larger divisions of the animal kingdom.

CHAPTER X

AT the present time there are two rival conceptions of organic evolution which represent a fundamental cleavage in scientific outlook. The one views the living organism as the resultant of variation (either spontaneous or induced by external factors) guided by the fortuitous changes of its environment. The other regards the organism as charged with a self-initiating capacity for development and adaptation and the modifications displayed in the course of evolution as the expression of this potential. The first, stressing the intimate relation of the organism with its environment, its apparent ' fit ' in the ecological complex, and the proof that evolution has proceeded by minute increments, finds the prime cause either in Natural Selection or in the direct moulding of the organism by the factors of the environment. The other emphasises the co-ordination and mutual interaction of the parts of the organism, its wholeness and organisation, and, unable to imagine that such organisation can be produced by the mechanical sieving of variants by selection or by the erratic stress of the environment, assigns the origin of evolutionary modifications to an internal energy. It is readily understood how this diversity of opinion has arisen, for the present incoherent and unrelated state of the data makes it easy to seize on certain kinds of evidence and treat them as decisive. We have stressed in a previous chapter the part played by prejudice and bias in evolutionary inquiry. It is not sufficiently realised, however, how limited and inadequate are our data for coming to a decision as to the causes of evolution. Any attempt, therefore, to form an unprejudiced conclusion labours under technical disadvantages which frustrate it and limit it to a summing of possibilities. We propose in this chapter to define as clearly as possible the limits of our knowledge on these matters, and in particular to indicate if the two theories above mentioned are to be reconciled or if one or the other is inadequate.

There appears to be no reason to question the orthodox and, indeed, inescapable [1] contention that evolution has taken place by a series of changes similar in dimensions to the differences in individual characters between races and species. It is possible that changes of an adaptive kind have arisen through mutations occurring *en bloc* (Chapter VI); but at present there is little evidence to support this belief.

Two features of this process impress themselves on our attention—the origin of groups of various kinds and the production of adaptations. We are led to contrast the continuous development of small divergences of the order of geographical races, colonies, subspecies and species with the sustained episodes in the course of which complex organs, protracted adaptive modification and the cumulative organisation of parts are established. According to one view these two features are different expressions of one and the same process; according to another, group formation and adaptation (using the term widely, Chapter IX) are due to different causes. Whatever the truth may be, it seems quite certain that adaptation itself appears to be established by the same sorts of changes that lead to the divergences of races and species. It may be, as we have suggested, that adaptive modification is established far more by correlated changes than we are aware of; but we have no right to assume this, and no evidence at least to suggest that this is general.

Now there is every reason to believe that the major groups of the animal kingdom are originated by divergences of the order of races and species—that they are, in short, the summation of such divergences. As a consequence, therefore, we are led to look on the whole process of evolution, at least as regards the stages by which it proceeds, as a unitary one. But as the taxonomic divergences become more emphasised, they become increasingly concerned with adaptive and functional modifications, so that, if we are right in assuming that the whole process is unitary, it seems that all divergences should be adaptive *ab initio*. The unitary nature of the process tends,

[1] Various authors (notably Cope and Wigand, see Philiptschenko, 1927, p. 91) have expressed strong doubts as to whether the higher systematic groups have arisen by the progressive modification of lower ones.

indeed, to suggest that the causes of divergence are the same at all stages.   But there may be a fallacy in this reasoning, for it does not follow that, because the divergences are of the same magnitude throughout, they are due to one and the same cause.

There is another ground for suspecting that, though the stages in evolution are of more or less uniform magnitude and the process seems to be unitary in this respect, it is not the result of a single main cause.   Many authors have expressed doubt as to whether the process of group formation and the origin of adaptation can be treated as part of the same process—whether, in short, the main adaptive tendencies are the expansion of minor useful divergences between races and species. Not only are there strong reasons for this doubt, but the fact that some divergence seems to precede adaptation suggests that adaptations have been, as it were, grafted on an already existing tendency.

In discussing these general aspects of the evolutionary process there is another point to bear in mind.   We have so far been using the term ' adaptation' in a broad sense.   But, as we have shown (Chapter IX), the term is given to several phenomena, of which we now single out two for special consideration. In the previous chapter (p. 365) we suggested that it is not easy to deal with the relations between organisation and specialisation—how far structures, etc., originally elaborated in relation to a particular environment become incorporated into the general organisation.   But we may press the question further and ask : is organisation, as we have defined it, the sum of divers specialisations, or is it an activity or quality having a separate origin?   We do not think that this question can be answered except by ascertaining if there is any cause efficient to accumulate and organise specialisations.   At first sight such a process appears unlikely.   Specialisation seems to be of a different order from organisation, the one involving local modification, the other a co-ordinating activity.   Yet we can at least conceive (Chapter IX, p. 366) that Natural Selection might act in such a way that survival value was determined by better organisation, and that those individuals were selected in which not only specialisation was most efficient, but also divers specialisations collectively contributed to survival.

The theory of Natural Selection (in its earlier and its modern form) postulates that the evolutionary process is unitary, and that not only are groups formed by the multiplication of single variants having survival value, but also that such divergences are amplified to produce adaptations (both specialisations and organisation). It has been customary to admit that certain ancillary processes are operative (isolation, correlation), but the importance of these, as active principles, is subordinate to selection. The evidence for the efficacy of selection is summarised in Chapter VII. It will be seen there that (a) it is very doubtful whether we have enough evidence of the right sort to form a judgment; (b) the direct evidence is negligible; and (c) the bulk of the circumstantial evidence is inadequate, although in some instances we are impelled to recognise that the action of selection is likely, if not proved. Conversely, there is a good deal of evidence that suggests that races and species arise independently of the survival value of their characters, unless we are prepared to make a very large appeal to ignorance. Apart from the strong *theoretical* case— which we do not regard as evidential—presented for Natural Selection as an agency adequate to account for the spread of new characters, it seems that the verdict must turn on the amount of weight we are prepared to allow to the various pieces of circumstantial evidence (mimicry, Cuckoo's eggs, etc.). We feel that these are by no means negligible and, in default of very convincing alternative explanations, they must remain as testimony that selection may be operative. Selection must therefore be retained as a likely factor. If this is admitted, it is only fair to ask : if the activity of Natural Selection is admitted as probable in some cases, may it not be more widely operative? Is it likely that such a principle should have only a partial or particular efficacy? Such questions plainly cannot be answered except on grounds so general as to be devoid of value. There is no *a priori* reason for considering that Natural Selection must have a universal activity, even if its efficacy is demonstrated in particular cases.

We attach considerable importance to the facts assembled in Chapter VII which suggest that the divergence of races and species is not influenced by selection. It has been suggested (p. 251) that, if mimetic resemblances are shown to be produced by selection, it involves a strong presupposition that specific divergences of the same order must be produced by this means. This analogy cannot have much weight in face of the very convincing suggestion that a great deal of specific and racial differentiation is due to isolation and chance survival. Finally, we believe that the special weaknesses of the selection theory render it unsuited to explain the origin of complex organs, and the more profound co-ordinative principles.

As the case for Natural Selection is of such a kind as to require what is virtually a suspense of judgment, we are driven to inquire as to the claims of the other theories.

When we turn to the suggestion that the prime factor in evolution is the inheritance of induced modification or of the effects of use and effort, it is possible to speak with more assurance.

As far as the experimental evidence is concerned, we believe that there is some likelihood that mutations may be induced by the direct effect of environmental factors on the germ cells. For the inherited effects on structure [1] of use and effort we find no evidence. We must admit that the time-factor has to be taken into account. The hereditary behaviour of ' Dauermodifikationen ' suggests that the germinal material is susceptible to temporary modifications, and we regard it as an open question whether stimuli applied for periods far exceeding those employed in experiment might not produce stable modifications. It is possible and even likely that such influences might account for much local differentiation, though we have little evidence for the transformation of whole populations by their means. But we do not believe they are capable of producing adaptations with their long-sustained history of modification in a given direction. ' Lamarckian ' processes involving long-continued use and effort would be suited to produce such results ; but we have no evidence for their occurrence.

The theory that various phenomena of determinate variation, excessive growth, and complexity are to be attributed to an inner momentum also labours under the disability that it does not account for the transformation of populations except on the assumption that such changes occur *en masse*.

---

[1] We think it possible that modifications of habit, perhaps not due to mutation at all, may nevertheless become permanent. The matter is still under investigation, but its importance in evolution may well be found to be considerable.

Some authors have nevertheless insisted that these phenomena are due to an internal impulse, and indeed the various theories (*cf.* Chapter VIII) by which it is sought to explain them as due to Natural Selection alone, or to selection combined with heterogony, are subject to the same general criticism as the selection theory. Analogy with physiological and pathological processes justifies us to some extent in a belief in an internal directive force, though the proof of its existence depends rather on the exclusion of other causes than on the direct demonstration of such a principle.

If it was correct to exclude other causes and to interpret the facts of orthogenesis as indicative of an internal potential, it would be possible to suggest a theoretical account of the origin of adaptations. We might assume that such a momentum affecting functionally associated parts could exert an organising influence on a part or on the whole animal, and even that, by what we might describe as a functional quickening, it could promote and attract to itself the kinds of mutations required in any adaptive situation. But for such a suggestion, of course, we have little evidence, and its chief justification is the poverty of the other theories.

If the estimation of the various theories just presented is a fair one, we are plainly left with a negative result and the inference that our knowledge is too defective to provide an answer. We may, perhaps, claim to have shown that group formation is, in part at least, independent of Natural Selection; that the effect of the environment alone cannot give rise to adaptations; and that Natural Selection cannot be excluded from the possible causes of adaptations, though it is more likely to have produced specialisation than the more fundamental processes of organisation.

Against this scepticism and uncertainty we are entitled to set certain impressions. It seems that organisation in its more fundamental manifestations, especially in development, is something for which the activities of Natural Selection, even if estimated in the most generous fashion, cannot well account. With more evidence, and particularly more knowledge of bionomics, it might be shown that selection does, in fact, produce certain kinds of specialisation. We find it hard to believe either that the ascertained ' fit ' of the organism to its environment could enable selection to work with the necessary accuracy and closeness of correlation, or that the selection of very rare mutants could produce that harmonious co-ordination in which one part depends on the appropriate appearance and degree of development of another part.

In suggesting that group-divergence and local variation are due to subordinate factors such as isolation of various kinds, random spread and the reshuffling of heritable characters, but that certain evolutionary tendencies may be referable to an innate ' momentum ' and self-regulation, we ought not to forget that after all one of the tests of an evolutionary theory is its capacity to account for the spreading of variants and the transformation of populations. In this respect, as we have admitted, Natural Selection enjoys a strong theoretical advantage. But it is only a theoretical advantage, and should not influence our judgment of the theory if the more important direct and circumstantial evidence is defective.

Finally, we would point out that, if indeed group divergence, specialisation and organisation are due to different causes, it is by no means easy to assign to these factors their particular spheres of influence with any accuracy. Some group divergences are almost certainly void of adaptive significance ; but in others we may discern the beginning of specialisation. Organisation, in its more profound expression an attribute of all living matter and independent of the temporary influences that evoke specialisation, may sometimes be guided along particular channels by specialisation.

In arguing that an element of self-regulation and self-organisation has had an influence in evolution we are aware that we are touching certain profound and speculative issues. If this organising activity is indeed an agent in producing the main adaptive tendencies in evolution, it might be argued that the gradual upbuilding and perfection of adaptations, because they involve so large an element of design, must also involve some reference to a purpose independent of survival value and chance, and existing as an end in itself. We have to admit that, if we were to relegate survival value to a sub-ordinate rôle in the causation of evolution, the element of design and purposefulness has to be explained. It is not likely that the mere interaction of developing parts and their reciprocal effects on one another could produce the ordered and purposeful designs which we see in adaptation. For those who believe that all organisation is produced by the material processes envisaged by the traditional theories, the scheme of evolution must seem to be clear, at least in outline. For those with whom the difficulties we have outlined in this work have any weight, it must remain to attempt a clearer definition of the purposeful activity with which we seem confronted.

BIBLIOGRAPHY

ACKERT, J. E. 1916. On the effects of selection in *Paramoecium*. Genetics, **1**, 387–405, 8 figs.

ADLERZ, G. 1902. *Ceropales maculata* Fab. en parasitisk Pompilid. Bihang K. Svenska Vet. Akad. Handl., **28**, afd. IV, no. 14, 20 pp.

—— 1902a. Periodische Massenvermehrung als Evolutionsfaktor. Biol. Centrbl., **22**, 108–119.

—— 1903. Lefnadsförhallanden och instinkter inom familjerna Pompilidae och Sphegidae. K. Svenska Vet. Akad. Handl., **37**, no. 5, 181 pp.

AGAR, W. E. 1913. The transmission of environmental effects . . . in *Simocephalus vetulus*. Phil. Trans. Roy. Soc. London, **203**B, 319–350, 6 tables.

—— 1931. A Lamarckian experiment involving a hundred generations with negative results. J. Exp. Biol., **8**, 95–107, 2 figs., 5 tables.

AGASSIZ, A. 1881. Challenger Reports : Zoology III. Echinoids, i–viii, 1–321, 45 plates.

ALKINS, W. E. 1921. Variation in Sphaeria. Mem. Proc. Manchester Lit. Phil. Soc., **65**, 1–10.

—— 1923. Variation in *Ena obscura*. Journ. Conch., **17**, 35–38.

—— 1923a. Note on the variation of *Clausilia itala*. Journ. Conch., **17**, 81–83.

—— 1923b. Morphogenesis in Brachiopoda. Mem. Proc. Manchester Lit. Phil. Soc., **67**, 109–136, 2 plates.

—— 1928. The Conchometric relationship of *Clausilia rugosa* and *Clausilia cravenensis*. Proc. Malac. Soc., **18**, pt. II, 50–69.

ALKINS, W. E., and COOK, M. 1921. Variation in Sphaeria II. Mem. Proc. Manchester Lit. Phil. Soc., **65**, 1–8.

ALKINS, W. E., and HARWOOD, J. 1921. Variation in Sphaeria III. Mem. Proc. Manchester Lit. Phil. Soc., **65**, 1–7.

ALLARD, H. A. 1929. Physiological differentiation in . . . Orthoptera. Canad. Ent., **61**, 195–198.

ALPATOV, W. W. 1924. Die Definition der untersten systematischen Kategorien . . . Zool. Anz., **60**, 161–168.

—— 1925. Ueber die Verkleinerung der Russellänge der Honigbiene vom Süden nach dem Norden hin. Zool. Anz., **65**, 103–111, 6 tables.

—— 1929. Biometrical studies in variation and races of the Honey Bee (*Apis mellifera* L.). Quart. Rev. Biol., **4**, 1–58, 21 figs., 25 tables.

ANNANDALE, N. 1915. Fauna of the Chilka Lake. Sponges. Mem. Ind. Mus. Calcutta, **5**, 23–54, 3 plates, 1 fig.

—— 1924. The evolution of the shell sculpture in freshwater snails of the family Viviparidae. Proc. R. Soc. London, **96**B, 60–76.

ANNANDALE, N., and HORA, S. L. 1922. Parallel evolution in the fish and tadpoles of mountain torrents. Rec. Ind. Mus., **24**, 505–510, 5 figs.

ANNANDALE, N., and RAO, H. S. 1925. Materials for a revision of the recent Indian Limnaeidae. Rec. Ind. Mus., **27**, 137–189, 15 figs.

ASHFORD, C. 1885 (1883–5). On the darts of British Helicidae. Journ. Conch., **4**, 69, 108, etc., 9 plates.

AUBERTIN, D. 1927. On the anatomy of the land snails *Cepea hortensis* and *Cepea nemoralis*. Proc. Zool. Soc. London, **1927**, 553–582, 4 plates.

AUBERTIN, D., ELLIS, A. E., and ROBSON, G. C. 1931. The natural history and variation of the Pointed Snail. Proc. Zool. Soc. London, **1930**, 1027–1055, 1 plate, 2 figs.

AVINOFF, A. 1929. A variable Palearctic Satyrid. Trans. Fourth Internat. Congress of Entomology, Ithaca, August 1928, **2**, 290–293.

BABCOCK, K. W. 1927. The European Cornborer, *Pyrausta nubilalis* Hübn. : A discussion of its seasonal history in relation to various climates. Ecology, **8**, 177–193, 4 tables.

BABCOCK, K. W., and VANCE, A. M. 1929. The Cornborer in Central Europe. A review of investigations from 1924 to 1927. U.S. Dept. Agric. Tech. Bull., **135**, 54 pp., 12 tables, 10 plates, 3 figs.

BACOT, A. 1917. A contribution to the bionomics of *Pediculus capitis* and *P. humanus*. Parasitology, **9**, 228–259, 4 figs.

BANKS, E. 1925. Variations in the colours of Palearctic birds in relation to the conditions in which they live. Proc. Zool. Soc. London, Pt. I, **1925**, 311–322, 2 graphs, 2 tables.

—— 1931. The forms of Prevost's squirrel found in Sarawak. Proc. Zool. Soc. London, **1931**, 1335–1348, 1 plate, 1 table.

BANNERMAN, D. A. 1927. Report on the birds collected during the British Museum Expedition to Tunisia. The Ibis, **12**, Suppt., 1–213, 9 plates.

BANTA, A. 1921. Selection in Cladocera . . . Carn. Inst. Washington Pubn., **305**, 1–170, 19 figs.

BARRETT, C., and CRANDALL, L. 1932. The Bower Birds and their bowers. Bull. N. York Zool. Soc., **35**, 55–68, 11 figs.

BARRETT-HAMILTON, G. E. H., and HINTON, M. A. C. 1910–1921. A History of British Mammals. London.

BARTSCH, P. 1920. Experiments in the breeding of *Cerions*. Dept. of Marine Biology, Carn. Inst. Washington, **14**, 1–54, 59 plates.

BATESON, W. 1889. On some variations of *Cardium edule* . . . Phil. Trans. Roy. Soc. London, **180**B, 297–330, 1 plate.

—— 1892. On variation in the colour of cocoons of *Eriogaster lanestris* and *Saturnia carpini*. Trans. Ent. Soc. London, **1892**, 45–52.

—— 1894. Materials for the study of variation. London.

—— 1909. Mendel's Principles of Heredity. Cambridge.

—— 1913. Problems of genetics. New Haven.

BATESON, W., and BRINDLEY, H. H. 1892. On some cases of variation in secondary sexual characters, statistically examined. Proc. Zool. Soc. London, **1892**, 585–594, 6 figs.

BATHER, F. A. 1927. Biological classification, past and future. Quart. Journ. Geol. Soc., **83**, pt. 2, lxii–civ.

BAUMBERGER, J. P. 1917. Hibernation : a periodical phenomenon. Ann. Ent. Soc. Amer., **10**, 179–186, 5 tables, 1 fig.

BEEBE, C. W. 1907. Geographic variation in birds . . . Zoologica, **1**, 1–41, 1 plate.

BEECHER, H. F. 1901. Studies in Evolution. Yale Univ. Bicentennial Pubns. New York, pp. 1–638, 34 plates, 132 figs.

BELJAJEFF, M. M. 1927. Ein Experiment über die Bedeutung der Schutz-färbung. Biol. Zentralbl., **47**, 107–113, 2 figs.

BENSON, S. B. 1932. Three new rodents from lava beds of Southern New Mexico. Univ. California Publ. Zool., **38**, 335–340, 1 plate.

BEQUAERT, J. 1919. A revision of the Vespidae of the Belgian Congo based on the collection of the American Museum Congo Expedition, with a list of Ethiopian wasps. Bull. Amer. Mus. Nat. Hist., **39**, pp. iv + 384, 6 plates, 267 figs, 2 maps.

—— 1931. The color forms of the Common Hornet, *Vespa crabro* L. Konowia, **10**, 101–109.

BERG, L. S. 1926. Nomogenesis or Evolution determined by Law. (English Transln.) London.

BERGSON, H. 1911. Creative Evolution. (English Transln.) London.

BERRY, E. W. 1928. Cephalopod adaptation . . . Quart. Rev. Biol., **3**, 92–108, 6 plates.

BEZZI, M. 1916. Riduzione e scomparsa delle ali negli insetti Ditteri. Riv. Sci. nat. ' Natura,' **7**, 85–182, 11 figs.

—— 1922. The first Eremochaetous Dipteron with vestigial wings. Ann. Mag. Nat. Hist. (9), **9**, 323–328, 1 fig.

BITTERA, J. VON. 1918. Einiges über die männlichen Copulationsorgane der Muriden und deren systematischen Bedeutung. Zool. Jahrb., Abt. f. Syst., **41**, 399–418, 1 plate.

BLAIR, K. G. 1931. The beetles of the Scilly Islands. Proc. Zool. Soc. London, **1931**, 1211–1258.

BLAND SUTTON, J. 1890. Evolution and Disease (Contemporary Science Series). London.

BODENHEIMER, F. S., and KLEIN, H. Z. 1930. Ueber die Temperatur-abhängigkeiten von Insekten. II. Die Abhängigkeit der Aktivität bei der Ernteameise *Messor semirufus* André von Temperatur und andere Faktoren. Zs. vergl. Phys., **11**, 345–384, 17 figs., 34 tables.

BOETTGER, C. R. 1921. *Otala tigri* und *Carabus morbillosus*. Abh. Senckenb. naturf. Ges. Frankfurt a/M., **37**, 321–325, 2 plates.

—— 1925. Die wissenschaftliche Bedeutung der Weichtierschalen. Ber. Senckenb. Ges. Frankfurt a/M., **55**, 101–109.

—— 1931. Die Entstehung von Populationen mit bestimmter Variant-anzahl bei . . . *Cepea*. Zs. ind. Abst. u. Vererblehre, **58**, 295–316.

—— 1932. Die funktionelle Bedeutung der Rippung bei Landschnecken-gehäusen. Zool. Anz., **98**, 209–213.

BOLK, L. 1919. On the topographical relations of the orbits in infantile and adult skulls in man and apes. Amsterdam Proc. Sci. K. Akad. Wet., **21**, 277–286, 13 figs.

BORODIN, N. A. 1927. Changes of environment as cause of the origin of varieties or subspecies. Amer. Nat., **61**, 266–271, 2 figs.

BOULANGÉ, H. 1924. Recherches sur l'appareil copulateur des Hyméno-ptères et spécialement des Chalastogastres. Mém. et Trav. Facultés Catholiques de Lille, Fasc. **28**, 444, 3 plates, 141 figs.

BOUVIER, E. 1904. Sur le genre *Ortmannia* . . . C. R. Ac. Sci. Paris, **138**, 446–449.

BOWATER, W. 1914. The Heredity of melanism in Lepidoptera. Journ. Genetics, **3**, 299–314, 1 plate.

BOYCOTT, A. E. 1919. Observations on the local variation of *Clausilia bidentata*. Journ. Conch., **16**, 10–23.

—— 1927. Further observations on the local variation of *Clausilia bidentata*. Journ. Conch., **18**, 131–135.

BOYCOTT, A. E., DIVER, C., and others. 1930. The inheritance of sinistrality in *Limnaea peregra*. Phil. Trans. Roy. Soc. London, **219**B, 51–131, 1 plate.

BOYCOTT, A. E., OLDHAM, C., and WATERSTON, A. 1932. Notes on the Lake Lymnaeas of S.W. Ireland. Proc. Malac. Soc., **20**, 105–126.

BRAIN, W. RUSSELL. 1927. Galatea or the future of Darwinism. London.

BRANDT, K. 1897. Die Fauna der Ostsee . . . Verh. deutschen Zool. Ges., **1897**, 10–34, 4 figs.

BRAUER, A. 1908. Die Tiefsee Fische, Th. II. : in Wiss. Ergebn. Deutsche Tiefsee Expedn., **15**, 19–266, 26 plates, 11 figs.

BRIDGES, C. 1923. Aberrations in chromosomal materials. Eugenics, Genetics and the Family, **1**, 76–81.

BRIDGMAN, P. W. 1932. Statistical mechanics and the second law of thermo-dynamics. Science, n.s., **75**, 419–428.

BRISTOWE, W. S. 1929. The Spiders of Lundy Island. Proc. Zool. Soc. London, **1929**, 235–244.

—— 1929a. The Spiders of the Scilly Isles. Proc. Zool. Soc. London, **1929**, 149–164.

—— 1929b. A Contribution to the knowledge of the spiders of the Channel Isles. Proc. Zool. Soc. London, **1929**, 181–188.

—— 1929c. The distribution and dispersal of spiders. Proc. Zool. Soc. London, **1929**, 633–657, 5 figs.

—— 1929d. The mating habits of spiders, with special reference to the problems surrounding sex dimorphism. Proc. Zool. Soc. London, **1929**, 309–358, 15 figs.

—— 1931. Notes on the biology of spiders, IV. Ann. Mag. Nat. Hist. (10), **8**, 457–465, 6 figs.

BRISTOWE, W. S., and LOCKET, G. H. 1926. The courtship of British Lycosid spiders, and its probable significance. Proc. Zool. Soc. London, **1926**, 317–347, 10 figs.

BRUES, C. T. 1928. A note on the genus *Pelecinus*. Psyche, **35**, 205–209.

BULLER, W. L. 1888. A History of the Birds of New Zealand, Vol. I. London.

BUMPUS, H. C. 1899 (1898). The elimination of the unfit as illustrated by the introduced Sparrow . . . Biol. Lectures, Mar. Biol. Lab. Woods Hole Lect., **11**, 209–226.

BURCKHARDT, G. 1900. Faunistische und Systematische Studien über das Zooplankton der grösseren Seen der Schweiz. Rev. Suisse de Zoologie, **7**, 353–713, 4 plates.

BURTON, M. 1928. A comparative study of . . . shallow water and deepwater sponges. Journ. Quekett Microscopical Club, **16**, 49–70, 1 plate, 7 figs.

BUTTEL-REEPEN, H. VON. 1915. Leben und Wesen der Bienen. Braunschweig.

BUXTON, P. A. 1923. Animal Life in Deserts. London.

CALMAN, W. T. 1930. Presidential Address, Section D, British Association Adv. Science, **1930**, 1–10.

CARPENTER, G. H. 1928. The Biology of Insects. London.

CARRELL, A. 1931. The new cytology. Science, n.s., **73**, 297–303.

CASTLE, W. E. 1919. Studies of heredity in Rabbits, etc. Carn. Inst. Washington Pubn., **288**, i–iv, 1–56, 3 plates, 5 figs.

—— 1932. Body size and body proportion in relation to growth rates and Natural Selection. Science, n.s., **76**, 365–366.

CASTLE, W. E., and PHILLIPS, J. 1911. On germinal transplantation in vertebrates. Carn. Inst. Washington Pubn., **144**, 1–26, 2 plates.

CASTLE, W. E., and WRIGHT, S. 1916. Studies of inheritance in Guinea Pigs and Rats. Carn. Inst. Washington Pubn., **241**, 1–192, 7 plates, 7 figs.

CESNOLA, A. P. DI. 1904. Preliminary note on the protective value of colour in *Mantis religiosa*. Biometrika, **3**, 58–59.

—— 1907. A first study of Natural Selection in *Helix arbustorum*. Biometrika, **5**, 387–399, 1 plate.

CHAMPY, C. 1924. Sexualité et Hormones. Paris.

CHAPMAN, F. M. 1923. Mutations among birds in the genus *Buarremon*. Bull. Amer. Mus. Nat. Hist., **48**, art. IX, 243–278, 1 map, 4 plates.

CHAPMAN, F. M., and GRISCOM, L. 1924. The House Wrens of the Genus *Troglodytes*. Bull. Amer. Mus. Nat. Hist., **50**, art. IV, 279–304, 2 maps.

CHAPMAN, R. N. 1931. Animal ecology with special reference to insects. London.

CHAPMAN, R. N., MICKEL, C. E., PARKER, J. R., and others. 1926. Studies in the ecology of sand dune insects. Ecology, **7**, 416–426.

CHAPMAN, T. A. 1913. Mimicry (?) in Erebias. Trans. Ent. Soc. London, Proc., **1913**, cvii–cx.

CHEESMAN, R. E. 1926. In Unknown Arabia. London.

CHEESMAN, R. E., and HINTON, M. A. C. 1924. On the mammals collected in the desert of Central Arabia by Major R. E. Cheesman. Ann. Mag. Nat. Hist. (9), **14**, 548–558.

CHRISTY, C. 1929. The African Buffaloes. Proc. Zool. Soc. London, **1929**, 445–462, 4 plates.

CLARK, A. H. 1932. The Butterflies of the District of Columbia and vicinity. U.S. Nat. Mus. Bull. **157**, 1–256, 64 plates.

COBLENTZ, W. W. 1911. The colour of the light emitted by the Lampyridae. Canad. Ent., **43**, 355–360, 5 figs.

COCKAYNE, L., and ALLAN, H. H. 1927. The Bearing of ecological studies in New Zealand on botanical taxonomic conceptions . . . J. Ecology, **15**, 234–277.

COLE, L., and BACHUBER, L. J. 1914. The effect of lead on the germ-cells of the male rabbit and fowl . . . Proc. Soc. Exp. Biol. and Med., **12**, 24–29.

COLLINGE, W. 1909. Colour variation in some British slugs. Journ. Conch., **12**, 235–237.

CONKLIN, E. 1898. Environmental and sexual dimorphism in *Crepidula*. Proc. Acad. Nat. Sci. Philadelphia, **1898**, 435–444, 3 plates.

COPE, E. D. 1887. The Origin of the Fittest. New York.

—— 1896. The Primary Factors of Organic Evolution. Chicago.

CORSET, J. 1931. Les coaptations chez les insectes. Bull. biol. France et Belg., suppl. XIII, Paris.

COTT, H. B. 1932. Exhibit and Lecture (not published in full). Proc. Zool. Soc. London, **1932**, 225.

COUTAGNE, G. 1895. Recherches sur la polymorphisme des mollusques de France. Ann. Soc. agric. Lyon (7), **3**, 291–453.

CRAMPTON, H. E. 1904. Variation and elimination in *Philosamia cynthia*. Biometrika, **3**, 113–130, 1 fig.

—— 1916. Studies on . . . the genus *Partula*. The species inhabiting Tahiti. Carn. Inst. Washington Pubn., **228**, 1–311, 34 plates.

CRAMPTON, H. E. 1925. Studies on . . . the genus *Partula*. The species inhabiting Guam, etc. *Op. cit.*, **228**A, 1–116, 14 plates.

—— 1932. Studies on . . . the genus *Partula*. Carn. Inst. Washington Pubn., **410**, i–v, 1–335, 24 plates, 6 figs.

CROZIER, W. 1918. Assortative mating in a Nudibranch, *Chromodoris zebra*. J. Exp. Zool., **27**, 247–292, 7 figs., 16 charts.

CUÉNOT, L. 1917. *Sepia officinalis* est une espèce en voie de dissociation. Arch. Zoologie exp. gén., **56**, 315–346, 4 figs.

—— 1921. La Génèse des Espèces animales. 2me Edn., Paris.

—— 1925. L'Adaptation. Paris.

CUNNINGHAM, J. T. 1928. Modern Biology. London.

DAKIN, W. J. 1928. The eyes of *Pecten*, etc. . . . Proc. Roy. Soc. London, **103**B, 355–365, 1 fig.

DARWIN, C. 1884. The Origin of Species. London. John Murray. 6th ed.

—— 1901. The Descent of Man and Selection in Relation to Sex. London. John Murray.

—— 1905. Variation of animals and plants under domestication. London. John Murray. Two vols.

DAVENPORT, C. 1908. Elimination in self-coloured birds. Nature, **78**, 101.

DAWSON, R. W. 1931. The problem of voltinism and dormancy in the polyphemus moth (*Telea polyphemus* Cramer). J. Exp. Zool., **59**, 87–131, 7 figs., 10 tables.

DELCOURT, A. 1909. Recherches sur la variabilité du genre *Notonecta*. Bull. sci. France et Belg., **43**, 373–461, 2 plates.

DEMAISON, L. 1927. Sur quelques aberrations de Lépidoptères. Bull. Soc. ent. France, **1927**, 295–296.

DENDY, A. 1911. Momentum in evolution. Repts. Brit. Assocn. Adv. Science (Portsmouth), London, **1911**, 277–280.

DETLEFSEN, J. A. 1925. The inheritance of acquired characters. Physiol. Reviews, **5**, 244–278.

DEWAR, D., and FINN, F. 1909. The Making of a Species. London.

DICE, L. R. 1929. Descriptions of two new pocket-mice and a new Woodrat . . . Occas. Papers, Mus. Zool. Univ. Michigan, **203**, 1–4.

—— 1931. The occurrence of two subspecies of one species in the same area. Journ. Mammalogy, **12**, 210–213.

DIETZE, K. 1913. Biologie der Eupithecien. Zweiter Teil, Text. Berlin.

DOBROVOLSKAIA-ZAVADSKAIA, N. 1929. The problem of species in view of the origin of some new forms in mice. Biol. Rev., **4**, 327–350, 4 plates.

DOBRZANSKY, T. 1924. Die geographische und individuelle Variabilität von *Harmonia axyridis*, Pall. in ihren Wechselbeziehungen. Biol. Zentrbl., **44**, 401–421, 2 figs.

DODDS, G. S., and HISAW, F. L. 1924*a*. Ecological studies of aquatic insects. I. Ecology, **5**, 137–148.

—— 1924*b*. Same title, II. *Ibid.*, **5**, 262–271.

DOFLEIN, F. 1908. Über Schutzanpassung durch Ähnlichkeit. Biol. Centrbl., **28**, 243–256.

DONCASTER, L. 1906. Collective enquiry as to progressive melanism in Lepidoptera. Ent. Record, **18**, 165–254 (*passim*).

DUERDEN, J. E. 1907. Genetics of the colour pattern in . . . the genus *Homopus* and its allies. Rec. Albany Museum, **2,** 65–92, 3 plates.

—— 1920. The inheritance of the callosities in the Ostrich. Amer. Nat., **54,** 289–312, 7 figs.

DUNBAR, C. 1924. Phases of Cephalopod adaptation *in* ' Organic Adaptation to Environment,' ed. M. Thorpe, 187–223, 4 figs.

DUNCAN, F. N. 1915. An attempt to produce mutations through hybridization. Amer. Nat., **49,** 575–582.

DUNCKER, H. 1896. Variation und Verwandschaft von *Pleuronectes flesus*. Wiss. Meeresunters. Kiel (Helgoland) (2), **2,** 47–104, 4 plates.

DÜRKEN, B. 1922. Korrelation und Artbegriff. Zs. ind. Abst. u. Vererb. lehre, **27,** 27–47.

—— 1923. Ueber die Wirkung farbigen Lichtes auf die Puppen des Kohlweisslings (*Pieris brassicae*) und des Verhalten der Nachkommen. Arch. Entw. Mech., **99,** 222–389, 1 plate, 9 figs.

DWIGHT, J. 1918. The Geographical distribution and colour . . . in the genus *Junco* . . . Bull. Amer. Mus. Nat. Hist., **38,** art. 9, 269–309, 3 plates.

EDELSTEN, H. M. 1907. Oviposition of *Nonagria cannae*. Trans. Ent. Soc. London, Proc., **1907,** l–liv.

EDWARDS, F. W. 1929. British non-biting midges (Diptera, Chironomidae). Trans. Ent. Soc. London, **77,** 279–430, 3 plates, 15 figs.

—— 1929*a*. Diptera of Patagonia and South Chile. Part II. Fasc. II. Blepharoceridae. British Museum, London.

EGGERS, F. 1925. Ueber estlandische Dalyelliden. Mit. einem Wort zur Artbildungsfrage. Zool. Jahrb. Abt. Syst., **49,** 449–468, 1 plate, 3 figs.

EIMER, T. 1881. Untersuchungen über das Variieren des Mauereidechse . . . Arch. Naturgesch., **47,** 239–517, 3 plates.

—— 1897. Orthogenesis der Schmetterlinge. Leipzig.

EISENTRAUT, M. 1929. Die Variation der balearischen Inseleidechse *Lacerta lilfordi*. Sitzungsber. Ges. naturf. Freunde, Berlin, **1929,** 24–36, 1 fig.

—— 1929*a*. Untersuchungen über die . . . Eidechsen auf das balearischen Inseln. (Cited in Rensch, 1929.)

EKMAN, S. 1913. Artbildung bei der Copepodengattung *Limnocalanus*. Zs. ind. Abst. u. Vererb.lehre, **11,** 39–104, 9 figs.

ELTON, C. S. 1924. Periodic fluctuations in the numbers of animals . . . Brit. Journ. Expt. Biology, **2,** 119–163.

—— 1925. Plague and the regulation of numbers in wild mammals. J. Hygiene, **24,** 138–163, 4 figs.

—— 1927. Animal Ecology. London.

—— 1930. Animal Ecology and Evolution. Oxford.

—— 1931. The study of epidemic diseases among wild animals. J. Hygiene, **31,** 435–456.

ELTRINGHAM, H. 1910. African Mimetic Butterflies. Oxford.

—— 1912. A monograph of the African species of the genus *Acraea* Fab., with a supplement on those of the Oriental region. Trans. Ent. Soc. London, **1912,** 1–374, 16 plates.

—— 1916. On specific and mimetic relationships in the genus *Heliconius* L. Trans. Ent. Soc. London, **1916,** 101–148, 7 plates.

ELTRINGHAM, H. 1919. Butterfly vision. Trans. Ent. Soc. London, **1919**, 1–49, 5 plates.

EWING, H. W. 1916. Eighty-seven generations in a parthenogenetic pure line of *Aphis avenae*. Biol. Bull., **31**, 53–112, 19 figs.

FABER, A. 1928. Die Bestimmung der deutschen Geradflügler (Orthoptera) nach ihren Lautäusserungen. Zs. wiss. Ins. Biol., **23**, 209–234.

FENTON, C. L. 1931. Studies of evolution in the genus *Spirifer*. Pubn. Wagner Free Inst. Philadelphia, **2**, 1–436, 50 plates, 204 figs.

FERNALD, H. T. 1906. The digger wasps of North America and the West Indies belonging to the subfamily Chlorioninae. Proc. U.S. Nat. Mus., **31**, 291–423, 5 plates.

—— 1926. Climate and coloration in some wasps. Ann. Ent. Soc. Amer., **19**, 87–92.

—— 1927. The digger-wasps of North America of the genus *Podalonia* (*Psammophila*). Proc. U.S. Nat. Mus., **71**, art. 9, pp. 42, 2 plates.

FERRONIÈRE, G. 1901. Études biologiques sur les zones supralittorales . . . Bull. Soc. sci. nat. Ouest de la France (2), **1**, I, 1–451, 6 plates.

FERRY, L., SHAPIRO, N. I., and SIDOROFF, B. N. 1930. On the Influence of temperature on the process of mutation . . . Amer. Nat., **64**, 570–574.

FERTON, C. 1901. Notes détachées sur l'instinct des Hyménoptères méllifères et ravisseurs avec la description de quelques espèces. Ann. Soc. ent. France, **70**, 83–148, 3 plates.

FEUERBORN, H. J. 1922. Der sexuelle Reizapparat (Schmuck-, Duft- und Berührungsorgane) der Psychodiden nach biologischen und physiologischen Gesichtspunkten untersucht. Arch. Naturges., **88**A, Heft 4, 1–137, 39 figs.

FILIPJEV, I. N. 1929. Life-zones in Russia and their injurious insects. Trans. Fourth Internat. Congress of Entomology, Ithaca, August 1928, **2**, 813–820, 3 maps.

FINLAY, G. F. 1924. The effect of different species lens antisera on pregnant mice . . . Brit. Journ. Exp. Biology, **1**, 201–213.

FISCHER, E. 1901. Experimentelle Untersuchungen . . . Allg. Zs. Ent., **6**, 49–51, 363–365, 377–381, 1 plate.

—— 1903. Lepidopterologische Experimental-Forschungen, III. Allg. Zs. Ent., **8**, 221–228, 269–284, 316–326, 356–368, 52 figs.

—— 1907. Zur Physiologie der Aberrationen und Varietätenbildung . . . Arch. Rass.- und Geschlechtsbiologie, **4**, 761. (Not seen.)

FISHER, R. A. 1930. The Genetical Theory of Natural Selection. Oxford.

—— 1931. The evolution of dominance. Biol. Rev., **6**, 345–368.

FISHER, R. A., and FORD, E. B. 1928. The variability of species in the Lepidoptera, with reference to abundance and sex. Trans. Ent. Soc. London, **1928**, 367–384, 1 plate.

FOOT, K., and STROBELL, E. C. 1914. Results of crossing *Euschistus variolarius* and *Euschistus servus* with reference to the inheritance of an exclusively male character. J. Linn. Soc. London, Zool., **32**, 337–373, 7 plates, 2 figs.

FORD, E. B. 1924 (1923). Geographical races of *Heodes phlaeas*. Trans. Ent. Soc. London, **1923**, 692–743, 1 plate.

—— 1930. The theory of dominance. Amer. Nat., **64**, 560–565.

—— 1931. Mendelism and Evolution. London.

FORD, E. B., and HUXLEY, J. S. 1929. Genetic rate-factors in *Gammarus*. Roux' Archiv f. Entwickl. u. Organ., **117**, 67–79.

FORD, H. D. and E. B. 1930. Fluctuation in numbers, and its influence on variation, in *Melitaea aurinia* Rott. (Lepidoptera). Trans. Ent. Soc. London, **78**, 345–351, 1 plate.

FOWLER, H. W., and BEAN, B. A. 1929. Contributions to the biology of the Philippine Archipelago . . . U.S. Nat. Mus. Bull., **100**, 1–352, 25 figs.

FOX, H. M. 1924. Note on Kammerer's experiments with *Ciona* . . . J. Genetics, **14**, 89–91, 1 plate.

FRANZ, V. 1928. Ueber Bastardpopulationen in der Gattung *Paludina*. Biol. Zentrbl., **48**, 79–93.

FRYER, J. C. F. 1913. An investigation by pedigree breeding into the polymorphism of *Papilio polytes* Linn. Phil. Trans. Roy. Soc. London, **204**B, 227–254.

—— 1928. Polymorphism in the moth *Acalla comariana* Zeller. J. Genetics, **20**, 157–178, 1 plate.

FULTON, B. B. 1925. Physiological variation in the Snowy Tree Cricket. . . . Ann. Ent. Soc. Amer., **18**, 363–383, 6 figs.

GADOW, H. 1903. Evolution of the colour-pattern and orthogenetic variation in . . . Mexican Lizards . . . Proc. Roy. Soc. London, **72**, 109–125, 3 plates, 7 figs.

—— 1911. Isotely and coral snakes. Zool. Jahrb. Abt. Syst., **31**, 1–24, 1 plate, 18 figs.

GARDNER, L. L. 1925. Adaptive modifications . . . of the tongue in birds. Proc. U.S. Nat. Mus., **67**, 1–33, 16 plates.

GATENBY, J. B. 1916. The transition of peritoneal epithelial cells . . . in *Rana temporaria*. Quart. J. Micr. Sci., **61**, 275–300, 2 plates, 1 fig.

GATES, R. R. 1924. Polyploidy. Brit. J. Expt. Biology, **2**, 153–182.

GAUSE, G. F. 1927. Zur Kenntnis der Variabilität der Wanderheusschrecke. Zs. angew. Ent., **13**, 247–266, 9 figs.

GEISER, S. W. 1923. Notes relative to the species of *Gambusia* in the U.S.A. Amer. Midland Naturalist, **8**, 175–188, 20 figs.

GÉNIEYS, P. 1922. Sur le déterminisme des variations de la coloration chez un Hyménoptère parasite. C. R. Soc. biol. Paris, **86**, 767–770, 1080–1083, 2 figs.

GEROULD, J. H. 1923. Inheritance of white wing color, a sex-limited (sex-controlled) variation in yellow Pierid butterflies. Genetics, **8**, 495–551.

GOLDSCHMIDT, R. 1922. *Argynnis paphia-valesina*, ein Fall geschlechtscontrollierter Vererbung. Genetica, **4**, 247–278.

—— 1923. The Mechanism and Physiology of Sex Determination. Trans. W. J. Dakin. London.

—— 1929. Experimentelle Mutation und das Problem der sogenannten Parallelinduktion. Biol. Zentrbl., **49**, 437–448.

GOODRICH, E. S. 1924. Living Organisms. Oxford.

GRAHAM KERR, J. 1926. Evolution. London.

GRASSÉ, P. P. 1924. Étude biologique sur *Phaneroptera* 4-*punctata* Br. et *Ph. falcata* Scop. Bull. biol. France et Belg., **58**, 454–472, 2 plates, 8 figs.

GRAY, H. M. 1930. Changing habits in gulls. Scottish Naturalist, **186**, 170.

GRINNELL, H. W. 1918. A synopsis of the bats of California. Univ. of California Pubns., Zool., **17**, 223–404, 11 plates.

GRINNELL, J., and SWARTH, H. S. 1913. An account of the birds and mammals of the San Jacinto area of S. California . . . Univ. of California Pubns., Zool., **10**, 197–406, 5 plates, 3 figs.

GROSVENOR, T. H. L. 1921. British species of *Zygaena*. Trans. Ent. Soc. London, Proc., **1921**, lxxiii–lxxiv.

GULICK, T. 1905. Evolution, racial and habitudinal. Carn. Inst. Washington Pubn., **25**, 1–269, 5 plates.

GURNEY, R. 1923. The Crustacean plankton of the English Lake District. Journ. Linn. Soc. London, Zool., **35**, 411–447, 1 plate, 3 figs.

—— 1929. Dimorphism and rate of growth in Copepoda. Int. Rev. Hydrobiol., **21**, 189–207, 9 figs., 5 tables.

GUYÉNOT, E. 1930. La variation et l'évolution. Tome II. L'évolution. Paris.

GUYER, M. F. 1923. The germ cell and serological influences. Proc. Amer. Phil. Soc., **62**, 274–291.

GUYER, M. F., and SMITH, E. 1920. Studies on cytolysis, II. J. Expt. Zool., **31**, 171–215, 4 plates, 7 figs.

HAACKE, W. 1897. Grundriss der Entwickelungsmechanik. (Not seen.)

HACHFELD, G. 1926. Zur Biologie der *Trachusa byssina* Pz. (Hym., Apid., Megach.). Zs. wiss. Ins. biol., **21**, 63–84, 1 plate, 16 figs.

HACKETT, L. W., and MISSIROLI, A. 1931. The natural disappearance of malaria in certain regions of Europe. Amer. J. Hygiene, **13**, 57–78.

HADWEN, S. 1929. Fly attack and animal coloration. Trans. 4th Internat. Congress of Entomology, Ithaca, August 1928, **2**, 199–202, 2 figs.

HAGEDOORN, A. L. and A. C. 1921. The relative value of the processes causing evolution. The Hague.

HALDANE, J. B. S. 1932. The Causes of Evolution. London.

—— 1932a. The time of action of genes . . . Amer. Nat., **66**, 5–24.

HALDANE, J. S. 1929. The Sciences and Philosophy. Gifford Lectures, University of Glasgow, 1927 and 1928. London.

HAMM, A. H., and RICHARDS, O. W. 1926. The biology of the British Crabronidae. Trans. Ent. Soc. London, **1926**, 298–331.

HAMMER, P., and HENRIKSEN, K. 1930. Zoology of the Faroes. Vol. 2, XXXII, Myriapoda, 1–6. Copenhagen.

HÄMMERLING, J. 1929. Dauermodifikationen : in Handbuch der Vererbungswissenschaft, Bd. 1, 1–69, 31 figs. Berlin.

HANSEN, H. J. 1911. The Genera and species of the order Euphausiacea. . . . Bull. Inst. Océanogr. Monaco, **210**, 1–54, 18 figs.

HANSON, F. B., and HEYS, F. 1928. The effects of radium in producing lethal mutations in *Drosophila melanogaster*. Science, n.s., **68**, 115–116.

HANSON, F. B., HEYS, F., and STANTON, E. 1931. The effects of increasing X-ray voltages on the production of lethal mutations in *Drosophila melanogaster*. Amer. Nat., **65**, 134–143, 1 fig., 1 table.

HARDY, G. H. 1908. Mendelian proportions in a mixed population. Science, n.s., **28**, 49–50.

HARMER, S. F. 1901. Presidential Address. Trans. Norfolk and Norwich Naturalists' Society, **7**, 115–137.

HARNISCH, W. 1915. Ueber den männlichen Begattungsapparat einiger Chrysomeliden. Zs. wiss. Zool., **114**, 1–94, 1 plate, 71 figs.

HARRIS, J. A. 1911. A neglected paper on Natural Selection in the English Sparrow. Amer. Nat., **45**, 314–318.

HARRISON, J. W. H. 1916. Studies in the hybrid Bistoninae. J. Genetics, **6**, 95–161, 11 figs.

—— 1920. Genetical studies in the moths of the . . . genus *Oporabia*. J. Genetics, **9**, 195–280, 13 figs.

—— 1927. Experiments on the egg-laying of the Sawfly *Pontania salicis* . . . Proc. Roy. Soc. London, **101**B, 115–126, 1 table.

—— 1928. A further induction of melanism in . . . *Selenia bilunaria*. Proc. Roy. Soc. London, **102**B, 338–346, 8 tables.

—— 1928a. Induced changes in . . . the Butterfly *Pieris napi*. Proc. Roy. Soc. London, **102**B, 347–353.

HARRISON, J. W. H., and CARTER, W. 1924. The British races of *Aricia medon* (Esper) with special reference to the areas in which they overlap. Trans. Nat. Hist. Soc. Durham and Newcastle-on-Tyne, **6**, 89–106, 1 plate, 1 map.

HARRISON, J. W. H., and GARRETT, F. 1926. The induction of melanism in the Lepidoptera . . . Proc. Roy. Soc. London, **99**B, 241–263.

HAUPT, H. 1927. Monographie der Psammocharidae (Pompilidae) Mittel-, Nord- und Osteuropas. Beiheft Deuts. ent. Zs., **1926-7**, 367 pp., 155 figs.

HAUSER, G. 1921. Die *Damaster-Coptolabrus* Gruppe der Gattung *Carabus*. Zool. Jahrb. Abt. Syst., **45**, 1–394, 11 plates.

HAVILAND, M., and PITT, F. 1919. The selection of *Helix nemoralis* by the Song Thrush. Ann. Mag. Nat. Hist. (9), **3**, 525–531.

HEADLEE, T. J. 1917. Some facts relative to the influence of atmospheric humidity on insect metabolism. J. Econ. Ent., **10**, 31–41.

—— 1921. The response of the bean weevil to different percentages of atmospheric moisture. J. Econ. Ent., **14**, 264–268, 1 fig.

HECHT, E. 1896. Contributions à l'étude des Nudibranches. Mém. Soc. zool. France, **8**, 539–711, 5 plates.

HEIKERTINGER, F. 1929. Schutzanpassungen im Tierreich. Karlsrühe in Baden.

—— 1929a. Ueber das Mimikryproblem und seine Schwesterprobleme. Trans. 4th Internat. Congress of Entomology, Ithaca, August 1928, **2**, 821–831.

HEINCKE, F. 1898. Naturgeschichte des Herings. Abh. deutsche See-fischerei Vereins, **2**, CXXXVI, 1–128, 26 plates.

HENRY, E. 1928. Classification and Uses of Fingerprints. H.M. Stationery Office, London, pp. 1–142, 5 plates, 42 figs., A–B.

HESSE, R. 1924. Tiergeographie. Jena.

HEWITT, J. 1914. Notes on the distribution and characters of Reptiles, etc., in S. Africa . . . S. Afr. J. Sci., **10**, 238–253, 4 maps.

—— 1918. A survey of the Scorpion Fauna of S. Africa. Trans. Roy. Soc. S. Africa, **6**, 189–192, 14 plates, 1 fig.

—— 1925. Facts and theories on the distribution of Scorpions in S. Africa. Trans. R. Soc. S. Africa, **12**, 249–276, 6 maps.

HIGGINS, L. G. 1930. Some Erebiid butterflies from Styria. Proc. Ent. Soc. London, **5**, 21.

HIMMER, A. 1932. Die Temperaturverhältnisse bei den sozialen Hymenopteren. Biol. Rev., **7**, 224–253, 10 figs.

HINGSTON, R. W. 1933. The Meaning of Animal Colour and Adornment. London.

HINTON, M. A. C. 1926. Monograph of the Voles and Lemmings. London, British Museum (Natural History).

HOGBEN, L. T. 1919. The progressive reduction of the jugal in the mammalia. Proc. Zool. Soc. London, **1919,** 71–78.

—— 1931. The Nature of Living Matter. London.

HOLLISTER, W. 1913. A synopsis of the American minks. Proc. U.S. Nat. Mus., **44,** 471–480.

HOLLOWAY, J. K. 1931. Temperature as a factor in the activity and development of the Chinese strain of *Tiphia popilliavora* (Rohw.) in New Jersey and Pennsylvania. J. N.Y. Ent. Soc., **39,** 555–564, 1 plate.

HORA, G. L. 1930. Ecology, Economics and Evolution of the Torrential Fauna . . . Phil. Trans. R. Soc. London, **218**B, 171–282, 4 plates, 22 figs.

HOWELL, A. B. 1924. Individual and age variation in *Microtus montanus yosemite.* J. Agric. Res., **28,** 977–1015, 25 figs.

HOWELL, A. H. 1915. Revision of the American Marmots. U.S. Dept. Agric., Bur. Biol. Survey, Bull. **37,** 1–80, 15 plates.

—— 1918. A Revision of the American Flying Squirrels. U.S. Dept. Agric., Bur. Biol. Survey, Bull. **44,** 1–64, 7 plates, 4 figs.

HOYLE, W. E. 1904. In Report . . . Pearl Oyster Fisheries of the Gulf of Manaar. Part II, Supp. Rep. XIV, pp. 185–200, 3 plates.

HUBBS, C. L. 1926. The Structural Consequences of Modifications of the Developmental Rate in Fishes . . . Amer. Nat., **60,** 57–81.

HUDSON, W. H. 1892. The Naturalist in La Plata. First ed. London.

—— 1924. Idle Days in Patagonia. London.

HUGHES, A. McK. 1932. Induced melanism in Lepidoptera. Proc. Roy. Soc. London, **110**B, 378–402.

HUTCHINSON, G. E. 1929. A revision of the Notonectidae and Corixidae of S. Africa. Ann. S. African Mus., **25,** 359–474, 15 plates.

HUXLEY, J. S. 1923. Courtship activities in the Red-throated Diver (*Colymbus stellatus* Pontopp.) ; together with a discussion of the evolution of courtship in birds. J. Linn. Soc. London, Zool., **35,** 253–292, 4 figs.

—— 1926. Article : ' Evolution ' (Introdn.) Encyclopædia Britannica, London. Ed. 13, vol. I, pp. 1069–1073.

—— 1932. Problems of Relative Growth. London.

HUXLEY, J. S., and CARR-SAUNDERS, A. M. 1924. Absence of prenatal effects of lens antibody in rabbits. Brit. J. Expt. Biol., **1,** 215–248.

HYATT, A. 1894. Phylogeny of an acquired characteristic. Proc. Amer. Phil. Soc., **32,** 349–640, 14 plates, 15 figs.

INGOLDBY, C. M. 1927. Some notes on the African Squirrels of the genus *Heliosciurus.* Proc. Zool. Soc. London, **1927,** 471–487, 4 plates.

JACKSON, D. J. 1928. The inheritance of long and short wings in the weevil (*Sitona hispidula*), with a discussion of wing reduction among beetles. Trans. Roy. Soc. Edinburgh, **55,** 665–735, 7 plates, 4 figs.

JAMESON, H. L. 1898. On a probable case of protective coloration in the House Mouse. J. Linn. Soc. London, Zool., **26,** 465–473, 1 plate.

JEANNEL, R. 1911. Revision des Bathysciinae (Coléoptères Silphides). Arch. Zool. exp. et génér. (5), **7,** 1–641, 24 plates.

—— 1926. Faune cavernicole de la France. Paris.

JENKINSON, J. W. 1909. Experimental Embryology. Oxford.

JENNINGS, H. S. 1910. Experimental evidence on the effectiveness of Selection. Amer. Nat., **44,** 136–145.

JENNINGS, H. S. 1916. Heredity, variation, etc., in *Difflugia corona*. Genetics, **1**, 408–534, 19 figs.

JENSEN, A. S. 1912. Lamellibranchia, Pt. I, in Danish Ingolf Expedn., II, 5, pp. 1–119, 4 plates. Copenhagen.

JOLLOS, V. 1930. Studien zum Evolutionsproblem. I. Ueber die experimentelle Hervorrufung und Steigerung von Mutationen bei *Drosophila melanogaster*. Biol. Zentrbl., **50**, 541–554.

JONES, F. MORTON. 1932. Insect coloration and the relative acceptability of insects to birds. Trans. Ent. Soc. London, **80**, 345–385, 11 plates.

JORDAN, K. 1896. On mechanical selection and other problems. Novit. Zool., **3**, 426–525, 4 plates.

—— 1905. Der Gegensatz zwischen geographischer und nicht-geographischer Variation. Zs. wiss. Biol., **83**, 151–210, 73 figs.

—— 1931. Presidential address. Proc. Ent. Soc. London, **5**, 128–142, 11 figs.

JOURDAIN, F. C. R. 1925. A Study of parasitism in the Cuckoos. Proc. Zool. Soc. London, **1925**, 639–667, 5 plates.

KAMMERER, P. 1909. Vererbung erzwungener Fortpflanzungsanpassungen, **III**. Arch. Entw. Mech., xxviii, pp. 447–545, 2 plates.

—— 1913. Vererbung erzwungener Farbveränderungen IV. Das Farbkleid des Feuersalamanders (*Salamandra maculosa* Laurenti) in seiner Abhängigkeit von der Umwelt. Arch. Entw. Mech., **36**, 193 pp., 16 plates.

—— 1919. Vererbung erzwungener Formveränderungen. Arch. Entw. Mech., **45**, 324–370, 2 plates.

—— 1923. Breeding experiments on the inheritance of acquired characters. Nature, **111**, 637–640.

—— 1926. Der Artenwandel auf Inseln. *Anhang* by Wettstein, O. Wien and Leipzig.

KANE, W. 1896. Observations on the development of melanism in *Camptogramma bilineata*. Irish Naturalist, **5**, 74–80.

—— 1897. Further Observations on the Development of Melanism in Moths. *Ibid.*, **6**, 44.

KEITH, A. 1922. The Evolution of human races in the light of the hormone theory. Johns Hopkins Hosp. Bull., **33**, 155 and 195.

KELLOGG, V. 1906. Is there determinate evolution? Science, n.s., **24**, 621–628.

—— 1907. Darwinism To-day. London.

KELLOGG, V., and BELL, R. 1904. Studies of variation in insects. Proc. Acad. Sci. Washington, **6**, 203–332, 81 figs.

KEMP, S. 1917. Notes on the fauna of the Matlah River. Rec. Ind. Mus., **13**, 233–241, 7 figs.

KIKUCHI, K. 1931. Formation of the lateral spines in *Brachionus pala*. J. Fac. Sci. Imp. Univ. Tokyo, **2**, 163–169, 1 fig.

KINSEY, A. C. 1930. The gall wasp genus *Cynips*. Indiana Univ. Studies, **16**, 577 pp., 429 figs.

KIRKMAN, F. B., and JOURDAIN, F. C. R. 1930. British Birds. London.

KIRKPATRICK, T. W. 1923. The Egyptian Cotton-seed Bug (*Oxycarenus hyalinipennis* Costa). Its bionomics, damage, and suggestions for remedial measures. Min. Agric. Egypt, Tech. and Sci. Serv., Bull. **35**, viii + 106 pp., 45 figs.

KNIGHT, H. H. 1924. On the nature of the color patterns in Heteroptera, with data on the effects produced by temperature and humidity. Ann. Soc. Ent. Amer., **17**, 258–271, 1 plate.

KOBELT, W. 1876. Iconographie der Land- und Süsswasser-Mollusken. Wiesbaden. Bd. IV.

KOFOID, C. A. 1906. A discussion of species characters in *Tripolosenia*. Univ. California Pubn., Zoology, **3**, 117–126.

KOHL, F. F. 1915. Die Crabronen der paläarktischen Region. Ann. k. k. Hofmus., **29**, 453 pp., 14 plates, 87 figs.

KOLBE, H. 1920. Über Mutationsformen bei Coleoptera. Zs. wiss. Ins. biol., **16**, 49–63.

KOSMINSKY, P. 1912. Zur Frage über die Unbeständigkeit der morphologischen Merkmale bei *Abraxas grossulariata* L. Rev. russe Ent., **12**, 313–328, 11 figs.

KÜHN, A. 1927. Die Pigmentierung von *Habrobracon juglandis* Ashmead, ihre Prädetermination und ihre Vererbung durch Gene und Plasmon. Nachr. Ges. Wiss. Göttingen, Math. Phys. Klasse, **1927**, 407–421.

KÜHN, A., and HENKE, K. 1929. Genetische und Entwicklungsphysiologische Untersuchungen an der Mehlmotte *Ephestia kühniella* Zeller. I–VII. Abh. Ges. Wiss. Göttingen, Math. Phys. Klasse, **15** n.f., pp. 121, 45 figs., 5 plates.

LACK, D. 1933. Habitat Selection in Birds . . . J. Animal Ecology, **2**, 239–262, 2 plates.

LACKSCHEWITZ, P. 1930. Die *oleracea*-Gruppe des Genus *Tipula* (Dipter., Nematoc. polyn.). Konowia, **9**, 257–278, 2 plates.

LANCEFIELD, D. E. 1929. A genetic study of crosses of two races or physiological species of *Drosophila obscura*. Zs. Abst. Vererb. lehre, **52**, 287–317, 2 figs., 10 tables.

LANG, W. D. 1920. A Handbook of British Mosquitoes. London, Natural History Museum.

—— 1921. Catalogue of the Fossil Bryozoa. British Museum (Natural History), London, vol. III, pt. I.

LAPOUGE, G. 1902. Degré de l'évolution du genre *Carabus* à l'époque du pleistocène moyen. Bull. Soc. sci. et méd. Ouest, **10**, 325–344 ; **11**, 306–317.

LASHLEY, K. 1916. Results of continued selection in *Hydra*. J. Exp. Zool., **20**, 19–25.

LEIGH-SHARPE, H. 1920. The comparative morphology of the secondary sexual characters of Elasmobranch fishes. J. Morphol., **34**, 245–265.

—— 1921. Same title. *Ibid.*, **35**, 359–380.

LENGERKEN, H. VON. 1917. Ueber *Cicindela hybrida* L. und subsp. *maritima* Latr. von der Ostpreussischen Küste. Deuts. ent. Zs., **1917**, 122–124, 3 figs.

LE SOUEF, A. S. 1930. Occasional notes. Australian Zool., **6**, 110–111.

LESTAGE, J. 1925. Contribution à l'étude des larves des Ephémères. Ann. Biol. Lacustre, **13**, 227–302, 14 figs.

LINSDALE, J. M. 1928. Variations in the Fox Sparrow. Univ. California Pubn., Zool., **30**, 251–392, 5 plates, 1 fig.

LITTLE, C., and BAGG, H. 1924. The occurrence of four inheritable morphological variations in Mice . . . Journ. Exp. Zool., **41**, 45–91, 12 figs.

LLOYD, R. E. 1912. The Growth of Groups in the Animal Kingdom. London.

LONGLEY, W. H. 1917. Studies on the biological significance of animal coloration. Amer. Nat., **51**, 257–285.

LONNBERG, E. 1903. On the adaptations to a molluscivorous diet in *Varanus niloticus*. Ark. Zool., **1**, 65–83.

—— 1911. Der Penisknochen zweier seltener Carnivoren. Anat. Anz., **38**, 230–232.

—— 1932. . . . on the relict forms of *Cottus quadricornis*. Ark. Zool., **24**A, no. 7, 1–23, 1 plate, 3 figs.

LOOMIS, F. B. 1905. Momentum in variation. Amer. Nat., **39**, 839–843.

LOTSY, J. P. 1916. Evolution by means of Hybridization. The Hague.

LOVE, H., and LEIGHTY, C. 1914. Variation and correlation in Oats (*Avena sativa*). Part I, Memoir 3. Cornell Agric. Exp. Sta., Ithaca. (Not seen.)

LOVERIDGE, A. 1928. Field notes on Vertebrates (E. Africa). Proc. U.S. Nat. Mus., **73**, 1–69, 4 plates.

LOWE, P. R. 1929. Hybridization in birds. Bull. Brit. Ornith. Club, **337**, 22–29.

LOWNDES, A. G. 1930. On Entomostraca from the New Hebrides collected by Dr. J. R. Baker. Proc. Zool. Soc. London, **1930**, 973–977, 2 plates.

LULL, R. S. 1917. Organic Evolution. New York.

LUNDBLAD, O. 1930. Zoology of the Faroes. Vol. 2, XLVIII : Hydracarina, pp. 1–65, 27 figs.

LUTZ, F. E. 1908. Variation and correlation in the taxonomic characters of *Gryllus*. Carn. Inst. Washington Pubn., **101**, 1–63, 6 figs.

—— 1911. Experiments with *Drosophila ampelophila* concerning evolution. Carn. Inst. Washington Pubn., **143**, iii + 40 pp.

—— 1915. Experiments with *Drosophila ampelophila* concerning Natural Selection. Bull. U.S. Nat. Mus., **34**, 605–624.

—— 1924. Apparently non-selective characters and combinations of characters, including a study of ultra-violet in relation to the flower-visiting habits of insects. Ann. N.Y. Acad. Sci., **29**, 181–283, 7 plates, 48 figs.

McATEE, W. L. 1932. Effectiveness in nature of the so-called protective adaptations in the animal kingdom, chiefly as illustrated by the food habits of Nearctic birds. Smithsonian Misc. Coll., **85**, no. 7, 201 pp.

MACBRIDE, E. W. 1924. The work of Tornier as affording a possible explanation of the causes of mutations. Eugenics Review, January, 1–11.

MACDERMOTT, F. A. 1910. A note on the light-emission of some American Lampyridae. Canad. Ent., **42**, 357–363.

—— 1911. Some further observations on the light-emission of American Lampyridae : the photogenic function as a mating adaptation in the Photinini. *Ibid.*, **43**, 399–406.

—— 1912*a*. Observations on the light-emission of American Lampyridae. *Ibid.*, **44**, 309–311.

—— 1912*b*. The light-emission of American Lampyridae : notes and corrections. *Ibid.*, **44**, 73.

MACDOUGALL, W. 1927. An experiment for the testing of the hypothesis of Lamarck. Brit. J. Psychol., **17**, 267–304, 10 tables, 2 figs.

—— 1930. Second report on a Lamarckian experiment. Brit. J. Psychol., **20**, 201–218, 1 fig., 1 table.

MACGILLAVRY, D. 1927. Notiz über das Vorkommen der *Cicindela hybrida* L. und *maritima* Latr. in Holland. Ent. Mitt., **16**, 205–210, 1 plate.

MACLAGAN, D. S. 1932. An ecological study of the ' Lucerne flea ' (*Smynthurus viridis* Linn.). II. Outdoor studies. Bull. Ent. Res., **23**, 151–190, 2 maps, 5 tables, 7 graphs, 1 diagr.

—— 1932a. The effect of population density upon rate of reproduction. . . . Proc. R. Soc. London, **111**B, 437–504, 4 figs., 5 tables.

MANHARDT, G. 1930. Einer neurer Obstschädling. Int. Ent. Zs., **24**, 385–386.

MARLATT, C. L. 1907. The periodical Cicada. U.S. Dept. Agric., Bur. Ent., Bull. **71**, 181 pp., 48 figs., 6 plates.

MARSHALL, G. A. K. 1902. Five years' observations and experiments (1896–1901) on the bionomics of South African insects, chiefly directed to the investigation of mimicry and warning colours. Trans. Ent. Soc. London, **1902**, 287–584, 15 plates.

MATTHEW, W. D. 1901. Tertiary Mammalia of N.E. Colorado. Mem. Amer. Mus. Nat. Hist., **1**, 353–447, 3 plates.

—— 1910. The phylogeny of the Felidae. Bull. Amer. Mus. Nat. Hist., **28**, 289–316, 15 figs.

MAVOR, J. W. 1922. The production of non-disjunction by X-rays. Science, n.s., **55**, 295–297.

MAYER, A. G. 1900. On the mating instinct in moths. Ann. Mag. Nat. Hist. (7), **5**, 183–190.

—— 1902. Some species of *Partula* from Tahiti. Mem. Mus. Harvard, **26**, 117–135, 1 plate.

MAYER, A. G., and SOULE, C. G. 1906. Reactions of caterpillars and moths. J. Exp. Zool., **3**, 415–433.

MERCIER, L. 1929. Contribution à la connaissance de l'espèce chez les Myodaires supérieurs. Bull. biol. France et Belg., **63**, 399–423, 8 figs.

MERRIAM, C. H. 1919. Criteria for the recognition of species and genera. J. Mamm., **1**, 6–9.

MERRIFIELD, F., and POULTON, E. B. 1899. The colour-relation between the pupæ of *Papilio machaon*, *Pieris napi* and many other species, and the surroundings of the larva preparing to pupate, etc. Trans. Ent. Soc. London, **1899**, 369–433.

MERTENS, R. 1931. *Ablepharus boutoni* . . . und seine Geographische Variation. Zool. Jahrb. Abt. Syst., **61**, 63–210, 3 plates, 6 figs.

METALNIKOV, S. 1924. Sur l'hérédité de l'immunité acquise. C. R. Acad. Sci. Paris, **179**, 514–516.

—— 1926. Contribution à l'étude de l'immunité chez les invertébrés. Ann. Inst. Pasteur, **40**, 787–826.

METCALF, M. M. 1928. Trends in evolution . . . J. Morph. Physiol., **45**, 1–45, 61 figs.

MICKEL, C. E. 1924. An analysis of a bimodal variation of the parasite *Dasymutilla bioculata* Cresson (Hymen., Mutillidae). Ent. News, **35**, 236–242, 1 plate, 1 fig.

—— 1928. Biological and taxonomic investigations on the Mutillid wasps. Bull. U.S. Nat. Mus., **143**, ix + 340 pp., 5 plates, 28 figs.

MIDDLETON, A. D. 1930. The ecology of the American Grey Squirrel. Proc. Zool. Soc. London, **1930**, 809–843, 6 plates, 4 figs.

—— 1931. The Grey Squirrel. London.

MILLER, G. S. 1909. The Mouse Deer of the Rhio-Ling Archipelago : a study of specific differentiation under uniform environment. Proc. U.S. Nat. Mus., **37**, 1–9, 3 plates, 2 figs.

MILLER, R. C. 1922. Variations in the shell of *Teredo navalis* . . . Univ. California Pubn., Zoology, **22**, 293–328, 5 plates.

Möbius, K. 1873. Die Fische . . . in der Ostsee . . . Jahresber. Comm. z. wiss. Unters. deutschen Meere, Berlin, **1**, 145–147 ; *l.c.* Mollusca, 153–154.

Morgan, A. 1913. A contribution to the biology of May Flies. Ann. Ent. Soc. Amer., **6**, 371–426, 13 plates.

Morgan, T. H. 1919. The Physical Basis of Heredity. Philadelphia.

—— 1932. The Scientific Basis of Evolution. New York.

—— 1932a. The rise of genetics, II. Science, n.s., **76**, 285–288.

Morgan, T. H., Bridges, C. B., and Sturtevant, A. H. 1925. The genetics of *Drosophila*. Bibliographia Genetica, **II**, 1–262, 6 plates, 62 figs.

Morrison, L. 1925. Note on mating experiments with *Tipula*. Proc. Roy. Phys. Soc. Edinburgh, **21**, 8–9.

Morrison, T. A. 1925. Species determination of the two common Craneflies, *Tipula paludosa* and *Tipula oleracea*. Proc. Roy. Phys. Soc. Edinburgh, **21**, 4–8, 2 figs.

Moss, J. E. 1933. The natural control of the caterpillars, *Pieris* spp. J. An. Ecol. **2**, 210–231, 2 figs.

Mottram, J. C. 1915. The distribution of secondary sexual characters amongst birds . . . Proc. Zool. Soc. London, **1915**, 663–678.

—— 1915a. Some observations on Pattern-blending . . . Proc. Zool. Soc. London, **1915**, 679–692, 5 figs.

Muir, F. 1931. The case of *Melitaea aurinia* Rott., its variation and fluctuations ; a discussion. Entomologist, **60**, 49–52.

Muller, H. J. 1928. The problem of genic modification. Verh. V. Internat. Kongr. f. Vererb., **1**, 234–260.

—— 1932. Further studies on the nature and causes of gene mutations. Proc. Sixth Internat. Congress of Genetics, **1**, 213–255.

Muller, H. J., and Mott Smith, L. 1930. Evidence that natural radioactivity is inadequate to explain the frequency of ' natural ' mutations. Proc. Nat. Acad. Sci. Philadelphia, **16**, 277–285.

Murray, J., and Hjort, J. 1912. The Depths of the Ocean. London.

Myers, J. G. 1926. New or little-known Australasian Cicadas of the genus *Melampsalta*, with notes on the songs by Iris Myers. Psyche, **33**, 61–76, 1 plate.

—— 1929. The Taxonomy, Phylogeny and Distribution of New Zealand Cicadas. Trans. Ent. Soc. London, **77**, 29–60, 3 plates.

—— 1931. Observations on the food of the Coati. Proc. Ent. Soc. London, **5**, 69–75.

Nabours, R. 1929. The genetics of the Tettigidae (Grouse Locusts). Bibliographia Genetica, **V**, 27–104, 4 plates, 5 figs.

—— 1930. Mutations and allelomorphism in the Grouse Locusts. Proc. Nat. Acad. Sci. Washington, **16**, 350–353.

Nägeli, C. von. 1883. Mechanisch-Physiologische Theorie der Abstammungslehre.

Nicholson, A. J. 1927. A new theory of mimicry in insects. Austr. Zool., **5**, 10–104, 14 plates, 3 figs.

Nicholson, E. M. 1929. Report on the ' British Birds ' census of Heronries. British Birds, **22**, 270–333.

Noble, G. K. 1926. Kammerer's *Alytes*. Nature, **118**, 209–210, 518.

Norman, J. R. 1931. A History of Fishes. London.

Nuttall, G. F. 1911. On the adaptation of ticks to the habits of their hosts. Parasitology, **4**, 46–67, 1 fig.

NUTTALL, G. F. 1914. The biology of *Pediculus humanus*. *Op. cit.* **10,** 80–185, 2 plates, 12 figs.

OMER COOPER, J. 1931. Species pairs among insects. Nature, **127,** 237.

OSBORN, H. F. 1912. Evolution as it·appears to the paleontologist. Proc. Seventh Int. Zoological Congress, Boston (1907), **1912,** 733–739.

—— 1929. The Titanotheres of Ancient Wyoming, Dakota and Nebraska, vol. 2. U.S. Geol. Survey, Monogr. **55,** pp. x + 703-882, 192 plates, 121 figs.

OSGOOD, W. H. 1909. Revision of the mice of the American genus *Peromyscus*. U.S. Dept. Agric., N. Amer. Fauna, **28,** 1–285, 8 plates.

PANTIN, C. F. 1932. Physiological adaptation. Journ. Linn. Soc. London, Zoology, **37,** 705–711.

PARKER, H. W. 1932. Parallel modifications in the skeleton of the Amphibia Salientia. Atti. XI° Congr. Zool. Padova, **3,** 1240–1248, 11 figs.

PARSHLEY, H. M. 1923. The distribution and forms of *Lygaeus kalmii* Stål, with remarks on insect zoogeography. (Hemiptera, Lygaeidae.) Canad. Ent., **55,** 81–84, 1 map.

PAYNE, F. 1911. *Drosophila ampelophila* Loew bred in the dark for sixty-nine generations. Biol. Bull., **21,** 297–301, 1 fig.

PAYNE, N. M. 1931. Effect of temperature upon the development and life-length of *Habrobracon juglandis* Ashmead. (Abstract.) Anat. Rec., **51,** 24.

PEACOCK, A. D. 1923. The biology of *Thrinax mixta* Kl. and *T. macula* Kl. Proc. Univ. Durham Philos. Soc., **6,** 365–374.

PEARL, R. 1911. Data on the relative conspicuousness of . . . Fowls. Amer. Nat., **45,** 107–117, 4 figs.

—— 1917. The Selection problem. Amer. Nat., **51,** 65–91.

—— 1927. The growth of populations. Quart. Rev. Biol., **2,** 532–548, 11 figs.

—— 1928. Experiments on longevity. Quart. Rev. Biol., **3,** 391–407, 10 figs.

—— 1930. Requirements of a proof that natural selection has altered a race. Scientia, **47,** 175–186.

—— 1932. The influence of density of population upon egg production in *Drosophila melanogaster*. J. Exp. Zool., **63,** 57–84, 5 tables, 8 figs.

PEARL, R., MINER, J. R., and PARKER, S. L. 1927. Experimental studies on the duration of life. XI. Density of population and life-duration in *Drosophila*. Amer. Nat., **61,** 289–318, 10 figs., 8 tables.

PEARSE, A. S. 1914. On the habits of the *Uca pugnax* . . . Trans. Wisconsin Acad. Sci. Madison, etc., **17,** 791–802, 1 fig.

PEARSON, K. 1903. Mathematical contributions to the theory of Evolution. Phil. Trans. Roy. Soc. London, **200**A, 1–66.

PELSENEER, P. 1920. Les variations et leur hérédité chez les Mollusques. Mém. couronn. 8° Belgique Acad. Roy. (2), **5,** 1–826.

PÉREZ, J. 1894. De l'organe copulateur mâle des Hyménoptères et de sa valeur taxonomique. Ann. Soc. ent. France, **63,** 74–81, 8 figs.

PERKINS, R. C. L. 1912. The colour-groups of Hawaiian wasps, etc. Trans. Ent. Soc. London, **1912,** 677–701.

PETERSEN, W. 1909. Ein Beitrag zur Kenntnis der Gattung *Eupithecia* Curt.—Vergleichende Untersuchung der Generationsorgane. Deuts. ent. Soc. Iris, **22,** 203–313, 28 + 4 plates, 5 figs.

PHILIPTSCHENKO, J. 1927. Variabilität und Variation. Berlin.

PHILLIPS, J. 1921. A further report of species crosses in Birds. Genetics, **6**, 366–383, 5 figs.

PIAGET, J. 1921. Malacologia Valaisienne. Thèse: Univ. de Neuchâtel, Sion, pp. 1–101.

PICKFORD, G. 1926. In Stephenson, J.: 'The Oligochaeta.' Oxford (1930), p. 431.

PICTET, A. 1910. Quelques exemplaires de l'hérédité des caractères acquis. Verh. Schweiz. Natf. Ges., **93**, 272–274.

—— 1913. Recherches expérimentales sur l'hibernation de *Lasiocampa quercus*. Bull. Soc. lépidopt. Génève, **2**, 179–206, 14 tables.

—— 1926. Localisation . . . d'une race constante de papillons. . . . Rev. suisse de Zoologie, **33**, 399–403, 1 map.

PIERCE, F. N., and METCALFE, J. W. 1922. The genitalia of the group Tortricidae of the Lepidoptera of the British Islands. Oundle.

PILSBRY, H. 1919. A review of the land mollusks of the Belgian Congo . . . Bull. Amer. Mus. Nat. Hist., **40**, 1–370, 23 plates, 1 fig.

PILSBRY, H., HYATT, H., and COOK, M. 1912. A Manual of Conchology. Philadelphia.

PLATE, L. 1913. Selektionsprinzip und Probleme der Artbildung. 4th edn. Leipzig and Berlin.

PLOUGH, H. H. 1930. Complete elimination of self-sterility in the Ascidian *Styela* by fertilizing in alkaline solutions. Proc. Nat. Acad. Sci. Washington, **16**, 800–804, 1 table.

—— 1932. Elimination of self-sterility in the *Styela* egg. A reinterpretation with further experiments. Proc. Nat. Acad. Sci. Washington, **18**, 131–135, 1 fig., 1 table.

PLUNKETT, C. R. 1927. The experimental production of melanism in Lepidoptera. Amer. Nat., **61**, 82–88.

POCOCK, R. I. 1916. Scent-glands in mammals. Proc. Zool. Soc. London, **1916**, 742–755, 2 figs.

—— 1923. Classification of the Sciuridae. Proc. Zool. Soc. London, **1923**, 209–246, 12 figs.

—— 1929. Tigers. J. Bombay N. H. Soc., **33**, 505–541, 13 plates.

PORTER, B. A. 1926. American wasps of the genus *Sceliphron* Klug. Proc. U.S. Nat. Mus., **70**, Art. 1, 1–22, 4 plates.

POULTON, E. B. 1892. Further experiments upon the colour-relations between certain Lepidopterous larvæ, pupæ, cocoons and imagines and their surroundings. Trans. Ent. Soc. London, **1892**, 293–487, 2 plates.

—— 1912. No title. Trans. Ent. Soc. London, Proc., **1912**, lvi–lxv.

—— 1926. Protective resemblance borne by certain African insects to the blackened areas caused by grass fires. Verh. III Internat. Ent. Kongr. Zürich, 19–25 Juli 1925, **2**, 433–451, 1 plate.

—— 1931. Further notes on *Hypolimnas bolina* L. Proc. Ent. Soc. London, **5**, 75–77.

POULTON, E. B., and SAUNDERS, C. 1899. An experimental inquiry into the struggle for Existence . . . Rept. Brit. Assocn. Adv. Science (1898), **1899**, 906–909.

PRASHAD, B. 1931. Some . . . examples of parallel evolution in Molluscan faunas . . . Proc. Roy. Soc. Edinburgh, **51**, 42–53.

PROMPTOFF, A. N. 1930. Die geographische Variabilität des Buchfinkenschlags (*Fringilla coelebs* L.) in Zusammenhang mit etlichen allgemeinen Fragen der Saison Vögelzuge. Biol. Zentrbl., **50**, 478–503, 4 figs., 3 tables.

PRZIBRAM, H. 1909. Uebertragungen erworbener Eigenschaften bei Säugethiere. Verh. Ges. Deutsch. Naturf. u. Aertzte, **81**, pp. 179–180.
PUNNETT, R. C. 1915. Mimicry in Butterflies. Cambridge.

RACOVITZA, E. 1907. Les problèmes Biospéologiques. Arch. Zool. Exp. Gén. (4), **6**, 371–488.
RADL, E. 1930. The History of Biological Theories. Oxford.
RAMSBOTTOM, J. 1926. Presidential Address. Trans. Brit. Mycol. Soc., **11**, 25–45.
REGAN, C. T. 1926. Presidential Address, Section D, Rept. Brit. Assocn. Adv. Science (1925), **1926**, 75–86.
REICHERT, E. 1919. A biochemic basis for the study of problems of taxonomy . . . Carn. Inst. Washington Pubn., **270**, pt. I., pp. xi + 376, 34 plates.
REIGHARD, J. 1908. An experimental Field Study of Warning Coloration . . . Dept. Mar. Biol. Carn. Inst. Washington. Papers from the Tortugas Laboratory, **2**, no. 9, 257–325, 5 plates.
REINHARD, E. G. 1929. The Witchery of Wasps. New York.
RENSCH, B. 1929. Das Prinzip geographischer Rassenkreise und das Problem der Artbildung. Berlin.
—— 1932. Über den Unterschied zwischen geographischer und individueller Variabilität . . . Arch. Naturges. (n.f.), **1**, 95–113, 1 plate.
RHINE, J. B., and MACDOUGALL, W. 1933. Third report on a Lamarckian experiment. Brit. J. Psychol., Gen. Sect., **24**, 213–235, 6 tables, 1 fig.
RICHARDS, O. W. 1926. Studies on the ecology of English heaths. III. Animal communities of the felling and burn successions at Oxshott Heath, Surrey. J. Ecol., **14**, 244–281, 2 figs.
—— 1927. Sexual selection and allied problems in the insects. Biol. Rev., **2**, 298–364, 8 figs.
—— 1927a. The specific characters of British humble-bees (Hymenoptera). Trans. Ent. Soc. London, **1927**, 233–268, 4 plates, 5 figs.
—— 1928. A revision of the European bees allied to *Psithyrus quadricolor* Lepeletier (Hymenoptera, Bombidae). Trans. Ent. Soc. London, **1928**, 345–365, 1 plate.
—— 1930. The British species of Sphaeroceridae (Borboridae, Diptera). Proc. Zool. Soc. London, **1930**, 261–345, 1 plate, 23 figs.
RICHARDS, O. W., and ROBSON, G. C. 1926. The land and freshwater Mollusca of the Scilly Is. and West Cornwall. Proc. Zool. Soc. London, **1926**, 1101–1124, 1 fig.
RIETZ, G. DU. 1930. The fundamental units of biological taxonomy. Svensk Bot. Tidskrift, **24**, 333–428.
RILEY, J. H. 1929. A review of the birds of the islands of Siberut and Sipora. Proc. U.S. Nat. Mus., **75**, art. 4, 1–45, 1 plate.
RILEY, N. D. 1924. Presidential Address. Proc. S. London Ent. and Nat. Hist. Soc., **1924**, 74–90.
ROBSON, G. C. 1923. Parthenogenesis in the mollusc *Paludestrina jenkinsi*. Brit. J. Exptl. Biol., **1**, 65–78.
—— 1925. The deep sea Octopoda. Proc. Zool. Soc. London, **1925**, 1323–1356, 4 figs.
—— 1928. The Species Problem. London.
—— 1929. The dispersal of the American Slipper Limpet in English waters. Proc. Malac. Soc. London, **18**, 272–275.
—— 1929a. Parthenogenesis in *Paludestrina jenkinsi*, pt. 2. Brit. J. Exptl. Biol., **3**, 149–160.

ROBSON, G. C. 1932. On Cephalopoda in the Raffles Museum. Bull. Raffles Museum, Singapore, no. 7, 21–33.

—— 1932a. A Monograph of the Recent Cephalopoda, II. British Museum, London.

ROKIZKY, P. T. 1930. Ueber das Hervorrufen erblicher Veränderungen bei *Drosophila* durch Temperatureinwirkung. Biol. Zentrbl., **50**, 554–566, 3 tables.

ROOSEVELT, T. 1911. Revealing and concealing coloration in birds and mammals. Bull. Amer. Mus. Nat. Hist., **30**, 119–231.

ROOSEVELT, T., and HELLER, E. 1915. Life Histories of African Game Animals. Vols. I–II. London.

ROSZKOWSKI, W. 1912. Notes sur les Limnées . . . du lac Léman. Zool. Anz., **40**, 375–381.

ROTHSCHILD, L. W. 1916. Some new Lepidoptera from Siam and Africa. Ann. Mag. Nat. Hist. (8), **17**, 474–476.

ROTHSCHILD, L. W., and HARTERT, E. 1915. The effect of environment on the evolution of species. Bull. Brit. Ornith. Club, **35**, 128–142.

ROTHSCHILD, L. W., and JORDAN, K. 1903. A revision of the Lepido-pterous family Sphingidae. Novit. Zool., **9**, i–cxxxv + 1–972, 67 plates.

RUSSELL, E. S. 1924. The Study of Living Things. London.

—— 1930. The Interpretation of Development and Heredity. Oxford.

—— 1932. Fishery research : its contribution to ecology. J. Ecol., **20**, 128–151.

RUTHVEN, A. G. 1908. Variations and genetic relationships of the Garter Snakes. Smithsonian Instn. U.S. Nat. Mus. Bull., **61**, 1–201, 82 figs.

RUXTON, A. E., and SCHWARZ, E. 1929. On hybrid Hartebeests . . . Proc. Zool. Soc. London, **1929**, 567–583, 2 plates, 1 map.

SALT, G. 1931. Parasites of the Wheat-stem Sawfly, *Cephus pygmaeus* Linnaeus, in England. Bull. Ent. Res., **22**, 479–545, 29 figs., 2 tables.

—— 1932. The natural control of the sheep blowfly, *Lucilia sericata* Meigen. Bull. Ent. Res., **23**, 235–245, 2 tables, 2 figs.

SCHILDER, F. A. 1925. Zur Variabilität von *Cepaea*. Zs. ind. Abst.- u. Vererbungsl., **39**, 249–280.

SCHLOTTKE, E. 1926. Ueber die Variabilität der schwarzen Pigmentier-ung und ihrer Beeinflüssbarkeit durch Temperaturen bei *Habrobracon juglandis* Ashmead. Zs. vergl. Physiol., **3**, 692–736, 37 figs., 17 curves, 5 tables.

SCHMALFUSS, H., and WERNER, H. 1926. Chemismus der Entstehung von Eigenschaften. Zs. ind. Abst.- u. Vererb.lehre, **41**, 285–358, 10 tables.

SCHMIDT, J. 1918. Racial studies in fishes, I. J. Genetics, **7**, 105–118, 1 plate, 7 figs.

—— 1919. Racial investigations, III. C.R. Trav. Lab. Carlsberg, **14**, 1–7.

—— 1920. Racial studies in fishes, IV. J. Genetics, **10**, 179–191.

—— 1930. Racial investigations, X. C.R. Trav. Lab. Carlsberg, **18**, 1–71, 9 plates.

—— 1931. Eels and conger eels of the North Atlantic. Nature, **128**, 602–604, 3 figs.

SCHNAKENBECK, W. 1931. Zum Rassenproblem bei den Fischen. Zs. Ökolog. u. Mikr. Anat. Tiere., **21**, 409–566, 50 figs.

SCHRÖDER, C. 1903. Ueber experimentell erzielte Instinktvariationen. Verh. Zool. Ges. Leipzig, **13**, 158–166.

SCHRÖDER, C. 1903a. Die Zeichnungs Variabilität von *Abraxas grossulariata*. Allg. Zs. Ent., **8**, 105–119, 145–157, 177–194, 228–234, 2 plates, 100 figs.

SCHUBERT, K. 1929. Die Odonaten der Umgegend von Neustadt O.-S. Zs. wiss. Ins. Biol., **24**, 178–189.

SCHWEPPENBURG, H. G. VON. 1924. Anmerkungen zur Subspecies-frage . . . Zool. Jahrb. Abt. Syst., **49**, 131–196.

SCOTT, A. 1909. Free-swimming . . . Copepoda. 'Siboga' Expedn. Reports, XXIXa, 1–323, plates 1–69.

SCUDDER, S. H. 1889. The butterflies of the Eastern United States and Canada, II. Cambridge, Mass.

SEITZ, A. 1894. Allgemeine Biologie der Schmetterlinge. III Teil. Fortpflanzung. Zool. Jahrb. Abt. Syst., **7**, 823–851.

SEMENOV-TIAN-SHANSKY, A. 1910. Die taxonomischen Grenze der Art und ihrer Unterabteilungen. Berlin.

SEXTON, E., CLARK, A., and SPOONER, G. M. 1930. Some new eye-colour changes in *Gammarus chevreuxi*. J. Mar. Biol. Assn., **17**, 189–218, 1 plate.

—— 1932. Some new colour-changes in *Gammarus* . . . J. Mar. Biol. Assocn. Plymouth, **18**, 307–336.

SHELDON, W. G. 1930–1931. Notes on the nomenclature and variation of British species of the *Peronea* group of the Tortricidae. Entomologist, **63**, 121–124, 148–151, 175–178, 193–198, 222–225, 242–246, 273–277 ; **64**, 2–6, 30–34, 60–64, 77–82, 99–103, 124–127, 1 plate.

SHELFORD, V. E. 1907. Preliminary note on the distribution of the Tiger Beetles and its relation to plant succession. Biol. Bull., **14**, 9–14.

—— 1909. Life histories and larval habits of the Tiger Beetles (Cicindelidae). J. Linn. Soc. London, Zool., **30**, 157–184.

SIKORA, H. 1917. Zur Kleiderlaus . . . Kopplausfrage. Arch. f. Schiffs- u. Tropenhygiene, **21**, 275–284, 3 figs.

SILFRAST, J. 1922. Ueber die Beziehungen des Mutterlichen Organismus zum Embryo . . . Klin. Monatsbl. Augenheilk., **69**, 815.

SIMPSON, C. T. 1929. The Florida Tree Snails of the Genus *Liguus*. Proc. U.S. Nat. Mus., **73**, art. 20, 1–144, 4 plates.

SMUTS, J. C. 1926. Holism and Evolution. London.

SNODGRASS, R. E. 1903. Notes on the anatomy of *Geospiza*, etc. The Auk, **20**, 402–417, 4 plates.

SONNEBORN, T. M. 1931. Macdougall's Lamarckian experiment. Amer. Nat., **65**, 541–550, 1 table.

SPENGEL, J. W. 1904. Ueber Schwimmblasen, Lungen und Keimentaschen der Wirbeltiere. Zool. Jahrb., Suppl., **7**, 727–749.

SPOONER, G. 1932. An experiment in breeding . . . *Gammarus chevreuxi*. J. Mar. Biol. Assocn. Plymouth, **18**, 337–353, 1 fig.

STANDFUSS, M. 1896. Handbuch der paläarktischen Gross-Schmetterlinge für Forscher und Sammler. Jena.

—— 1898. Experimentelle zoologische Studien . . . Neue Denks. allgem. Schweiz. Ges. Naturwiss., **36**, 1–82, 5 plates.

STELFOX, A. W. 1930. Wasps' nests : their normal and some unusual situations. Irish Nat. J., **3**, 98–101.

STEPHENSON, J. 1930. The Oligochaeta. Oxford.

STEPHENSON, T. A. 1929. On methods of reproduction as specific characters. J. Mar. Biol. Assocn. Plymouth, **16**, 131–172, 11 figs.

STERNFELD, R. 1913. Die Erscheinungen der Mimikry bei den Schlangen. Sitzber. Ges. naturforsch. Freunde, Berlin, **1913**, 98–117, 4 figs.

STOCKARD, C., and PAPANICOLAOU, G. 1916. A further analysis of the hereditary transmission of degeneracy . . . by the descendants of alcoholized Mammals, II. Amer. Nat., **50**, 144–177, 6 figs.

STRESEMANN, E. 1925. Über Färbungsmutationen bei nichtdomestizierten Vögeln. Verh. Deutsche Zool. Ges. Leipzig, **30**, 159–166.

STUART BAKER, E. C. 1923. Cuckoos' eggs and evolution. Proc. Zool. Soc. London, **1923**, 277–294, 4 plates.

—— 1931. The game birds of the Indian Empire. V. The waders and other semi-sporting birds. Part XV. J. Bombay Nat. Hist. Soc., **35**, 241–253, 1 plate.

STURANY, R. 1916. Beitrage z. Naturgeschichte d. Scoglien und Kleineren Inseln Suddalmatiens. Denkschr. k. Akad. Wiss., Wien, **92**, 19, Mollusca, 397–404.

STURTEVANT, A. H. 1915. Experiments on sex recognition and the problem of sexual selection in *Drosophila*. J. Anim. Behav., **5**, 351–366.

—— 1920. Genetic studies on *Drosophila simulans*. I. Introduction. Hybrids with *D. melanogaster*. Genetics, **5**, 488–500.

—— 1921. Genetic studies on *Drosophila simulans*. III. Autosomal genes. General discussion. Genetics, **6**, 179–207, 4 figs.

—— 1921a. The North American species of *Drosophila*. Carn. Inst. Washington Pubn., **301**, 1–150, 3 plates, 49 figs.

SUMNER, F. B. 1915. Genetic studies of several geographic races of . . . Deer-mice. Amer. Nat., **49**, 688–701, 1 map.

—— 1917. The rôle of isolation in the formation of . . . a race of Deer-mice. Amer. Nat., **51**, 173–185, 1 fig.

—— 1918. . . . Inheritance in *Peromyscus*. Amer. Nat., **52**, 177–208, 12 figs.

—— 1920. Geographic variation and Mendelian inheritance. J. Expt. Zool., **30**, 369–402, 6 figs.

—— 1921. Desert and lava-dwelling mice . . . J. Mammalogy, **2**, 75–86.

—— 1923. Origin and inheritance of specific characters. Amer. Nat., **57**, 238–254.

—— 1928. An analysis of geographic variation in mice of the *Peromyscus polionotus* group . . . J. Mammalogy, **7**, 149–184, 4 plates, 9 figs.

—— 1929. Analysis of a concrete case of intergradation between two subspecies (I). Proc. Nat. Acad. Sci. Washington, **15**, 110–120, 3 figs.

—— 1929a. Analysis of a concrete case of Intergradation between two subspecies (II). *Ibid.*, 481–493, 3 figs.

—— 1932. Genetic . . . studies of the subspecies of . . . *Peromyscus*. Bibliographia Genetica, **9**, 1–106, 24 figs.

SWARTH, H. S. 1920. Revision of the avian genus *Passerella* . . . Univ. California Pubn., Zool., **21**, 75–224, 4 plates, 30 figs.

SWINNERTON, H. H. 1921. The use of graphs in palæontology. Geol. Mag., **58**, 357–364, 397–408, 10 figs.

—— 1930. Outlines of Palæontology. London.

SWYNNERTON, C. F. M. 1919. Experiments and observations on the explanation of form and colouring, 1908–1913. J. Linn. Soc. London, Zool., **33**, 203–385.

—— 1926. An investigation into the defences of butterflies of the genus *Charaxes*. 3rd Int. Entom. Congress, Zurich, **2**, 478–506, 1 plate.

TAYLOR, J. 1907. Monograph of the Land and Freshwater Mollusca of the British Isles. Leeds. (Vol. Testacellidae, etc.)

THOMAS, O., and WROUGHTON, R. C. 1916. Sci. Results from the Mammal Survey, no. XII. J. Bombay Nat. Hist. Soc., **24**, 224–245, 1 plate, 1 map.

THOMPSON, E., BELL, J., and PEARSON, K. 1911. A third co-operative study of *Vespa vulgaris*. Biometrika, **8**, 1–12.

THOMPSON, W. D'ARCY. 1917. On Growth and Form. Cambridge.

THOMPSON, W. R. 1928. A contribution to the study of biological control . . . Parasitology, **20**, 90–112, 5 figs.

—— 1929. A contribution to the study of morphogenesis in the Muscoid Diptera. Trans. Ent. Soc. London, **77**, 195–244, 30 figs.

THOMPSON, W. R., and PARKER, H. L. 1927. The problem of host relations with special reference to entomophagous parasites. Parasitology, **19**, 1–34.

—— 1928. The European Corn-borer and its controlling factors in Europe. U.S. Dept. Agric. Tech. Bull., **59**, 1–62, 21 tables, 3 figs.

THOMSEN, M., and LEMCHE, H. 1933. Experimente zur Erzielung eines erblichen Melanismus . . . Biol. Zentralbl., **53**, 541–560.

THORPE, W. H. 1929. Biological races in *Hyponomeuta padella* L. J. Linn. Soc. London, Zool., **36**, 621–634, 3 tables.

—— 1930. Biological races in insects and allied groups. Biol. Rev., **5**, 177–212, 3 tables.

—— 1930a. Observations on the parasites of the pine-shoot moth, *Rhyacionia buoliana* Schiff. Bull. Ent. Res., **21**, 387–412, 8 figs.

—— 1931. Further observations on biological races in *Hyponomeuta padella* (L.). J. Linn. Soc. London, Zool., **37** (1930), 489–492.

THORSON, G., and TUXEN, S. 1930. Die Variabilität von *Carychium minimum* Müll. in Dänemark. Vid. Medd. Dansk. naturh. Foren., **88**, 293–300, 3 figs.

TILLYARD, R. J. 1917. The Biology of Dragon-flies. Cambridge.

TIMOFEEF-RESSOVSKY, H. A. and N. W. 1927. Genetische Analyse einer freilebenden *Drosophila melanogaster*-Population. Arch. entw. Mech., **109**, 70–109, 18 tables, 26 figs.

TOMS, H. S. 1922. The Pointed Snail *Cochlicella acuta* Muller in Sussex. Ann. Rept. Brighton and Hove Nat. Hist. Soc., **1922**, 9–12, 1 plate.

TONNOIR, A. L. 1924. Les Blepharoceridae de la Tasmanie. Ann. Biol. Lacustre, **13**, 1–67.

TOWER, W. 1906. An investigation of evolution in Chrysomelid beetles . . . Carn. Inst. Washington Pubn., **48**, pp. x + 320, 1 plate, maps.

TOYAMA, K. 1912. On certain characteristics of the silkworm which are apparently non-Mendelian. Biol. Centralbl., **32**, 593–607.

TRUEMAN, A. E. 1916. Shell banding as a means of protection. Ann. Mag. Nat. Hist. (8), **18**, 341–342.

—— 1930. Results of some recent statistical investigations of invertebrate Fossils. Biol. Rev., **5**, 296–308, 9 figs.

TSCHULOCK, S. 1922. Deszendenzlehre. Jena.

TUTT, J. W. 1909. Discussion of affinities of *Agriades thetis* (*bellargus*) and *A. coridon*. Trans. Ent. Soc. London, Proc., **1909**, lxxiv–lxxx.

—— 1910. The same title. *Ibid.*, Proc., **1910**, vi–xi.

UVAROV, B. P. 1924. A revision of the Old World Cyrtacanthacrini (Orthoptera, Acrididae). V. Genera *Cyrtacanthacris* to *Loiteria*. Ann. Mag. Nat. Hist. (9), **14**, 96–113, 2 figs.

—— 1931. Insects and climate. Trans. Ent. Soc. London, **79**, 1–247, 40 tables, 53 figs.

VANDEL, A. 1928. La parthénogénèse géographique. Bull. biol. France et Belg., **62**, 164–281.

VERLAINE, L. 1925. Sur la précarité des caractères distinctifs des *Vespa vulgaris* L. et *germanica* F. et sa signification biologique. Ann. et Bull. Soc. ent. Belgique, **65,** 315–349.

VERNON, H. M. 1903. Variation in Animals and Plants. London.

WAGNER, M. 1889. Die Entstehung der Arten durch räumliche Sonderung. Basel.

WALKER, E. M. 1912. The North American dragon-flies of the genus *Aeshna.* Toronto Univ. Studies Biol., **11,** pp. viii + 213, 28 plates.

WARD, H. L. 1904. A study in the variation of proportions in bats . . . Trans. Wisconsin Acad. Sci. (1903), **14,** 630–649, 5 plates.

WARREN, B. C. S. 1926. Monograph of the tribe Hesperidi (European species), with a revised classification of the subfamily Hesperiinae (Palearctic species) based on the genital armature of the male. Trans. Ent. Soc. London, **74,** 1–170, 60 plates, 2 figs.

WARREN, E. 1896. Variation in *Portunus depurator.* Proc. Roy. Soc. London, Biol., **60**B, 221–243, 6 figs.

WATERHOUSE, G. A. 1922. Presidential address. Proc. Linn. Soc. N.S.W., **47,** i–xvii, 3 plates.

WATERHOUSE, G. A., and LYELL, G. 1914. The Butterflies of Australia. Sydney.

WATERS, E. G. R. 1926. Micro-Lepidoptera in South Devon, August, 1925. Entomologist, **59,** 158–161.

—— 1928. Observations on *Coleophora caespititiella* Z. and *C. glaucicolella* Wood. Ent. Mo. Mag., **64,** 47–51, 1 fig.

WATSON, D. M. S. 1930. Adaptation. Presidential Address, Section D, Brit. Assocn. Adv. Science (1929), **1930,** 88–99.

WEBER, H. 1931. Lebensweise und Umweltbeziehungen von *Trialeurodes vaporariorum* (Westwood). (Homoptera—Aleurodina.) Erster Beitrag zur einer Monographie dieser Art. Zs. Morph. Oekol. Tiere, **23,** 575–753, 59 figs.

WEBSTER, F. M., and PHILLIPS, W. J. 1912. The spring grain-aphis or ' green bug.' Bull. Bur. Ent. U.S. Dept. Agric., **110,** 153 pp., 9 plates, 48 figs., 5 diagrs.

WELDON, W. F. R. 1899. Presidential Address, Section D, Brit. Assocn. Adv. Science (1898), **1899,** 887–902, 6 figs.

—— 1901. A first study of Natural Selection in *Clausilia laminata.* Biometrika, **1,** 109–124, 3 figs.

—— 1904. Note on a race of *Clausilia itala.* Biometrika, **3,** 299–307, 2 figs.

WESENBERG-LUND, C. 1926. Contribution to the biology of the genus *Daphnia* . . . Skr. K. Dansk. Vid. Selsk. Kjobenhavn, (8) **11,** 89–251, 1 plate, 21 figs.

WHEDON, A. D. 1918. The comparative morphology and possible adaptations of the abdomen in the Odonata. Trans. Ent. Soc. Amer., **44,** 373–437, 9 plates.

WHEELER, W. M. 1913. Ants. Their structure, development and behavior. New York.

—— 1923. Social Life among the Insects. London.

—— 1928. Foibles of Insects and Men. New York.

WHITING, P. W. 1919. Genetic studies on the Mediterranean flour-moth, *Ephestia kühniella* Zeller. J. Exp. Zool., **28,** 413–441, 2 plates.

—— 1921. Heredity in wasps. A study of heredity in a parthenogenetic insect, the parasitic wasp, *Habrobracon.* J. Hered., **12,** 262–266, 6 figs.

WHITMAN, C. O. 1919. Orthogenetic evolution in pigeons. (Post. Works, vol. I.) Carn. Inst. Washington Pubn., **257**, pp. x + 194, 88 plates, 1 fig.

WILLEY, A. 1911. Convergence in Evolution. London.

—— 1930. Lectures on Darwinism. Boston.

WILLIS, A. G. 1922. Age and Area. Cambridge.

WLADIMIRSKY, A. P. 1928. Ueber die Vererbung experimentell erzeugter Färbung von Puppen der Kohlmotte *Plutella maculipennis*. Biol. Zentrbl., **48**, 739–759, 5 tables, 8 figs.

WODSEDALEK, J. E. 1917. Five years of starvation of larvæ. Science, n.s., **46**, 366.

WOLTERECK, R. 1908. Ueber natürliche und Künstliche Varietäten-Bildung bei Daphniden. Verh. Deutsche Zool. Ges., **18**, 234–240.

—— 1911. Transmutation und Präinduktion bei *Daphnia*. *Ibid.*, **21**, 141–172.

—— 1919. Variation und Artbildung. Bern.

—— 1921. Variation und Artbildung (. . . Untersuchungen an . . . Cladoceren). Int. Rev. Ges. Hydrobiol. u. Hydrogr., **9**, 1–146, 6 plates, 55 figs.

—— 1928. Ueber die Population Frederiksborgerschloss-See von *Daphnia cucullata* . . . *Ibid.*, **19**, 172–203, 11 figs.

WOOD JONES, F. 1910. Corals and Atolls. London.

WOODGER, J. 1929. Biological Principles. London.

WOODRUFFE-PEACOCK, A. 1909. Thrush stones and *Helix nemoralis*. The Naturalist, London, **1909**, 171–174, 257–259.

WOODWARD, A. S. 1909. Presidential Address, Geological Section, Brit. Assocn. Adv. Sci. (1908), **1909**, 462–471.

WRIGHT, S. 1929. Fisher's theory of dominance. Amer. Nat., **63**, 274–279.

—— 1931. Evolution in Mendelian populations. Genetics, **16**, 97–159.

ZELENY, C., and MATTOON, E. W. 1915. The effect of selection on the ' Bar-eye ' mutation of *Drosophila*. J. Exp. Zool., **19**, 515–529.

ZIMMERMANN, K. 1930. Zur Systematik der paläarktischen *Polistes* (Hym., Vesp.). Mitt. Zool. Mus. Berlin, **15**, 607–621, 3 figs., 5 maps.

—— 1931. Studien über individuelle und geographische Variabilität paläarktischer *Polistes* und verwandter Vespiden. Zs. Morph. Oekol. Tiere, **22**, 173–230, 1 plate, 5 tables, 28 figs.

INDEX

Printed in England at THE BALLANTYNE PRESS
SPOTTISWOODE, BALLANTYNE & CO. LTD.
Colchester, London & Eton